American Harvest

American Harvest

TWENTY YEARS OF

CREATIVE WRITING

IN THE UNITED STATES

EDITED BY ALLEN TATE

AND JOHN PEALE BISHOP

Garden City Publishing Co., Inc.

Garden City, New York

1943
GARDEN CITY PUBLISHING CO., INC.

MANUFACTURED IN THE U.S.A.

CONTENTS

II

III

6

INTRODUCTION

FOR THE first time in the history of this country it is possible to produce an anthology in which the editors can feel confidence that it represents what is, properly speaking, a literature. It may be that the period 1920-1940, which is roughly the period covered by this book, did not bring forth a writer of the stature of Hawthorne, Melville or Henry James, of Poe or Whitman. Yet a few great writers do not make a literature. Hawthorne, Melville and Whitman were contemporaries. Anthologies of the mid-nineteenth century could have included them as mountain peaks surrounded, on one side, by colonial imitators of the British and, on the other by provincial amateurs of whom some, like Augustus Longstreet (the forerunner of Mark Twain) had genius, but of whom few or none had any conception of literature as an art.

In the nineteenth century, then, we had, apart from the great figures, two varieties of insularity, of which the colonial and imitative sort was undoubtedly the less promising. So long as the colonial spirit prevails, a people cannot but look at itself through the eyes of the mother country and will not be able to bring to the conditions of its own life that sharp, intense scrutiny which alone gathers substance and gives authentic value to a literature. The provincial mind, narrow, complacent, and cut off from the world, has nevertheless accepted the life of its region as a normal manifestation of humanity. Of this mind, something may be expected. And it was out of this complacent dream that the new literature represented in this anthology came into being.

Behind the new literature there was a complex historical process, to which justice cannot be done here in all its interesting phases. Let it be sufficient to say that the war of 1914-1918 shocked the people of all sections of the United States into a new awareness of the world at large, into what may be called a comparative awareness of American life and of the cultures of Europe. For the first time in this country we began to take for granted, as part of a larger culture, French literature from Stendhal and Flaubert to Proust and Valéry, whom we found to be as close to us as Yeats and Joyce in our own language.

But probably the capital point in all this was not that we found new models to imitate, though there was some imitation, but rather that we began to look as artists on the literary materials offered by American life. We ceased to look at America as chauvinists, moralists and snobs. From our experience of Europe, we learned first how to be Americans and then how to be American writers. And as we began to apply to our own materials the various lessons in the techniques and crafts of literature that we had learned from Europe, our writings became more intensely American. Is it not a commonplace of literary history that the writer cannot know his subject until he knows it through form? And is not technique the means by which we discover the material itself?

The editors of this anthology made no attempt to represent, in terms of historical or aesthetic theory, the period under consideration. The chief guide to selection was our own memory of a period in which we had participated in most of its phases. Although there may be, as we have indicated, a lack of figures of the highest stature, this anthology ought to be a source of satisfaction to all those who are concerned with the creation of a sound literature. Professional, as distinguished from commercial, standards of competence, critical intelligence and an informed approach to literary problems, are, we think, the prominent features of the prose and poetry we have gathered here. They indicate the presence in America for the first time of a literature in the sense in which the French understand that word.

The United States are culturally and economically divided—not like Gaul into three—but into five parts. Each has had its special history; each has a somewhat special way of life. There are New England, the South, the Middle West, the Southwest and the West Coast. No attempt was made to give these sections equal representation in this book. But when we had chosen the poems, stories and essays, we found that they represented in varying proportions all the great sections. And this alone will indicate how widespread literary activity on a high level has been since the last war. New York is the city where books and magazines (but not all of them and not always the best) are published; it is the city where writers go to make a living. The energy that has gone into the contents of this anthology has derived some substance from the sidewalks of New York; its origin is to be sought in the New England village, the Ohio factory town, the Wisconsin farm, the Southern plantation, the dry plains of New Mexico.

And this is as it should be. We have perhaps no writer to compare with such writers of our age as Proust, Mann and Yeats. But the great writers abroad in these years have been scattered in several countries and each, to all appearances, has been as lonely in his living and his art as was ever in our own past a Melville or a Poe. It is safe to say that from no other land than ours, within the limits of time we set ourselves, could there have been gathered together a body of writing so various and so vigorous, so serious in intent and so accomplished in craft.

A.T.
J.P.B.

I

ACKNOWLEDGMENTS

Ernest Hemingway, THE UNDEFEATED from "Men Without Women," copyright 1932 by Ernest Hemingway (Charles Scribner's Sons); Sherwood Anderson, THE EGG from "The Triumph of the Egg," copyright 1921 by Mrs. Sherwood Anderson (The Viking Press, Inc.); Stephen Vincent Benét, THE DEVIL AND DANIEL WEBSTER, copyright 1937 by Stephen Vincent Benét (Farrar & Rinehart, Inc.); Willa Cather, THE SCULPTOR'S FUNERAL from "Youth and the Bright Medusa," copyright 1920 by Alfred A. Knopf, Inc.; Ring Lardner, HAIRCUT from "Round Up," copyright 1929 by Charles Scribner's Sons; John Dos Passos, RED, WHITE AND BLUE THANKSGIVING from "Adventures of a Young Man," copyright 1938, 1939 by John Dos Passos (Harcourt, Brace & Co., Inc.); Jerome Weidman, THE TUXEDOS, by permission of Simon and Schuster, Inc.; James Thurber, THE SECRET LIFE OF WALTER MITTY, by permission of Simon and Schuster, Inc.; Robert Penn Warren, WHEN THE LIGHT GETS GREEN, by permission of Robert Penn Warren; Erskine Caldwell, PRIMING THE WELL from "Jackpot," copyright 1940 by Duell, Sloan and Pearce, Inc.; Andrew Lytle, JERICHO, JERICHO, JERICHO, copyright 1942 by L. B. Fischer Publishing Corp.; Thomas Wolfe, IN THE SLEEPER from "Of Time and the River," copyright 1935 by Charles Scribner's Sons; Conrad Aiken, SILENT SNOW, SECRET SNOW from "Among the Lost People," copyright 1934 by Conrad Aiken (Charles Scribner's Sons).

Ernest Hemingway

THE UNDEFEATED

MANUEL GARCIA climbed the stairs to Don Miguel Retana's office. He set down his suitcase and knocked on the door. There was no answer. Manuel, standing in the hallway, felt there was some one in the room. He felt it through the door.

"Retana," he said, listening.

There was no answer.

He's there, all right, Manuel thought.

"Retana," he said and banged the door.

"Who's there?" said some one in the office.

"Me, Manolo," Manuel said.

"What do you want?" asked the voice.

"I want to work," Manuel said.

Something in the door clicked several times and it swung open. Manuel went in, carrying his suitcase.

A little man sat behind a desk at the far side of the room. Over his head was a bull's head, stuffed by a Madrid taxidermist; on the walls were framed photographs and bull-fight posters.

The little man sat looking at Manuel.

"I thought they'd killed you," he said.

Manuel knocked with his knuckles on the desk. The little man sat looking at him across the desk.

"How many corridas you had this year?" Retana asked.

"One," he answered.

"Just that one?" the little man asked.

"That's all."

"I read about it in the papers," Retana said. He leaned back in the chair and looked at Manuel.

Manuel looked up at the stuffed bull. He had seen it often before. He felt a certain family interest in it. It had killed his brother, the promising one, about nine years ago. Manuel remembered the day. There was a brass plate on the oak shield the bull's head was mounted on. Manuel could not read it, but he imagined it was in memory of his brother. Well, he had been a good kid.

The plate said: "The Bull 'Mariposa' of the Duke of Veragua, which accepted 9 varas for 7 caballos, and caused the death of Antonio Garcia, Novillero, April 27, 1909."

Retana saw him looking at the stuffed bull's head.

"The lot the Duke sent me for Sunday will make a scandal," he said. "They're all bad in the legs. What do they say about them at the Café?"

"I don't know," Manuel said. "I just got in."

"Yes," Retana said. "You still have your bag."

He looked at Manuel, leaning back behind the big desk.

"Sit down," he said. "Take off your cap."

Manuel sat down; his cap off, his face was changed. He looked pale, and his coleta pinned forward on his head, so that it would not show under the cap, gave him a strange look.

"You don't look well," Retana said.

"I just got out of the hospital," Manuel said.

"I heard they'd cut your leg off," Retana said.

"No," said Manuel. "It got all right."

Retana leaned forward across the desk and pushed a wooden box of cigarettes toward Manuel.

"Have a cigarette," he said.

"Thanks."

Manuel lit it.

"Smoke?" he said, offering the match to Retana.

"No," Retana waved his hand, "I never smoke."

Retana watched him smoking.

16

"Why don't you get a job and go to work?" he said.

"I don't want to work," Manuel said. "I am a bull-fighter."

"There aren't any bull-fighters any more," Retana said.

"I'm a bull-fighter," Manuel said.

"Yes, while you're in there," Retana said.

Manuel laughed.

Retana sat, saying nothing and looking at Manuel.

"I'll put you in a nocturnal if you want," Retana offered.

"When?" Manuel asked.

"To-morrow night."

"I don't like to substitute for anybody," Manuel said. That was the way they all got killed. That was the way Salvador got killed. He tapped with his knuckles on the table.

"It's all I've got," Retana said.

"Why don't you put me on next week?" Manuel suggested.

"You wouldn't draw," Retana said. "All they want is Litri and Rubito and La Torre. Those kids are good."

"They'd come to see me get it," Manuel said, hopefully.

"No, they wouldn't. They don't know who you are any more."

"I've got a lot of stuff," Manuel said.

"I'm offering to put you on to-morrow night," Retana said. "You can work with young Hernandez and kill two novillos after the Charlots."

"Whose novillos?" Manuel asked.

"I don't know. Whatever stuff they've got in the corrals. What the veterinaries won't pass in the daytime."

"I don't like to substitute," Manuel said.

"You can take it or leave it," Retana said. He leaned forward over the papers. He was no longer interested. The appeal that Manuel had made to him for a moment when he thought of the old days was gone. He would like to get him to substitute for Larita because he could get him cheaply. He could get others cheaply too. He would like to help him though. Still he had given him the chance. It was up to him.

"How much do I get?" Manuel asked. He was still playing with the idea of refusing. But he knew he could not refuse.

"Two hundred and fifty pesetas," Retana said. He had thought of five hundred, but when he opened his mouth it said two hundred and fifty.

"You pay Villalta seven thousand," Manuel said.

"You're not Villalta," Retana said.

"I know it," Manuel said.

"He draws it, Manolo," Retana said in explanation.

"Sure," said Manuel. He stood up. "Give me three hundred, Retana."

"All right," Retana agreed. He reached in the drawer for a paper.

"Can I have fifty now?" Manuel asked.

"Sure," said Retana. He took a fifty peseta note out of his pocket-book and laid it, spread out flat, on the table.

Manuel picked it up and put it in his pocket.

"What about a cuadrilla?" he asked.

"There's the boys that always work for me nights," Retana said. "They're all right."

"How about picadors?" Manuel asked.

"They're not much," Retana admitted.

"I've got to have one good pic," Manuel said.

"Get him then," Retana said. "Go and get him."

"Not out of this," Manuel said. "I'm not paying for any cuadrilla out of sixty duros."

Retana said nothing but looked at Manuel across the big desk.

"You know I've got to have one good pic," Manuel said.

Retana said nothing but looked at Manuel from a long way off.

"It isn't right," Manuel said.

Retana was still considering him, leaning back in his chair, considering him from a long way away.

"There're the regular pics," he offered.

"I know," Manuel said. "I know your regular pics."

Retana did not smile. Manuel knew it was over.

"All I want is an even break," Manuel said reasoningly. "When I go out there I want to be able to call my shots on the bull. It only takes one good picador."

He was talking to a man who was no longer listening.

"If you want something extra," Retana said, "go and get it. There will be a regular cuadrilla out there. Bring as many of your own pics as you want. The charlotada is over by 10.30."

"All right," Manuel said. "If that's the way you feel about it."

"That's the way," Retana said.

"I'll see you to-morrow night," Manuel said.

"I'll be out there," Retana said.

Manuel picked up his suitcase and went out.

"Shut the door," Retana called.

Manuel looked back. Retana was sitting forward looking at some papers. Manuel pulled the door tight until it clicked.

He went down the stairs and out of the door into the hot brightness of the street. It was very hot in the street and the light on the white buildings was sudden and hard on his eyes. He walked down the shady side of the steep street toward the Puerta del Sol. The shade felt solid and cool as running water. The heat came suddenly as he crossed the intersecting streets. Manuel saw no one he knew in all the people he passed.

Just before the Puerto del Sol he turned into a café.

It was quiet in the café. There were a few men sitting at tables against the wall. At one table four men played cards. Most of the men sat against the wall smoking, empty coffee-cups and liqueur-glasses before them on the tables. Manuel went through the long room to a small room in back. A man sat at a table in the corner asleep. Manuel sat down at one of the tables.

A waiter came in and stood beside Manuel's table.

"Have you seen Zurito?" Manuel asked him.

"He was in before lunch," the waiter answered. "He won't be back before five o'clock."

"Bring me some coffee and milk and a shot of the ordinary," Manuel said.

The waiter came back into the room carrying a tray with a big coffee-glass and a liqueur-glass on it. In his left hand he held a bottle of brandy. He swung these down to the table and a boy who had followed him poured coffee and milk into the glass from two shiny, spouted pots with long handles.

Manuel took off his cap and the waiter noticed his pigtail pinned forward on his head. He winked at the coffee-boy as he poured out the brandy into the little glass beside Manuel's coffee. The coffee-boy looked at Manuel's pale face curiously.

"You fighting here?" asked the waiter, corking up the bottle.

"Yes," Manuel said. "To-morrow."

The waiter stood there, holding the bottle on one hip.

"You in the Charlie Chaplins?" he asked.

The coffee-boy looked away, embarrassed.

"No. In the ordinary."

"I thought they were going to have Chaves and Hernandez," the waiter said.

"No. Me and another."

"Who? Chaves or Hernandez?"

"Hernandez, I think."

"What's the matter with Chaves?"

"He got hurt."

"Where did you hear that?"

"Retana."

"Hey, Looie," the waiter called to the next room, "Chaves got cogida."

Manuel had taken the wrapper off the lumps of sugar and dropped them into his coffee. He stirred it and drank it down, sweet, hot, and warming in his empty stomach. He drank off the brandy.

20

"Give me another shot of that," he said to the waiter.

The waiter uncorked the bottle and poured the glass full, slopping another drink into the saucer. Another waiter had come up in front of the table. The coffee-boy was gone.

"Is Chaves hurt bad?" the second waiter asked Manuel.

"I don't know," Manuel said, "Retana didn't say."

"A hell of a lot he cares," the tall waiter said. Manuel had not seen him before. He must have just come up.

"If you stand in with Retana in this town, you're a made man," the tall waiter said. "If you aren't in with him, you might just as well go out and shoot yourself."

"You said it," the other waiter who had come in said. "You said it then."

"You're right I said it," said the tall waiter. "I know what I'm talking about when I talk about that bird."

"Look what he's done for Villalta," the first waiter said.

"And that ain't all," the tall waiter said. "Look what he's done for Marcial Lalanda. Look what he's done for Nacional."

"You said it, kid," agreed the short waiter.

Manuel looked at them, standing talking in front of his table. He had drunk his second brandy. They had forgotten about him. They were not interested in him.

"Look at that bunch of camels," the tall waiter went on. "Did you ever see this Nacional II?"

"I seen him last Sunday, didn't I?" the original waiter said.

"He's a giraffe," the short waiter said.

"What did I tell you?" the tall waiter said. "Those are Retana's boys."

"Say, give me another shot of that," Manuel said. He had poured the brandy the waiter had slopped over in the saucer into his glass and drank it while they were talking.

The original waiter poured his glass full mechanically, and the three of them went out of the room talking.

In the far corner the man was still asleep, snoring slightly on the intaking breath, his head back against the wall.

Manuel drank his brandy. He felt sleepy himself. It was too hot to go out into the town. Besides there was nothing to do. He wanted to see Zurito. He would go to sleep while he waited. He kicked his suitcase under the table to be sure it was there. Perhaps it would be better to put it back under the seat, against the wall. He leaned down and shoved it under. Then he leaned forward on the table and went to sleep.

When he woke there was some one sitting across the table from him. It was a big man with a heavy brown face like an Indian. He had been sitting there some time. He had waved the waiter away and sat reading the paper and occasionally looking down at Manuel, asleep, his head on the table. He read the paper laboriously, forming the words with his lips as he read. When it tired him he looked at Manuel. He sat heavily in the chair, his black Cordoba hat tipped forward.

Manuel sat up and looked at him.

"Hello, Zurito," he said.

"Hello, kid," the big man said.

"I've been asleep." Manuel rubbed his forehead with the back of his fist.

"I thought maybe you were."

"How's everything?"

"Good. How is everything with you?"

"Not so good."

They were both silent, Zurito, the picador, looked at Manuel's white face. Manuel looked down at the picador's enormous hands folding the paper to put away in his pocket.

"I got a favor to ask you, Manos," Manuel said.

Manosduros was Zurito's nickname. He never heard it without thinking of his huge hands. He put them forward on the table self-consciously.

"Let's have a drink," he said.

"Sure," said Manuel.

The waiter came and went and came again. He went out of the room looking back at the two men at the table.

22

"What's the matter, Manolo?" Zurito set down his glass.

"Would you pic two bulls for me to-morrow night?" Manuel asked, looking up at Zurito across the table.

"No," said Zurito. "I'm not pic-ing."

Manuel looked down at his glass. He had expected that answer; now he had it. Well, he had it.

"I'm sorry, Manolo, but I'm not pic-ing." Zurito looked at his hands.

"That's all right," Manuel said.

"I'm too old," Zurito said.

"I just asked you," Manuel said.

"Is it the nocturnal to-morrow?"

"That's it. I figured if I had just one good pic, I could get away with it."

"How much are you getting?"

"Three hundred pesetas."

"I get more than that for pic-ing."

"I know," said Manuel. "I didn't have any right to ask you."

"What do you keep on doing it for?" Zurito asked. "Why don't you cut off your coleta, Manolo?"

"I don't know," Manuel said.

"You're pretty near as old as I am," Zurito said.

"I don't know," Manuel said. "I got to do it. If I can fix it so that I get an even break, that's all I want. I got to stick with it, Manos."

"No, you don't."

"Yes, I do. I've tried keeping away from it."

"I know how you feel. But it isn't right. You ought to get out and stay out."

"I can't do it. Besides, I've been going good lately."

Zurito looked at his face.

"You've been in the hospital."

"But I was going great when I got hurt."

Zurito said nothing. He tipped the cognac out of his saucer into his glass.

23

"The papers said they never saw a better faena," Manuel said.

Zurito looked at him.

"You know when I get going I'm good," Manuel said.

"You're too old," the picador said.

"No," said Manuel. "You're ten years older than I am."

"With me it's different."

"I'm not too old," Manuel said.

They sat silent, Manuel watching the picador's face.

"I was going great till I got hurt," Manuel offered.

"You ought to have seen me, Manos," Manuel said, reproachfully.

"I don't want to see you," Zurito said. "It makes me nervous."

"You haven't seen me lately."

"I've seen you plenty."

Zurito looked at Manuel, avoiding his eyes.

"You ought to quit it, Manolo."

"I can't," Manuel said. "I'm going good now, I tell you."

Zurito leaned forward, his hands on the table.

"Listen. I'll pic for you and if you don't go big to-morrow night, you'll quit. See? Will you do that?"

"Sure."

Zurito leaned back, relieved.

"You got to quit," he said. "No monkey business. You got to cut the coleta."

"I won't have to quit," Manuel said. "You watch me. I've got the stuff."

Zurito stood up. He felt tired from arguing.

"You got to quit," he said. "I'll cut your coleta myself."

"No, you won't," Manuel said. "You won't have a chance."

Zurito called the waiter.

"Come on," said Zurito. "Come on up to the house."

Manuel reached under the seat for his suitcase. He was

happy. He knew Zurito would pic for him. He was the best picador living. It was all simple now.

"Come on up to the house and we'll eat," Zurito said.

Manuel stood in the patio de caballos waiting for the Charlie Chaplins to be over. Zurito stood beside him. Where they stood it was dark. The high door that led into the bull-ring was shut. Above them they heard a shout, then another shout of laughter. Then there was silence. Manuel liked the smell of the stables about the patio de caballos. It smelt good in the dark. There was another roar from the arena and then applause, prolonged applause, going on and on.

"You ever seen these fellows?" Zurito asked, big and looming beside Manuel in the dark.

"No," Manuel said.

"They're pretty funny." Zurito said. He smiled to himself in the dark.

The high, double, tight-fitting door into the bull-ring swung open and Manuel saw the ring in the hard light of the arc-lights, the plaza, dark all the way around, rising high; around the edge of the ring were running and bowing two men dressed like tramps, followed by a third in the uniform of a hotel bell-boy who stooped and picked up the hats and canes thrown down onto the sand and tossed them back up into the darkness.

The electric light went on in the patio.

"I'll climb onto one of those ponies while you collect the kids," Zurito said.

Behind them came the jingle of the mules, coming out to go into the arena and be hitched onto the dead bull.

The members of the cuadrilla, who had been watching the burlesque from the runway between the barrera and the seats, came walking back and stood in a group talking, under the electric light in the patio. A good-looking lad in a silver-and-orange suit came up to Manuel and smiled.

"I'm Hernandez," he said and put out his hand.

25

Manuel shook it.

"They're regular elephants we've got to-night," the boy said cheerfully.

"They're big ones with horns," Manuel agreed.

"You drew the worst lot," the boy said.

"That's all right," Manuel said. "The bigger they are, the more meat for the poor."

"Where did you get that one?" Hernandez grinned.

"That's an old one," Manuel said. "You line up your cuadrilla, so I can see what I've got."

"You've got some good kids," Hernandez said. He was very cheerful. He had been on twice before in nocturnals and was beginning to get a following in Madrid. He was happy the fight would start in a few minutes.

"Where are the pics?" Manuel asked.

"They're back in the corrals fighting about who gets the beautiful horses," Hernandez grinned.

The mules came through the gate in a rush, the whips snapping, bells jangling and the young bull ploughing a furrow of sand.

They formed up for the paseo as soon as the bull had gone through.

Manuel and Hernandez stood in front. The youths of the cuadrillas were behind, their heavy capes furled over their arms. In back, the four picadors, mounted, holding their steel-tipped push-poles erect in the half-dark of the corral.

"It's a wonder Retana wouldn't give us enough light to see the horses by," one picador said.

"He knows we'll be happier if we don't get too good a look at these skins," another pic answered.

"This thing I'm on barely keeps me off the ground," the first picador said.

"Well, they're horses."

"Sure, they're horses."

They talked, sitting their gaunt horses in the dark.

Zurito said nothing. He had the only steady horse of the

lot. He had tried him, wheeling him in the corrals and he responded to the bit and the spurs. He had taken the bandage off his right eye and cut the strings where they had tied his ears tight shut at the base. He was a good, solid horse, solid on his legs. That was all he needed. He intended to ride him all through the corrida. He had already, since he had mounted, sitting in the half-dark in the big, quilted saddle, waiting for the paseo, pic-ed through the whole corrida in his mind. The other picadors went on talking on both sides of him. He did not hear them.

The two matadors stood together in front of their three peones, their capes furled over their left arms in the same fashion. Manuel was thinking about the three lads in back of him. They were all three Madrilenos, like Hernandez, boys about nineteen. One of them, a gypsy, serious, aloof, and dark-faced, he liked the look of. He turned.

"What's your name, kid?" he asked the gypsy.

"Fuentes," the gypsy said.

"That's a good name," Manuel said.

The gypsy smiled, showing his teeth.

"You take the bull and give him a little run when he comes out," Manuel said.

"All right," the gypsy said. His face was serious. He began to think about just what he would do.

"Here she goes," Manuel said to Hernandez.

"All right. We'll go."

Heads up, swinging with the music, their right arms swinging free, they stepped out, crossing the sanded arena under the arc-lights, the cuadrillas opening out behind, the picadors riding after, behind came the bull-ring servants and the jingling mules. The crowd applauded Hernandez as they marched across the arena. Arrogant, swinging, they looked straight ahead as they marched.

They bowed before the president, and the procession broke up into its component parts. The bull-fighters went over to the barrera and changed their heavy mantles for the light fighting capes. The mules went out. The picadors gal-loped jerkily around the ring, and two rode out the gate they had come in by. The servants swept the sand smooth.

Manuel drank a glass of water poured for him by one of Retana's deputies, who was acting as his manager and sword-handler. Hernandez came over from speaking with his own manager.

"You got a good hand, kid," Manuel complimented him.

"They like me," Hernandez said happily.

"How did the paseo go?" Manuel asked Retana's man.

"Like a wedding," said the handler. "Fine. You came out like Joselito and Belmonte."

Zurito rode by, a bulky equestrian statue. He wheeled his horse and faced him toward the toril on the far side of the ring where the bull would come out. It was strange under the arc-light. He pic-ed in the hot afternoon sun for big money. He didn't like this arc-light business. He wished they would get started.

Manuel went up to him.

"Pic him, Manos," he said. "Cut him down to size for me."

"I'll pic him, kid," Zurito spat on the sand. "I'll make him jump out of the ring."

"Lean on him, Manos," Manuel said.

"I'll lean on him," Zurito said. "What's holding it up?"

"He's coming now," Manuel said.

Zurito sat there, his feet in the box-stirrups, his great legs in the buckskin-covered armor gripping the horse, the reins in his left hand, the long pic held in his right hand, his broad hat well down over his eyes to shade them from the lights, watching the distant door of the toril. His horse's ears quiv-ered. Zurito patted him with his left hand.

The red door of the toril swung back and for a moment Zurito looked into the empty passageway far across the arena. Then the bull came out in a rush, skidding on his four legs as he came out under the lights, then charging in a gallop, moving softly in a fast gallop, silent except as he woofed

28

through wide nostrils as he charged, glad to be free after the dark pen.

In the first row of seats, slightly bored, leaning forward to write on the cement wall in front of his knees, the substitute bull-fight critic of *El Heraldo* scribbled: "Campagnero, Negro, 42, came out at 90 miles an hour with plenty of gas——"

Manuel, leaning against the barrera, watching the bull, waved his hand and the gypsy ran out, trailing his cape. The bull, in full gallop, pivoted and charged the cape, his head down, his tail rising. The gypsy moved in a zigzag, and as he passed, the bull caught sight of him and abandoned the cape to charge the man. The gyp sprinted and vaulted the red fence of the barrera as the bull struck it with his horns. He tossed into it twice with his horns, banging into the wood blindly.

The critic of *El Heraldo* lit a cigarette and tossed the match at the bull, then wrote in his note-book, "large and with enough horns to satisfy the cash customers, Campagnero showed a tendency to cut into the terrane of the bull-fighters."

Manuel stepped out on the hard sand as the bull banged into the fence. Out of the corner of his eye he saw Zurito sitting the white horse close to the barrera, about a quarter of the way around the ring to the left. Manuel held the cape close in front of him, a fold in each hand, and shouted at the bull. "Huh! Huh!" The bull turned, seemed to brace against the fence as he charged in a scramble, driving into the cape as Manuel side-stepped, pivoted on his heels with the charge of the bull, and swung the cape just ahead of the horns. At the end of the swing he was facing the bull again and held the cape in the same position close in front of his body, and pivoted again as the bull recharged. Each time, as he swung, the crowd shouted.

Four times he swung with the bull, lifting the cape so it billowed full, and each time bringing the bull around to

29

charge again. Then, at the end of the fifth swing, he held the cape against his hip and pivoted, so the cape swung out like a ballet dancer's skirt and wound the bull around himself like a belt, to step clear, leaving the bull facing Zurito on the white horse, come up and planted firm, the horse facing the bull, its ears forward, its lips nervous, Zurito, his hat over his eyes, leaning forward, the long pole sticking out before and behind in a sharp angle under his right arm, held half-way down, the triangular iron point facing the bull.

El Heraldo's second-string critic, drawing on his cigarette, his eyes on the bull, wrote: "the veteran Manolo designed a series of acceptable veronicas, ending in a very Belmontistic recorte that earned applause from the regulars, and we entered the tercio of the cavalry."

Zurito sat his horse, measuring the distance between the bull and the end of the pic. As he looked, the bull gathered himself together and charged, his eyes on the horse's chest. As he lowered his head to hook, Zurito sunk the point of the pic in the swelling hump of muscle above the bull's shoulder, leaned all his weight on the shaft, and with his left hand pulled the white horse into the air, front hoofs pawing, and swung him to the right as he pushed the bull under and through so the horns passed safely under the horse's belly and the horse came down, quivering, the bull's tail brushing his chest as he charged the cape Hernandez offered him.

Hernandez ran sideways, taking the bull out and away with the cape, toward the other picador. He fixed him with a swing of the cape, squarely facing the horse and rider, and stepped back. As the bull saw the horse he charged. The picador's lance slid along his back, and as the shock of the charge lifted the horse, the picador was already half-way out of the saddle, lifting his right leg clear as he missed with the lance and falling to the left side to keep the horse between him and the bull. The horse, lifted and gored, crashed over with the bull driving into him, the picador gave a shove with his boots against the horse and lay clear, waiting to be lifted and hauled away and put on his feet.

Manuel let the bull drive into the fallen horse; he was in no hurry, the picador was safe; besides, it did a picador like that good to worry. He'd stay on longer next time. Lousy pics! He looked across the sand at Zurito a little way out from the barrera, his horse rigid, waiting.

"Huh!" he called to the bull, "Tomar!" holding the cape in both hands so it would catch his eye. The bull detached himself from the horse and charged the cape, and Manuel, running sideways and holding the cape spread wide, stopped, swung on his heels, and brought the bull sharply around facing Zurito.

"Campagnero accepted a pair of varas for the death of one rosinante, with Hernandez and Manolo at the quites," *El Heraldo's* critic wrote. "He pressed on the iron and clearly showed he was no horse-lover. The veteran Zurito resurrected some of his old stuff with the pike-pole, notably the suerte——"

"Olé! Olé!" the man sitting beside him shouted. The shout was lost in the roar of the crowd, and he slapped the critic on the back. The critic looked up to see Zurito, directly below him, leaning far out over his horse, the length of the pic rising in a sharp angle under his armpit, holding the pic almost by the point, bearing down with all his weight, holding the bull off, the bull pushing and driving to get at the horse, and Zurito, far out, on top of him, holding him, holding him, and slowly pivoting the horse against the pressure, so that at last he was clear. Zurito felt the moment when the horse was clear and the bull could come past, and relaxed the absolute steel lock of his resistance, and the triangular steel point of the pic ripped in the bull's hump of shoulder muscle as he tore loose to find Hernandez's cape before his muzzle. He charged blindly into the cape and the boy took him out into the open arena.

Zurito sat patting his horse and looking at the bull charging the cape that Hernandez swung for him out under the bright light while the crowd shouted.

"You see that one?" he said to Manuel.

"It was a wonder," Manuel said.

"I got him that time," Zurito said. "Look at him now."

At the conclusion of a closely turned pass of the cape the bull slid to his knees. He was up at once, but far out across the sand Manuel and Zurito saw the shine of the pumping flow of blood, smooth against the black of the bull's shoulder.

"I got him that time," Zurito said.

"He's a good bull," Manuel said.

"If they gave me another shot at him, I'd kill him," Zurito said.

"They'll change the thirds on us," Manuel said.

"Look at him now," Zurito said.

"I got to go over there," Manuel said, and started on a run for the other side of the ring, where the monos were leading a horse out by the bridle toward the bull, whacking him on the legs with rods and all, in a procession, trying to get him toward the bull, who stood, dropping his head, pawing, unable to make up his mind to charge.

Zurito, sitting his horse, walking him toward the scene, not missing any detail, scowled.

Finally the bull charged, the horse leaders ran for the barrera, the picador hit too far back, and the bull got under the horse, lifted him, threw him onto his back.

Zurito watched. The monos, in their red shirts, running out to drag the picador clear. The picador, now on his feet, swearing and flopping his arms. Manuel and Hernandez standing ready with their capes. And the bull, the great, black bull, with a horse on his back, hooves dangling, the bridle caught in the horns. Black bull with a horse on his back, staggering short-legged, then arching his neck and lifting, thrusting, charging to slide the horse off, horse sliding down. Then the bull into a lunging charge at the cape Manuel spread for him.

32

The bull was slower now, Manuel felt. He was bleeding badly. There was a sheen of blood all down his flank.

Manuel offered him the cape again. There he came, eyes open, ugly, watching the cape. Manuel stepped to the side and raised his arms, tightening the cape ahead of the bull for the veronica.

Now he was facing the bull. Yes, his head was going down a little. He was carrying it lower. That was Zurito.

Manuel flopped the cape; there he comes; he side-stepped and swung in another veronica. He's shooting awfully accurately, he thought. He's had enough fight, so he's watching now. He's hunting now. Got his eye on me. But I always give him the cape.

He shook the cape at the bull; there he comes; he side-stepped. Awful close that time. I don't want to work that close to him.

The edge of the cape was wet with blood where it had swept along the bull's back as he went by.

All right, here's the last one.

Manuel, facing the bull, having turned with him each charge, offered the cape with his two hands. The bull looked at him. Eyes watching, horns straight forward, the bull looked at him, watching.

"Huh!" Manuel said, "Toro!" and leaning back, swung the cape forward. Here he comes. He side-stepped, swung the cape in back of him, and pivoted, so the bull followed a swirl of cape and then was left with nothing, fixed by the pass, dominated by the cape. Manuel swung the cape under his muzzle with one hand, to show the bull was fixed, and walked away.

There was no applause.

Manuel walked across the sand toward the barrera, while Zurito rode out of the ring. The trumpet had blown to change the act to the planting of the banderillos while Manuel had been working with the bull. He had not consciously noticed it. The monos were spreading canvas over the two dead horses and sprinkling sawdust around them.

Manuel came up to the barrera for a drink of water. Retana's man handed him the heavy porous jug.

Fuentes, the tall gypsy, was standing holding a pair of banderillos, holding them together, slim, red sticks, fish-hook points out. He looked at Manuel.

"Go on out there," Manuel said.

The gypsy trotted out. Manuel set down the jug and watched. He wiped his face with his handkerchief.

The critic of *El Heraldo* reached for the bottle of warm champagne that stood between his feet, took a drink, and finished his paragraph.

"—the aged Manolo rated no applause for a vulgar series of lances with the cape and we entered the third of the palings."

Alone in the centre of the ring the bull stood, still fixed. Fuentes, tall, flat-backed, walking toward him arrogantly, his arms spread out, the two slim, red sticks, one in each hand, held by the fingers, points straight forward. Fuentes walked forward. Back of him and to one side was a peon with a cape. The bull looked at him and was no longer fixed.

His eyes watched Fuentes, now standing still. Now he leaned back, calling to him. Fuentes twitched the two banderillos and the light on the steel points caught the bull's eye.

His tail went up and he charged.

He came straight, his eyes on the man. Fuentes stood still, leaning back, the banderillos pointing forward. As the bull lowered his head to hook, Fuentes leaned backward, his arms came together and rose, his two hands touching, the banderillos two descending red lines, and leaning forward drove the points into the bull's shoulder, leaning far in over the bull's horns and pivoting on the two upright sticks, his legs tight together, his body curving to one side to let the bull pass.

"Olé!" from the crowd.

The bull was hooking wildly, jumping like a trout, all

34

four feet off the ground. The red shaft of the banderillos tossed as he jumped.

Manuel standing at the barrera, noticed that he hooked always to the right.

"Tell him to drop the next pair on the right," he said to the kid who started to run out to Fuentes with the new banderillos.

A heavy hand fell on his shoulder. It was Zurito.

"How do you feel, kid?" he asked.

Manuel was watching the bull.

Zurito leaned forward on the barrera, leaning the weight of his body on his arms. Manuel turned to him.

"You're going good," Zurito said.

Manuel shook his head. He had nothing to do now until the next third. The gypsy was very good with the banderillos. The bull would come to him in the next third in good shape. He was a good bull. It had all been easy up to now. The final stuff with the sword was all he worried over. He did not really worry. He did not even think about it. But standing there he had a heavy sense of apprehension. He looked out at the bull, planning his faena, his work with the red cloth that was to reduce the bull, to make him manageable.

The gypsy was walking out toward the bull again, walking heel-and-toe, insultingly, like a ball-room dancer, the red shafts of the banderillos twitching with his walk. The bull watched him, not fixed now, hunting him, but waiting to get close enough so he could be sure of getting him, getting the horns into him.

As Fuentes walked forward the bull charged. Fuentes ran across the quarter of a circle as the bull charged and, as he passed running backward, stopped, swung forward, rose on his toes, arms straight out, and sunk the banderillos straight down into the tight of the big shoulder muscles as the bull missed him.

The crowd were wild about it.

35

"That kid won't stay in this night stuff long," Retana's man said to Zurito.

"He's good," Zurito said.

"Watch him now."

They watched.

Fuentes was standing with his back against the barrera. Two of the cuadrilla were back of him, with their capes ready to flop over the fence to distract the bull.

The bull, with his tongue out, his barrel heaving, was watching the gypsy. He thought he had him now. Back against the red planks. Only a short charge away. The bull watched him.

The gypsy bent back, drew back his arms, the banderillos pointing at the bull. He called to the bull, stamped one foot. The bull was suspicious. He wanted the man. No more barbs in the shoulder.

Fuentes walked a little closer to the bull. Bent back. Called again. Somebody in the crowd shouted a warning.

"He's too damn close," Zurito said.

"Watch him," Retana's man said.

Leaning back, inciting the bull with the banderillos, Fuentes jumped, both feet off the ground. As he jumped the bull's tail rose and he charged. Fuentes came down on his toes, arms straight out, whole body arching forward, and drove the shafts straight down as he swung his body clear of the right horn.

The bull crashed into the barrera where the flopping capes had attracted his eye as he lost the man.

The gypsy came running along the barrera toward Manuel, taking the applause of the crowd. His vest was ripped where he had not quite cleared the point of the horn. He was happy about it, showing it to the spectators. He made the tour of the ring. Zurito saw him go by, smiling, pointing at his vest. He smiled.

Somebody else was planting the last pair of banderillos. Nobody was paying any attention.

36

Retana's man tucked a baton inside the red cloth of a muleta, folded the cloth over it, and handed it over the barrera to Manuel. He reached in the leather sword-case, took out a sword, and holding it by its leather scabbard, reached it over the fence to Manuel. Manuel pulled the blade out by the red hilt and the scabbard fell limp.

He looked at Zurito. The big man saw he was sweating.

"Now you get him, kid," Zurito said.

Manuel nodded.

"He's in good shape," Zurito said.

"Just like you want him," Retana's man assured him.

Manuel nodded.

The trumpeter, up under the roof, blew for the final act, and Manuel walked across the arena toward where, up in the dark boxes, the president must be.

In the front row of seats the substitute bull-fight critic of *El Heraldo* took a long drink of the warm champagne. He had decided it was not worth while to write a running story and would write up the corrida back in the office. What the hell was it anyway? Only a nocturnal. If he missed anything he would get it out of the morning papers. He took another drink of the champagne. He had a date at Maxim's at twelve. Who were these bull-fighters anyway? Kids and bums. A bunch of bums. He put his pad of paper in his pocket and looked over toward Manuel, standing very much alone in the ring, gesturing with his hat in a salute toward a box he could not see high up in the dark plaza. Out in the ring the bull stood quiet, looking at nothing.

"I dedicate this bull to you, Mr. President, and to the public of Madrid, the most intelligent and generous of the world," was what Manuel was saying. It was a formula. He said it all. It was a little long for nocturnal use.

He bowed at the dark, straightened, tossed his hat over his shoulder, and, carrying the muleta in his left hand and the sword in his right, walked out toward the bull.

Manuel walked toward the bull. The bull looked at him;

his eyes were quick. Manuel noticed the way the banderillos hung down on his left shoulder and the steady sheen of blood from Zurito's pic-ing. He noticed the way the bull's feet were. As he walked forward, holding the muleta in his left hand and the sword in his right, he watched the bull's feet. The bull could not charge without gathering his feet together. Now he stood square on them, dully.

Manuel walked toward him, watching his feet. This was all right. He could do this. He must work to get the bull's head down, so he could go in past the horns and kill him. He did not think about the sword, not about killing the bull. He thought about one thing at a time. The coming things oppressed him, though. Walking forward, watching the bull's feet, he saw successively his eyes, his wet muzzle, and the wide, forward-pointing spread of his horns. The bull had light circles about his eyes. His eyes watched Manuel. He felt he was going to get this little one with the white face.

Standing still now and spreading the red cloth of the muleta with the sword, pricking the point into the cloth so that the sword, now held in his left hand, spread the red flannel like the jib of a boat, Manuel noticed the points of the bull's horns. One of them was splintered from banging against the barrera. The other was sharp as a porcupine quill. Manuel noticed while spreading the muleta that the white base of the horn was stained red. While he noticed these things he did not lose sight of the bull's feet. The bull watched Manuel steadily.

He's on the defensive now, Manuel thought. He's reserving himself. I've got to bring him out of that and get his head down. Always get his head down. Zurito had his head down once, but he's come back. He'll bleed when I start him going and that will bring it down.

Holding the muleta, with the sword in his left hand widening it in front of him, he called to the bull.

The bull looked at him.

38

He leaned back insultingly and shook the wide-spread flannel.

The bull saw the muleta. It was a bright scarlet under the arc-light. The bull's legs tightened.

Here he comes. Whoosh! Manuel turned as the bull came and raised the muleta so that it passed over the bull's horns and swept down his broad back from head to tail. The bull had gone clean up in the air with the charge, Manuel had not moved.

At the end of the pass the bull turned like a cat coming around a corner and faced Manuel.

He was on the offensive again. His heaviness was gone. Manuel noted the fresh blood shining down the black shoulder and dripping down the bull's leg. He drew the sword out of the muleta and held it in his right hand. The muleta held low down in his left hand, leaning toward the left, he called to the bull. The bull's legs tightened, his eyes on the muleta. Here he comes, Manuel thought. Yuh!

He swung with the charge, sweeping the muleta ahead of the bull, his feet firm, the sword following the curve, a point of light under the arcs.

The bull recharged as the pase natural finished and Manuel raised the muleta for a pase de pecho. Firmly planted, the bull came by his chest under the raised muleta. Manuel leaned his head back to avoid the clattering banderillo shafts. The hot, black bull body touched his chest as it passed.

Too damn close, Manuel thought. Zurito, leaning on the barrera, spoke rapidly to the gypsy, who trotted out toward Manuel with a cape. Zurito pulled his hat down low and looked out across the arena at Manuel.

Manuel was facing the bull again, the muleta held low and to the left. The bull's head was down as he watched the muleta.

"If it was Belmonte doing that stuff, they'd go crazy," Retana's man said.

Zurito said nothing. He was watching Manuel out in the centre of the arena.

"Where did the boss dig this fellow up?" Retana's man asked.

"Out of the hospital," Zurito said.

"That's where he's going damn quick," Retana's man said. Zurito turned on him.

"Knock on that," he said, pointing to the barrera.

"I was just kidding, man," Retana's man said.

"Knock on the wood."

Retana's man leaned forward and knocked three times on the barrera.

"Watch the faena," Zurito said.

Out in the centre of the ring, under the lights, Manuel was kneeling, facing the bull, and as he raised the muleta in both hands the bull charged, tail up.

Manuel swung his body clear and, as the bull recharged, brought around the muleta in a half-circle that pulled the bull to his knees.

"Why, that one's a great bull-fighter," Retana's man said.

"No, he's not," said Zurito.

Manuel stood up and, the muleta in his left hand, the sword in his right, acknowledged the applause from the dark plaza.

The bull had humped himself up from his knees and stood waiting, his head hung low.

Zurito spoke to two of the other lads of the cuadrilla and they ran out to stand back of Manuel with their capes. There were four men back of him now. Hernandez had followed him since he first came out with the muleta. Fuentes stood watching, his cape held against his body, tall, in repose, watching lazy-eyed. Now the two came up. Hernandez motioned them to stand one at each side. Manuel stood alone, facing the bull.

Manuel waved back the men with the capes. Stepping back cautiously, they saw his face was white and sweating.

Didn't they know enough to keep back? Did they want

40

to catch the bull's eye with the capes after he was fixed and ready? He had enough to worry about without that kind of thing.

The bull was standing, his four feet square, looking at the muleta. Manuel furled the muleta in his left hand. The bull's eyes watched it. His body was heavy on his feet. He carried his head low, but not too low.

Manuel lifted the muleta at him. The bull did not move. Only his eyes watched.

He's all lead, Manuel thought. He's all square. He's framed right. He'll take it.

He thought in bull-fight terms. Sometimes he had a thought and the particular piece of slang would not come into his mind and he could not realize the thought. His instincts and his knowledge worked automatically, and his brain worked slowly and in words. He knew all about bulls. He did not have to think about them. He just did the right thing. His eyes noted things and his body performed the necessary measures without thought. If he thought about it, he would be gone.

Now, facing the bull, he was conscious of many things at the same time. There were the horns, the one splintered, the other smoothly sharp, the need to profile himself toward the left horn, lance himself short and straight, lower the muleta so the bull would follow it, and, going in over the horns, put the sword all the way into a little spot about as big as a five-peseta piece straight in back of the neck, between the sharp pitch of the bull's shoulders. He must do all this and must then come out from between the horns. He was conscious he must do all this, but his only thought was in words: "Corto y derecho."

"Corto y derecho," he thought, furling the muleta. Short and straight. Corto y derecho, he drew the sword out of the muleta, profiled on the splintered left horn, dropped the muleta across his body, so his right hand with the sword on the level with his eye made the sign of the cross, and, rising on his toes, sighted along the dipping blade of the sword at the spot high up between the bull's shoulders.

Corto y derecho he lanced himself on the bull.

There was a shock, and he felt himself go up in the air. He pushed on the sword as he went up and over, and it flew out of his hand. He hit the ground and the bull was on him. Manuel, lying on the ground, kicked at the bull's muzzle with his slippered feet. Kicking, kicking, the bull after him, missing him in his excitement, bumping him with his head, driving the horns into the sand. Kicking like a man keeping a ball in the air, Manuel kept the bull from getting a clean thrust at him.

Manuel felt the wind on his back from the capes flopping at the bull, and then the bull was gone, gone over him in a rush. Dark, as his belly went over. Not even stepped on.

Manuel stood up and picked up the muleta. Fuentes handed him the sword. It was bent where it had struck the shoulder-blade. Manuel straightened it on his knee and ran toward the bull, standing now beside one of the dead horses. As he ran, his jacket flopped where it had been ripped under his armpit.

"Get him out of there," Manuel shouted to the gypsy. The bull had smelled the blood of the dead horse and ripped into the canvas-cover with his horns. He charged Fuentes's cape, with the canvas hanging from his splintered horn, and the crowd laughed. Out in the ring, he tossed his head to rid himself of the canvas. Hernandez, running up from behind him, grabbed the end of the canvas and neatly lifted it off the horn.

The bull followed it in a half-charge and stopped still. He was on the defensive again. Manuel was walking toward him with the sword and muleta. Manuel swung the muleta before him. The bull would not charge.

Manuel profiled toward the bull, sighting along the dipping blade of the sword. The bull was motionless, seemingly dead on his feet, incapable of another charge.

42

Manuel rose to his toes, sighting along the steel, and charged.

Again there was the shock and he felt himself being borne back in a rush, to strike hard on the sand. There was no chance of kicking this time. The bull was on top of him. Manuel lay as though dead, his head on his arms, and the bull bumped him. Bumped his back, bumped his face in the sand. He felt the horn go into the sand between his folded arms. The bull hit him in the small of the back. His face drove into the sand. The horn drove through one of his sleeves and the bull ripped it off. Manuel was tossed clear and the bull followed the capes.

Manuel got up, found the sword and muleta, tried the point of the sword with his thumb, and then ran toward the barrera for a new sword.

Retana's man handed him the sword over the edge of the barrera.

"Wipe off your face," he said.

Manuel, running again toward the bull, wiped his bloody face with his handkerchief. He had not seen Zurito. Where was Zurito?

The cuadrilla had stepped away from the bull and waited with their capes. The bull stood, heavy and dull again after the action.

Manuel walked toward him with the muleta. He stopped and shook it. The bull did not respond. He passed it right and left, left and right before the bull's muzzle. The bull's eyes watched it and turned with the swing, but he would not charge. He was waiting for Manuel.

Manuel was worried. There was nothing to do but go in. Corto y derecho. He profiled close to the bull, crossed the muleta in front of his body and charged. As he pushed in the sword, he jerked his body to the left to clear the horn. The bull passed him and the sword shot up in the air, twinkling under the arc-lights, to fall red-hilted on the sand.

43

Manuel ran over and picked it up. It was bent and he straightened it over his knee.

As he came running toward the bull, fixed again now, he passed Hernandez standing with his cape.

"He's all bone," the boy said encouragingly.

Manuel nodded, wiping his face. He put the bloody handkerchief in his pocket.

There was the bull. He was close to the barrera now. Damn him. Maybe he was all bone. Maybe there was not any place for the sword to go in. The hell there wasn't! He'd show them.

He tried a pass with the muleta and the bull did not move. Manuel chopped the muleta back and forth in front of the bull. Nothing doing.

He furled the muleta, drew the sword out, profiled and drove in on the bull. He felt the sword buckle as he shoved it in, leaning his weight on it, and then it shot high in the air, end-over-ending into the crowd. Manuel had jerked clear as the sword jumped.

The first cushions thrown down out of the dark missed him. Then one hit him in the face, his bloody face looking toward the crowd. They were coming down fast. Spotting the sand. Somebody threw an empty champagne-bottle from close range. It hit Manuel on the foot. He stood there watching the dark, where the things were coming from. Then something whished through the air and struck by him. Manuel leaned over and picked it up. It was his sword. He straightened it over his knee and gestured with it to the crowd.

"Thank you," he said. "Thank you."

Oh, the dirty bastards! Dirty bastards! Oh, the lousy, dirty bastards! He kicked into a cushion as he ran.

There was the bull. The same as ever. All right, you dirty, lousy bastard!

Manuel passed the muleta in front of the bull's black muzzle.

44

Nothing doing.

You won't! All right. He stepped close and jammed the sharp peak of the muleta into the bull's damp muzzle.

The bull was on him as he jumped back and as he tripped on a cushion he felt the horn go into him, into his side. He grabbed the horn with his two hands and rode backward, holding tight onto the place. The bull tossed him and he was clear. He lay still. It was all right. The bull was gone.

He got up coughing and feeling broken and gone. The dirty bastards!

"Give me the sword," he shouted. "Give me the stuff."

Fuentes came up with the muleta and the sword.

Hernandez put his arm around him.

"Go on to the infirmary, man," he said. "Don't be a damn fool."

"Get away from me," Manuel said. "Get to hell away from me."

He twisted free. Hernandez shrugged his shoulders. Manuel ran toward the bull.

There was the bull standing, heavy, firmly planted.

All right, you bastard! Manuel drew the sword out of the muleta, sighted with the same movement, and flung himself onto the bull. He felt the sword go in all the way. Right up to the guard. Four fingers and his thumb into the bull. The blood was hot on his knuckles, and he was on top of the bull.

The bull lurched with him as he lay on, and seemed to sink; then he was standing clear. He looked at the bull going down slowly over on his side, then suddenly four feet in the air.

Then he gestured at the crowd, his hand warm from the bull blood.

All right, you bastards! He wanted to say something, but he started to cough. It was hot and choking. He looked down for the muleta. He must go over and salute the president. President hell! He was sitting down looking at something. It was the bull. His four feet up. Thick tongue out. Things

45

crawling around on his belly and under his legs. Crawling where the hair was thin. Dead bull. To hell with the bull! To hell with them all! He started to get to his feet and commenced to cough. He sat down again, coughing. Somebody came and pushed him up.

They carried him across the ring to the infirmary, running with him across the sand, standing blocked at the gate as the mules came in, then around under the dark passageway, men grunting as they took him up the stairway, and then laid him down.

The doctor and two men in white were waiting for him. They laid him out on the table. They were cutting away his shirt. Manuel felt tired. His whole chest felt scalding inside. He started to cough and they held something to his mouth. Everybody was very busy.

There was an electric light in his eyes. He shut his eyes.

He heard some one coming very heavily up the stairs. Then he did not hear it. Then he heard a noise far off. That was the crowd. Well, somebody would have to kill his other bull. They had cut away all his shirt. The doctor smiled at him. There was Retana.

"Hello, Retana!" Manuel said. He could not hear his voice.

Retana smiled at him and said something. Manuel could not hear it.

Zurito stood beside the table, bending over where the doctor was working. He was in his picador clothes, without his hat.

Zurito said something to him. Manuel could not hear it.

Zurito was speaking to Retana. One of the men in white smiled and handed Retana a pair of scissors. Retana gave them to Zurito. Zurito said something to Manuel. He could not hear it.

To hell with this operating-table! He'd been on plenty of operating-tables before. He was not going to die. There would be a priest if he was going to die.

Zurito was saying something to him. Holding up the scissors.

That was it. They were going to cut off his coleta. They were going to cut off his pigtail.

Manuel sat up on the operating-table. The doctor stepped back, angry. Some one grabbed him and held him.

"You couldn't do a thing like that, Manos," he said.

He heard suddenly, clearly, Zurito's voice.

"That's all right," Zurito said. "I won't do it. I was joking."

"I was going good," Manuel said. "I didn't have any luck. That was all."

Manuel lay back. They had put something over his face. It was all familiar. He inhaled deeply. He felt very tired. He was very, very tired. They took the thing away from his face.

"I was going good," Manuel said weakly. "I was going great."

Retana looked at Zurito and started for the door.

"I'll stay here with him," Zurito said.

Retana shrugged his shoulders.

Manuel opened his eyes and looked at Zurito.

"Wasn't I going good, Manos?" he asked, for confirmation.

"Sure," said Zurito. "You were going great."

The doctor's assistant put the cone over Manuel's face and he inhaled deeply. Zurito stood awkwardly, watching.

Sherwood Anderson

THE EGG

MY FATHER was, I am sure, intended by nature to be a cheerful, kindly man. Until he was thirty-four years old he worked as a farm-hand for a man named Thomas Butterworth whose place lay near the town of Bidwell, Ohio. He had then a horse of his own and on Saturday evenings drove into town to spend a few hours in social intercourse with other farm-hands. In town he drank several glasses of beer and stood about in Ben Head's saloon—crowded on Saturday evenings with visiting farm-hands. Songs were sung and glasses thumped on the bar. At ten o'clock father drove home along a lonely country road, made his horse comfortable for the night and himself went to bed, quite happy in his position in life. He had at that time no notion of trying to rise in the world.

It was in the spring of his thirty-fifth year that father married my mother, then a country school-teacher, and in the following spring I came wriggling and crying into the world. Something happened to the two people. They became ambitious. The American passion for getting up in the world took possession of them.

It may have been that mother was responsible. Being a school-teacher she had no doubt read books and magazines. She had, I presume, read of how Garfield, Lincoln, and other Americans rose from poverty to fame and greatness and as I lay beside her—in the days of her lying-in—she may have dreamed that I would some day rule men and cities. At any rate she induced father to give up his place as a farm-hand, sell his horse and embark on an independent enterprise of his own. She was a tall silent woman with a long nose and trou-

48

bled grey eyes. For herself she wanted nothing. For father and myself she was incurably ambitious.

The first venture into which the two people went turned out badly. They rented ten acres of poor stony land on Griggs's Road, eight miles from Bidwell, and launched into chicken raising. I grew into boyhood on the place and got my first impressions of life there. From the beginning they were impressions of disaster and if, in my turn, I am a gloomy man inclined to see the darker side of life, I attribute it to the fact that what should have been for me the happy joyous days of childhood were spent on a chicken farm.

One unversed in such matters can have no notion of the many and tragic things that can happen to a chicken. It is born out of an egg, lives for a few weeks as a tiny fluffy thing such as you will see pictured on Easter cards, then becomes hideously naked, eats quantities of corn and meal bought by the sweat of your father's brow, gets diseases called pip, cholera, and other names, stands looking with stupid eyes at the sun, becomes sick and dies. A few hens and now and then a rooster, intended to serve God's mysterious ends, struggle through to maturity. The hens lay eggs out of which come other chickens and the dreadful cycle is thus made complete. It is all unbelievably complex. Most philosophers must have been raised on chicken farms. One hopes for so much from a chicken and is so dreadfully disillusioned. Small chickens, just setting out on the journey of life, look so bright and alert and they are in fact so dreadfully stupid. They are so much like people they mix one up in one's judgments of life. If disease does not kill them they wait until your expectations are thoroughly aroused and then walk under the wheels of a wagon—to go squashed and dead back to their maker. Vermin infest their youth, and fortunes must be spent for curative powders. In later life I have seen how a literature has been built up on the subject of fortunes to be made out of the raising of chickens. It is intended to be read by the gods who have just eaten of the tree of the knowledge of good and evil. It is a hopeful literature and declares that much may be done by simple ambitious people who own a few hens. Do not be led astray by it. It was not written for you. Go hunt for gold on the frozen hills of Alaska, put your faith in the honesty of a politician, believe if you will that the world is daily growing better and that good will triumph over evil, but do not read and believe the literature that is written concerning the hen. It was not written for you.

I, however, digress. My tale does not primarily concern itself with the hen. If correctly told it will centre on the egg. For ten years my father and mother struggled to make our chicken farm pay and then they gave up that struggle and began another. They moved into the town of Bidwell, Ohio and embarked in the restaurant business. After ten years of worry with incubators that did not hatch, and with tiny—and in their own way lovely—balls of fluff that passed on into semi-naked pullethood and from that into dead henhood, we threw all aside and packing our belongings on a wagon drove down Griggs's Road toward Bidwell, a tiny caravan of hope looking for a new place from which to start on our upward journey through life.

We must have been a sad looking lot, not, I fancy, unlike refugees fleeing from a battlefield. Mother and I walked in the road. The wagon that contained our goods had been borrowed for the day from Mr. Albert Griggs, a neighbor. Out of its sides stuck the legs of cheap chairs and at the back of the pile of beds, tables, and boxes filled with kitchen utensils was a crate of live chickens, and on top of that the baby carriage in which I had been wheeled about in my infancy. Why we stuck to the baby carriage I don't know. It was unlikely other children would be born and the wheels were broken. People who have few possessions cling tightly to those they have. That is one of the facts that make life so discouraging.

Father rode on top of the wagon. He was then a bald-headed man of forty-five, a little fat and from long association with mother and the chickens he had become habitually silent and discouraged. All during our ten years on the chicken farm he had worked as a laborer on neighboring farms and most of the money he had earned had been spent for remedies to cure chicken diseases, on Wilmer's White Wonder Cholera Cure or Professor Bidlow's Egg Producer or some other preparations that mother found advertised in the poultry papers. There were two little patches of hair on father's head just above his ears. I remember that as a child I used to sit looking at him when he had gone to sleep in a chair before the stove on Sunday afternoons in the winter. I had at that time already begun to read books and have notions of my own and the bald path that led over the top of his head was, I fancied, something like a broad road, such a road as Caesar might have made on which to lead his legions out of Rome and into the wonders of an unknown world. The tufts of hair that grew above father's ears were, I thought, like forests. I fell into a half-sleeping, half-waking state and dreamed I was a tiny thing going along the road into a far beautiful place where there were no chicken farms and where life was a happy eggless affair.

One might write a book concerning our flight from the chicken farm into town. Mother and I walked the entire eight miles—she to be sure that nothing fell from the wagon and I to see the wonders of the world. On the seat of the wagon beside father was his greatest treasure. I will tell you of that.

On a chicken farm where hundreds and even thousands of chickens come out of eggs surprising things sometimes happen. Grotesques are born out of eggs as out of people. The accident does not often occur—perhaps once in a thousand births. A chicken is, you see, born that has four legs, two pairs of wings, two heads or what not. The things do not live. They go quickly back to the hand of their maker that has for a moment trembled. The fact that the poor little things could not live was one of the tragedies of life to father. He

51

had some sort of notion that if he could but bring into hen-hood or roosterhood a five-legged hen or a two-headed rooster his fortune would be made. He dreamed of taking the wonder about to county fairs and of growing rich by exhibiting it to other farm-hands.

At any rate he saved all the little monstrous things that had been born on our chicken farm. They were preserved in alcohol and put each in its own glass bottle. These he had carefully put into a box and on our journey into town it was carried on the wagon seat beside him. He drove the horses with one hand and with the other clung to the box. When we got to our destination the box was taken down at once and the bottles removed. All during our days as keepers of a restaurant in the town of Bidwell, Ohio, the grotesques in their little glass bottles sat on a shelf back of the counter. Mother sometimes protested but father was a rock on the subject of his treasure. The grotesques were, he declared, valuable. People, he said, liked to look at strange and wonderful things.

Did I say that we embarked in the restaurant business in the town of Bidwell, Ohio? I exaggerated a little. The town itself lay at the foot of a low hill and on the shore of a small river. The railroad did not run through the town and the station was a mile away to the north at a place called Pickle-ville. There had been a cider mill and pickle factory at the station, but before the time of our coming they had both gone out of business. In the morning and in the evening busses came down to the station along a road called Turner's Pike from the hotel on the main street of Bidwell. Our going to the out of the way place to embark in the restaurant business was mother's idea. She talked of it for a year and then one day went off and rented an empty store building opposite the railroad station. It was her idea that the restaurant would be profitable. Travelling men, she said, would be always waiting around to take trains out of town and town people would come to the station to await incoming trains. They would come to the restaurant to buy pieces of pie and drink

52

coffee. Now that I am older I know that she had another motive in going. She was ambitious for me. She wanted me to rise in the world, to get into a town school and become a man of the towns.

At Pickleville father and mother worked hard as they always had done. At first there was the necessity of putting our place into shape to be a restaurant. That took a month. Father built a shelf on which he put tins of vegetables. He painted a sign on which he put his name in large red letters. Below his name was the sharp command—"EAT HERE"—that was so seldom obeyed. A show case was bought and filled with cigars and tobacco. Mother scrubbed the floor and the walls of the room. I went to school in the town and was glad to be away from the farm and from the presence of the discouraged, sad-looking chickens. Still I was not very joyous. In the evening I walked home from school along Turner's Pike and remembered the children I had seen playing in the town school yard. A troop of little girls had gone hopping about and singing. I tried that. Down along the frozen road I went hopping solemnly on one leg. "Hippity Hop To The Barber Shop," I sang shrilly. Then I stopped and looked doubtfully about. I was afraid of being seen in my gay mood. It must have seemed to me that I was doing a thing that should not be done by one who, like myself, had been raised on a chicken farm where death was a daily visitor.

Mother decided that our restaurant should remain open at night. At ten in the evening a passenger train went north past our door followed by a local freight. The freight crew had switching to do in Pickleville and when the work was done they came to our restaurant for hot coffee and food. Sometimes one of them ordered a fried egg. In the morning at four they returned north-bound and again visited us. A little trade began to grow up. Mother slept at night and during the day tended the restaurant and fed our boarders while father slept. He slept in the same bed mother had occupied during the night and I went off to the town of Bidwell and

53

to school. During the long nights, while mother and I slept, father cooked meats that were to go into sandwiches for the lunch baskets of our boarders. Then an idea in regard to getting up in the world came into his head. The American spirit took hold of him. He also became ambitious.

In the long nights when there was little to do father had time to think. That was his undoing. He decided that he had in the past been an unsuccessful man because he had not been cheerful enough and that in the future he would adopt a cheerful outlook on life. In the early morning he came upstairs and got into bed with mother. She woke and the two talked. From my bed in the corner I listened.

It was father's idea that both he and mother should try to entertain the people who came to eat at our restaurant. I cannot now remember his words, but he gave the impression of one about to become in some obscure way a kind of public entertainer. When people, particularly young people from the town of Bidwell, came into our place, as on very rare occasions they did, bright entertaining conversation was to be made. From father's words I gathered that something of the jolly inn-keeper effect was to be sought. Mother must have been doubtful from the first, but she said nothing discouraging. It was father's notion that a passion for the company of himself and mother would spring up in the breasts of the younger people of the town of Bidwell. In the evening bright happy groups would come singing down Turner's Pike. They would troop shouting with joy and laughter into our place. There would be song and festivity. I do not mean to give the impression that father spoke so elaborately of the matter. He was as I have said an uncommunicative man. "They want some place to go. I tell you they want some place to go," he said over and over. That was as far as he got. My own imagination has filled in the blanks.

For two or three weeks this notion of father's invaded our house. We did not talk much, but in our daily lives tried earnestly to make smiles take the place of glum looks. Mother smiled at the boarders and I, catching the infection, smiled at our cat. Father became a little feverish in his anxiety to please. There was no doubt, lurking somewhere in him, a touch of the spirit of the showman. He did not waste much of his ammunition on the railroad men he served at night but seemed to be waiting for a young man or woman from Bidwell to come in to show what he could do. On the counter in the restaurant there was a wire basket kept always filled with eggs, and it must have been before his eyes when the idea of being entertaining was born in his brain. There was something pre-natal about the way eggs kept themselves connected with the development of his idea. At any rate an egg ruined his new impulse in life. Late one night I was awakened by a roar of anger coming from father's throat. Both mother and I sat upright in our beds. With trembling hands she lighted a lamp that stood on a table by her head. Downstairs the front door of our restaurant went shut with a bang and in a few minutes father tramped up the stairs. He held an egg in his hand and his hand trembled as though he were having a chill. There was a half insane light in his eyes. As he stood glaring at us I was sure he intended throwing the egg at either mother or me. Then he laid it gently on the table beside the lamp and dropped on his knees beside mother's bed. He began to cry like a boy and I, carried away by his grief, cried with him. The two of us filled the little upstairs room with our wailing voices. It is ridiculous, but of the picture we made I can remember only the fact that mother's hand continually stroked the bald path that ran across the top of his head. I have forgotten what mother said to him and how she induced him to tell her of what had happened downstairs. His explanation also has gone out of my mind. I remember only my own grief and fright and the shiny path over father's head glowing in the lamp light as he knelt by the bed.

As to what happened downstairs. For some unexplainable reason I know the story as well as though I had been a witness to my father's discomfiture. One in time gets to know many unexplainable things. On that evening young Joe Kane, son of a merchant of Bidwell, came to Pickleville to meet his father, who was expected on the ten o'clock evening train from the South. The train was three hours late and Joe came into our place to loaf about and to wait for its arrival. The local freight train came in and the freight crew were fed. Joe was left alone in the restaurant with father.

From the moment he came into our place the Bidwell young man must have been puzzled by my father's actions. It was his notion that father was angry at him for hanging around. He noticed that the restaurant keeper was apparently disturbed by his presence and he thought of going out. However, it began to rain and he did not fancy the long walk to town and back. He bought a five-cent cigar and ordered a cup of coffee. He had a newspaper in his pocket and took it out and began to read. "I'm waiting for the evening train. It's late," he said apologetically.

For a long time father, whom Joe Kane had never seen before, remained silently gazing at his visitor. He was no doubt suffering from an attack of stage fright. As so often happens in life he had thought so much and so often of the situation that now confronted him that he was somewhat nervous in its presence.

For one thing, he did not know what to do with his hands. He thrust one of them nervously over the counter and shook hands with Joe Kane. "How-de-do," he said. Joe Kane put his newspaper down and stared at him. Father's eye lighted on the basket of eggs that sat on the counter and he began to talk. "Well," he began hesitatingly, "well, you have heard of Christopher Columbus, eh?" He seemed to be angry. "That Christopher Columbus was a cheat," he declared emphatically. "He talked of making an egg stand on its end. He talked, he did, and then he went and broke the end of the egg."

My father seemed to his visitor to be beside himself at the
56

duplicity of Christopher Columbus. He muttered and swore. He declared it was wrong to teach children that Christopher Columbus was a great man when, after all, he cheated at the critical moment. He had declared he would make an egg stand on end and then when his bluff had been called he had done a trick. Still grumbling at Columbus, father took an egg from the basket on the counter and began to walk up and down. He rolled the egg between the palms of his hands. He smiled genially. He began to mumble words regarding the effect to be produced on an egg by the electricity that comes out of the human body. He declared that without breaking its shell and by virtue of rolling it back and forth in his hands he could stand the egg on its end. He explained that the warmth of his hands and the gentle rolling movement he gave the egg created a new centre of gravity, and Joe Kane was mildly interested. "I have handled thousands of eggs," father said. "No one knows more about eggs than I do."

He stood the egg on the counter and it fell on its side. He tried the trick again and again, each time rolling the egg between the palms of his hands and saying the words regarding the wonders of electricity and the laws of gravity. When after a half hour's effort he did succeed in making the egg stand for a moment he looked up to find that his visitor was no longer watching. By the time he had succeeded in calling Joe Kane's attention to the success of his effort the egg had again rolled over and lay on its side.

Afire with the showman's passion and at the same time a good deal disconcerted by the failure of his first effort, father now took the bottles containing the poultry monstrosities down from their place on the shelf and began to show them to his visitor. "How would you like to have seven legs and two heads like this fellow?" he asked, exhibiting the most remarkable of his treasures. A cheerful smile played over his face. He reached over the counter and tried to slap Joe Kane on the shoulder as he had seen men do in Ben Head's saloon when he was a young farm-hand and drove to town on Saturday evenings. His visitor was made a little ill by the sight of the body of the terribly deformed bird floating in the alcohol in the bottle and got up to go. Coming from behind the counter father took hold of the young man's arm and led him back to his seat. He grew a little angry and for a moment had to turn his face away and force himself to smile. Then he put the bottles back on the shelf. In an outburst of generosity he fairly compelled Joe Kane to have a fresh cup of coffee and another cigar at his expense. Then he took a pan and filling it with vinegar, taken from a jug that sat beneath the counter, he declared himself about to do a new trick. "I will heat this egg in this pan of vinegar," he said. "Then I will put it through the neck of a bottle without breaking the shell. When the egg is inside the bottle it will resume its normal shape and the shell will become hard again. Then I will give the bottle with the egg in it to you. You can take it about with you wherever you go. People will want to know how you got the egg in the bottle. Don't tell them. Keep them guessing. That is the way to have fun with this trick."

Father grinned and winked at his visitor. Joe Kane decided that the man who confronted him was mildly insane but harmless. He drank the cup of coffee that had been given him and began to read his paper again. When the egg had been heated in vinegar father carried it on a spoon to the counter and going into a back room got an empty bottle. He was angry because his visitor did not watch him as he began to do his trick, but nevertheless went cheerfully to work. For a long time he struggled, trying to get the egg to go through the neck of the bottle. He put the pan of vinegar back on the stove, intending to reheat the egg, then picked it up and burned his fingers. After a second bath in the hot vinegar the shell of the egg had been softened a little but not enough for his purpose. He worked and worked and a spirit of desperate determination took possession of him. When he thought that at last the trick was about to be consummated the delayed train came in at the station and Joe Kane started to go nonchalantly out at the door. Father made a last desperate effort to conquer the egg and make it do the thing that would establish his reputation as one who knew how to entertain guests who came into his restaurant. He worried the egg. He attempted to be somewhat rough with it. He swore and the sweat stood out on his forehead. The egg broke under his hand. When the contents spurted over his clothes, Joe Kane, who had stopped at the door, turned and laughed.

A roar of anger rose from my father's throat. He danced and shouted a string of inarticulate words. Grabbing another egg from the basket on the counter, he threw it, just missing the head of the young man as he dodged through the door and escaped.

Father came upstairs to mother and me with an egg in his hand. I do not know what he intended to do. I imagine he had some idea of destroying it, of destroying all eggs, and that he intended to let mother and me see him begin. When, however, he got into the presence of mother something happened to him. He laid the egg gently on the table and dropped on his knees by the bed as I have already explained. He later decided to close the restaurant for the night and to come upstairs and get into bed. When he did so he blew out the light and after much muttered conversation both he and mother went to sleep. I suppose I went to sleep also, but my sleep was troubled. I awoke at dawn and for a long time looked at the egg that lay on the table. I wondered why eggs had to be and why from the egg came the hen who again laid the egg. The question got into my blood. It has stayed there, I imagine, because I am the son of my father. At any rate, the problem remains unsolved in my mind. And that, I conclude, is but another evidence of the complete and final triumph of the egg—at least as far as my family is concerned.

Stephen Vincent Benét

THE DEVIL AND DANIEL WEBSTER

IT'S A story they tell in the border country, where Massachusetts joins Vermont and New Hampshire.

Yes, Dan'l Webster's dead—or, at least, they buried him. But every time there's a thunderstorm around Marshfield, they say you can hear his rolling voice in the hollows of the sky. And they say that if you go to his grave and speak loud and clear, "Dan'l Webster—Dan'l Webster!" the ground'll begin to shiver and the trees begin to shake. And after a while you'll hear a deep voice saying, "Neighbor, how stands the Union?" Then you better answer the Union stands as she stood, rock-bottomed and copper-sheathed, one and indivisible, or he's liable to rear right out of the ground. At least, that's what I was told when I was a youngster.

You see, for a while, he was the biggest man in the country. He never got to be President, but he was the biggest man. There were thousands that trusted in him right next to God Almighty, and they told stories about him and all the things that belonged to him that were like the stories of patriarchs and such. They said, when he stood up to speak, stars and stripes came right out in the sky, and once he spoke against a river and made it sink into the ground. They said, when he walked the woods with his fishing rod, Killall, the trout would jump out of the streams right into his pockets, for they knew it was no use putting up a fight against him; and, when he argued a case, he could turn on the harps of the blessed and the shaking of the earth underground. That was the kind of man he was, and his big farm up at Marshfield was suitable to him. The chickens he raised were all white meat down through the drumsticks, the cows were tended like children, and the big ram he called Goliath had horns with a curl like a morning-glory vine and could butt through an iron door. But Dan'l wasn't one of your gentlemen farmers; he knew all the ways of the land, and he'd be up by candlelight to see that the chores got done. A man with a mouth like a mastiff, a brow like a mountain and eyes like burning anthracite—that was Dan'l Webster in his prime. And the biggest case he argued never got written down in the books, for he argued it against the devil, nip and tuck and no holds barred. And this is the way I used to hear it told.

There was a man named Jabez Stone, lived at Cross Corners, New Hampshire. He wasn't a bad man to start with, but he was an unlucky man. If he planted corn, he got borers; if he planted potatoes, he got blight. He had good-enough land, but it didn't prosper him; he had a decent wife and children, but the more children he had, the less there was to feed them. If stones cropped up in his neighbor's field, boulders boiled up in his; if he had a horse with the spavins, he'd trade it for one with the staggers and give something extra. There's some folks bound to be like that, apparently. But one day Jabez Stone got sick of the whole business.

He'd been plowing that morning and he'd just broke the plowshare on a rock that he could have sworn hadn't been there yesterday. And, as he stood looking at the plowshare, the off horse began to cough—that ropy kind of cough that means sickness and horse doctors. There were two children down with the measles, his wife was ailing, and he had a whitlow on his thumb. It was about the last straw for Jabez Stone. "I vow," he said, and he looked around him kind of desperate—"I vow it's enough to make a man want to sell his soul to the devil! And I would, too, for two cents!"

Then he felt a kind of queerness come over him at having said what he'd said; though, naturally, being a New Hampshireman, he wouldn't take it back. But, all the same, when it got to be evening and, as far as he could see, no notice had been taken, he felt relieved in his mind, for he was a religious man. But notice is always taken, sooner or later, just like the Good Book says. And, sure enough, next day, about supper-time, a soft-spoken, dark-dressed stranger drove up in a handsome buggy and asked for Jabez Stone.

Well, Jabez told his family it was a lawyer, come to see him about a legacy. But he knew who it was. He didn't like the looks of the stranger, nor the way he smiled with his teeth. They were white teeth, and plentiful—some say they were filed to a point, but I wouldn't vouch for that. And he didn't like it when the dog took one look at the stranger and ran away howling, with his tail between his legs. But having passed his word, more or less, he stuck to it, and they went out behind the barn and made their bargain. Jabez Stone had to prick his finger to sign, and the stranger lent him a silver pin. The wound healed clean, but it left a little white scar.

II

After that, all of a sudden, things began to pick up and prosper for Jabez Stone. His cows got fat and his horses sleek, his crops were the envy of the neighborhood, and lightning might strike all over the valley, but it wouldn't strike his barn. Pretty soon, he was one of the prosperous people of the county; they asked him to stand for selectman, and he stood for it; there began to be talk of running him for state senate. All in all, you might say the Stone family was as happy and contented as cats in a dairy. And so they were, except for Jabez Stone.

He'd been contented enough, the first few years. It's a great thing when bad luck turns; it drives most other things out of your head. True, every now and then, especially in rainy weather, the little white scar on his finger would give him a twinge. And once a year, punctual as clockwork, the stranger with the handsome buggy would come driving by. But the sixth year, the stranger lighted, and, after that, his peace was over for Jabez Stone.

The stranger came up through the lower field, switching his boots with a cane—they were handsome black boots, but

Jabez Stone never liked the look of them, particularly the toes. And, after he'd passed the time of day, he said, "Well, Mr. Stone, you're a hummer! It's a very pretty property you've got here, Mr. Stone."

"Well, some might favor it and others might not," said Jabez Stone, for he was a New Hampshireman.

"Oh, no need to decry your industry!" said the stranger, very easy, showing his teeth in a smile. "After all, we know what's been done, and it's been according to contract and specifications. So when—ahem—the mortgage falls due next year, you shouldn't have any regrets."

"Speaking of that mortgage, mister," said Jabez Stone, and he looked around for help to the earth and the sky, "I'm beginning to have one or two doubts about it."

"Doubts?" said the stranger, not quite so pleasantly.

"Why, yes," said Jabez Stone. "This being the U. S. A. and me always having been a religious man." He cleared his throat and got bolder. "Yes, sir," he said, "I'm beginning to have considerable doubts as to that mortgage holding in court."

"There's courts and courts," said the stranger, clicking his teeth. "Still, we might as well have a look at the original document." And he hauled out a big black pocketbook, full of papers. "Sherwin, Slater, Stevens, Stone," he muttered. "I, Jabez Stone, for a term of seven years—Oh, it's quite in order, I think."

But Jabez Stone wasn't listening, for he saw something else flutter out of the black pocketbook. It was something that looked like a moth, but it wasn't a moth. And as Jabez Stone stared at it, it seemed to speak to him in a small sort of piping voice, terrible small and thin, but terrible human.

"Neighbor Stone!" it squeaked. "Neighbor Stone! Help me! For God's sake, help me!"

But before Jabez Stone could stir hand or foot, the stranger whipped out a big bandanna handkerchief, caught the creature in it, just like a butterfly, and started tying up the ends of the bandanna.

"Sorry for the interruption," he said. "As I was saying—"

But Jabez Stone was shaking all over like a scared horse. "That's Miser Stevens' voice!" he said, in a croak. "And you've got him in your handkerchief!"

The stranger looked a little embarrassed.

"Yes, I really should have transferred him to the collecting box," he said with a simper, "but there were some rather unusual specimens there and I didn't want them crowded. Well, well, these little contretemps will occur."

"I don't know what you mean by contertan," said Jabez Stone, "but that was Miser Stevens' voice! And he ain't dead! You can't tell me he is! He was just as spry and mean as a woodchuck, Tuesday!"

"In the midst of life—" said the stranger, kind of pious. "Listen!" Then a bell began to toll in the valley and Jabez Stone listened, with the sweat running down his face. For he knew it was tolled for Miser Stevens and that he was dead.

"These long-standing accounts," said the stranger with a sigh; "one really hates to close them. But business is business."

He still had the bandanna in his hand, and Jabez Stone felt sick as he saw the cloth struggle and flutter.

"Are they all as small as that?" he asked hoarsely.

"Small?" said the stranger. "Oh, I see what you mean. Why, they vary." He measured Jabez Stone with his eyes, and his teeth showed. "Don't worry, Mr. Stone," he said. "You'll go with a very good grade. I wouldn't trust you outside the collecting box. Now, a man like Dan'l Webster, of course—well, we'd have to build a special box for him, and even at that, I imagine the wing spread would astonish you. He'd certainly be a prize. I wish we could see our way clear to him. But, in your case, as I was saying—"

"Put that handkerchief away!" said Jabez Stone, and he

64

began to beg and to pray. But the best he could get at the end was a three years' extension, with conditions.

But till you make a bargain like that, you've got no idea of how fast four years can run. By the last months of those years, Jabez Stone's known all over the state and there's talk of running him for governor—and it's dust and ashes in his mouth. For every day, when he gets up, he thinks, "There's one more night gone," and every night when he lies down, he thinks of the black pocketbook and the soul of Miser Stevens, and it makes him sick at heart. Till, finally, he can't bear it any longer, and, in the last days of the last year, he hitches up his horse and drives off to seek Dan'l Webster. For Dan'l was born in New Hampshire, only a few miles from Cross Corners, and it's well known that he has a particular soft spot for old neighbors.

III

It was early in the morning when he got to Marshfield, but Dan'l was up already, talking Latin to the farm hands and wrestling with the ram, Goliath, and trying out a new trotter and working up speeches to make against John C. Calhoun. But when he heard a New Hampshireman had come to see him, he dropped everything else he was doing, for that was Dan'l's way. He gave Jabez Stone a breakfast that five men couldn't eat, went into the living history of every man and woman in Cross Corners, and finally asked him how he could serve him.

Jabez Stone allowed that it was a kind of mortgage case.

"Well, I haven't pleaded a mortgage case in a long time, and I don't generally plead now, except before the Supreme Court," said Dan'l, "but if I can, I'll help you."

"Then I've got hope for the first time in ten years," said Jabez Stone, and told him the details.

Dan'l walked up and down as he listened, hands behind his back, now and then asking a question, now and then plunging his eyes at the floor, as if they'd bore through it

65

like gimlets. When Jabez Stone had finished, Dan'l puffed out his cheeks and blew. Then he turned to Jabez Stone and a smile broke over his face like the sunrise over Monadnock.

"You've certainly given yourself the devil's own row to hoe, Neighbor Stone," he said, "but I'll take your case."

"You'll take it?" said Jabez Stone, hardly daring to believe.

"Yes," said Dan'l Webster. "I've got about seventy-five other things to do and the Missouri Compromise to straighten out, but I'll take your case. For if two New Hampshiremen aren't a match for the devil, we might as well give the country back to the Indians."

Then he shook Jabez Stone by the hand and said, "Did you come down here in a hurry?"

"Well, I admit I made time," said Jabez Stone.

"You'll go back faster," said Dan'l Webster, and he told 'em to hitch up Constitution and Constellation to the carriage. They were matched grays with one white forefoot, and they stepped like greased lightning.

Well, I won't describe how excited and pleased the whole Stone family was to have the great Dan'l Webster for a guest, when they finally got there. Jabez Stone had lost his hat on the way, blown off when they overtook a wind, but he didn't take much account of that. But after supper he sent the family off to bed, for he had most particular business with Mr. Webster. Mrs. Stone wanted them to sit in the front parlor, but Dan'l Webster knew front parlors and said he preferred the kitchen. So it was there they sat, waiting for the stranger, with a jug on the table between them and a bright fire on the hearth—the stranger being scheduled to show up on the stroke of midnight, according to specification.

Well, most men wouldn't have asked for better company than Dan'l Webster and a jug. But with every tick of the clock Jabez Stone got sadder and sadder. His eyes roved round, and though he sampled the jug you could see he couldn't taste it. Finally, on the stroke of 11:30 he reached over and grabbed Dan'l Webster by the arm.

"Mr. Webster, Mr. Webster!" he said, and his voice was shaking with fear and a desperate courage. "For God's sake, Mr. Webster, harness your horses and get away from this place while you can!"

"You've brought me a long way, neighbor, to tell me you don't like my company," said Dan'l Webster, quite peaceable, pulling at the jug.

"Miserable wretch that I am!" groaned Jabez Stone. "I've brought you a devilish way, and now I see my folly. Let him take me if he wills. I don't hanker after it, I must say, but I can stand it. But you're the Union's stay and New Hampshire's pride! He mustn't get you, Mr. Webster! He mustn't get you!"

Dan'l Webster looked at the distracted man, all gray and shaking in the firelight, and laid a hand on his shoulder.

"I'm obliged to you, Neighbor Stone," he said gently. "It's kindly thought of. But there's a jug on the table and a case in hand. And I never left a jug or a case half finished in my life."

And just at that moment there was a sharp rap on the door.

"Ah," said Dan'l Webster, very coolly, "I thought your clock was a trifle slow, Neighbor Stone." He stepped to the door and opened it. "Come in!" he said.

The stranger came in—very dark and tall he looked in the firelight. He was carrying a box under his arm—a black, japanned box with little air holes in the lid. At the sight of the box, Jabez Stone gave a low cry and shrank into a corner of the room.

"Mr. Webster, I presume," said the stranger, very polite, but with his eyes glowing like a fox's deep in the woods.

"Attorney of record for Jabez Stone," said Dan'l Webster, but his eyes were glowing too. "Might I ask your name?"

"I've gone by a good many," said the stranger carelessly.

67

"Perhaps Scratch will do for the evening. I'm often called that in these regions."

Then he sat down at the table and poured himself a drink from the jug. The liquor was cold in the jug, but it came steaming into the glass.

"And now," said the stranger, smiling and showing his teeth, "I shall call upon you, as a law-abiding citizen, to assist me in taking possession of my property."

Well, with that the argument began—and it went hot and heavy. At first, Jabez Stone had a flicker of hope, but when he saw Dan'l Webster being forced back at point after point, he just sat scrunched in his corner, with his eyes on that japanned box. For there wasn't any doubt as to the deed or the signature—that was the worst of it. Dan'l Webster twisted and turned and thumped his fist on the table, but he couldn't get away from that. He offered to compromise the case; the stranger wouldn't hear of it. He pointed out the property had increased in value, and state senators ought to be worth more; the stranger stuck to the letter of the law. He was a great lawyer, Dan'l Webster, but we know who's the King of Lawyers, as the Good Book tells us, and it seemed as if, for the first time, Dan'l Webster had met his match.

Finally, the stranger yawned a little. "Your spirited efforts on behalf of your client do you credit, Mr. Webster," he said, "but if you have no more arguments to adduce, I'm rather pressed for time—" and Jabez Stone shuddered.

Dan'l Webster's brow looked dark as a thundercloud. "Pressed or not, you shall not have this man!" he thundered. "Mr. Stone is an American citizen, and no American citizen may be forced into the service of a foreign prince. We fought England for that in '12 and we'll fight all hell for it again!"

"Foreign?" said the stranger. "And who calls me a foreigner?"

"Well, I never yet heard of the dev—of your claiming American citizenship," said Dan'l Webster with surprise.

"And who with better right?" said the stranger, with one

of his terrible smiles. "When the first wrong was done to the first Indian, I was there. When the first slaver put out for the Congo, I stood on her deck. Am I not in your books and stories and beliefs, from the first settlements on? Am I not spoken of, still, in every church in New England? 'Tis true the North claims me for a Southerner, and the South for a Northerner, but I am neither. I am merely an honest American like yourself—and of the best descent—for, to tell the truth, Mr. Webster, though I don't like to boast of it, my name is older in this country than yours."

"Aha!" said Dan'l Webster, with the veins standing out in his forehead. "Then I stand on the Constitution! I demand a trial for my client!"

"The case is hardly one for an ordinary court," said the stranger, his eyes flickering. "And, indeed, the lateness of the hour—"

"Let it be any court you choose, so it is an American judge and an American jury!" said Dan'l Webster in his pride. "Let it be the quick or the dead; I'll abide the issue!"

"You have said it," said the stranger, and pointed his finger at the door. And with that, and all of a sudden, there was a rushing of wind outside and a noise of footsteps. They came, clear and distinct, through the night. And yet, they were not like the footsteps of living men.

"In God's name, who comes by so late?" cried Jabez Stone, in an ague of fear.

"The jury Mr. Webster demands," said the stranger, sipping at his boiling glass. "You must pardon the rough appearance of one or two; they will have come a long way."

IV

And with that the fire burned blue and the door blew open and twelve men entered, one by one.

If Jabez Stone had been sick with terror before, he was blind with terror now. For there was Walter Butler, the loyalist, who spread fire and horror through the Mohawk

Valley in the times of the Revolution; and there was Simon Girty, the renegade, who saw white men burned at the stake and whooped with the Indians to see them burn. His eyes were green, like a catamount's, and the stains on his hunting shirt did not come from the blood of the deer. King Philip was there, wild and proud as he had been in life, with the great gash in his head that gave him his death wound, and cruel Governor Dale, who broke men on the wheel. There was Morton of Merry Mount, who so vexed the Plymouth Colony, with his flushed, loose, handsome face and his hate of the godly. There was Teach, the bloody pirate, with his black beard curling on his breast. The Reverend John Smeet, with his strangler's hands and his Geneva gown, walked as daintily as he had to the gallows. The red print of the rope was still around his neck, but he carried a perfumed handkerchief in one hand. One and all, they came into the room with the fires of hell still upon them, and the stranger named their names and their deeds as they came, till the tale of twelve was told. Yet the stranger had told the truth—they had all played a part in America.

"Are you satisfied with the jury, Mr. Webster?" said the stranger mockingly, when they had taken their places.

The sweat stood upon Dan'l Webster's brow, but his voice was clear.

"Quite satisfied," he said. "Though I miss General Arnold from the company."

"Benedict Arnold is engaged upon other business," said the stranger, with a glower. "Ah, you asked for a justice, I believe."

He pointed his finger once more, and a tall man, soberly clad in Puritan garb, with the burning gaze of the fanatic, stalked into the room and took his judge's place.

"Justice Hathorne is a jurist of experience," said the stranger. "He presided at certain witch trials once held in Salem. There were others who repented of the business later, but not he."

"Repent of such notable wonders and undertakings?" said the stern old justice. "Nay, hang them—hang them all!" And he muttered to himself in a way that struck ice into the soul of Jabez Stone.

Then the trial began, and, as you might expect, it didn't look anyways good for the defense. And Jabez Stone didn't make much of a witness in his own behalf. He took one look at Simon Girty and screeched, and they had to put him back in his corner in a kind of swoon.

It didn't halt the trial, though; the trial went on, as trials do. Dan'l Webster had faced some hard juries and hanging judges in his time, but this was the hardest he'd ever faced, and he knew it. They sat there with a kind of glitter in their eyes, and the stranger's smooth voice went on and on. Every time he'd raise an objection, it'd be "Objection sustained," but whenever Dan'l objected, it'd be "Objection denied." Well, you couldn't expect fair play from a fellow like this Mr. Scratch.

It got to Dan'l in the end, and he began to heat, like iron in the forge. When he got up to speak he was going to flay that stranger with every trick known to the law, and the judge and jury too. He didn't care if it was contempt of court or what would happen to him for it. He didn't care any more what happened to Jabez Stone. He just got madder and madder, thinking of what he'd say. And yet, curiously enough, the more he thought about it, the less he was able to arrange his speech in his mind.

Till, finally, it was time for him to get up on his feet, and he did so, all ready to bust out with lightnings and denunciations. But before he started he looked over the judge and jury for a moment, such being his custom. And he noticed the glitter in their eyes was twice as strong as before, and they all leaned forward. Like hounds just before they get the fox, they looked, and the blue mist of evil in the room thickened as he watched them. Then he saw what he'd been about to do, and he wiped his forehead, as a man might who's just escaped falling into a pit in the dark.

For it was him they'd come for, not only Jabez Stone. He read it in the glitter of their eyes and in the way the stranger hid his mouth with one hand. And if he fought them with their own weapons, he'd fall into their power; he knew that, though he couldn't have told you how. It was his own anger and horror that burned in their eyes; and he'd have to wipe that out or the case was lost. He stood there for a moment, his black eyes burning like anthracite. And then he began to speak.

He started off in a low voice, though you could hear every word. They say he could call on the harps of the blessed when he chose. And this was just as simple and easy as a man could talk. But he didn't start out by condemning or reviling. He was talking about the things that make a country a country, and a man a man.

And he began with the simple things that everybody's known and felt—the freshness of a fine morning when you're young, and the taste of food when you're hungry, and the new day that's every day when you're a child. He took them up and he turned them in his hands. They were good things for any man. But without freedom, they sickened. And when he talked of those enslaved, and the sorrows of slavery, his voice got like a big bell. He talked of the early days of America and the men who had made those days. It wasn't a spread-eagle speech, but he made you see it. He admitted all the wrong that had ever been done. But he showed how, out of the wrong and the right, the suffering and the starvations, something new had come. And everybody had played a part in it, even the traitors.

Then he turned to Jabez Stone and showed him as he was —an ordinary man who'd had hard luck and wanted to change it. And, because he'd wanted to change it, now he was going to be punished for all eternity. And yet there was good

72

in Jabez Stone, and he showed that good. He was hard and mean, in some ways, but he was a man. There was sadness in being a man, but it was a proud thing too. And he showed what the pride of it was till you couldn't help feeling it. Yes, even in hell, if a man was a man, you'd know it. And he wasn't pleading for any one person any more, though his voice rang like an organ. He was telling the story and the failures and the endless journey of mankind. They got tricked and trapped and bamboozled, but it was a great journey. And no demon that was ever foaled could know the inwardness of it—it took a man to do that.

V

The fire began to die on the hearth and the wind before morning to blow. The light was getting gray in the room when Dan'l Webster finished. And his words came back at the end to New Hampshire ground, and the one spot of land that each man loves and clings to. He painted a picture of that, and to each one of that jury he spoke of things long forgotten. For his voice could search the heart, and that was his gift and his strength. And to one, his voice was like the forest and its secrecy, and to another like the sea and the storms of the sea; and one heard the cry of his lost nation in it, and another saw a little harmless scene he hadn't remembered for years. But each saw something. And when Dan'l Webster finished he didn't know whether or not he'd saved Jabez Stone. But he knew he'd done a miracle. For the glitter was gone from the eyes of judge and jury, and, for the moment, they were men again, and knew they were men.

"The defense rests," said Dan'l Webster, and stood there like a mountain. His ears were still ringing with his speech, and he didn't hear anything else till he heard Judge Hathorne say, "The jury will retire to consider its verdict."

Walter Butler rose in his place and his face had a dark, gay pride on it.

73

"The jury has considered its verdict," he said, and looked the stranger full in the eye. "We find for the defendant, Jabez Stone."

With that, the smile left the stranger's face, but Walter Butler did not flinch.

"Perhaps 'tis not strictly in accordance with the evidence," he said, "but even the damned may salute the eloquence of Mr. Webster."

With that, the long crow of a rooster split the gray morning sky, and judge and jury were gone from the room like a puff of smoke and as if they had never been there. The stranger turned to Dan'l Webster, smiling wryly. "Major Butler was always a bold man," he said. "I had not thought him quite so bold. Nevertheless, my congratulations, as between two gentlemen."

"I'll have that paper first, if you please," said Dan'l Webster, and he took it and tore it into four pieces. It was queerly warm to the touch. "And now," he said, "I'll have you!" and his hand came down like a bear trap on the stranger's arm. For he knew that once you bested anybody like Mr. Scratch in fair fight, his power on you was gone. And he could see that Mr. Scratch knew it too.

The stranger twisted and wriggled, but he couldn't get out of that grip. "Come, come, Mr. Webster," he said, smiling palely. "This sort of thing is ridic—ouch!—is ridiculous. If you're worried about the costs of the case, naturally, I'd be glad to pay—"

"And so you shall!" said Dan'l Webster, shaking him till his teeth rattled. "For you'll sit right down at that table and draw up a document, promising never to bother Jabez Stone nor his heirs or assigns nor any other New Hampshireman till doomsday! For any hades we want to raise in this state, we can raise ourselves, without assistance from strangers."

"Ouch!" said the stranger. "Ouch! Well, they never did run very big to the barrel, but—ouch!—I agree!"

74

So he sat down and drew up the document. But **Dan'l** Webster kept his hand on his coat collar all the time.

"And, now, may I go?" said the stranger, quite humble, when Dan'l'd seen the document was in proper and legal form.

"Go?" said Dan'l, giving him another shake. "I'm still trying to figure out what I'll do with you. For you've settled the costs of the case, but you haven't settled with me. I think I'll take you back to Marshfield," he said, kind of reflective. "I've got a ram there named Goliath that can butt through an iron door. I'd kind of like to turn you loose in his field and see what he'd do."

Well, with that the stranger began to beg and to plead. And he begged and he pled so humble that finally Dan'l, who was naturally kindhearted, agreed to let him go. The stranger seemed terrible grateful for that and said, just to show they were friends, he'd tell Dan'l's fortune before leaving. So Dan'l agreed to that, though he didn't take much stock in fortunate-tellers ordinarily.

But, naturally, the stranger was a little different. Well, he pried and he peered at the lines in Dan'l's hands. And he told him one thing and another that was quite remarkable. But they were all in the past.

"Yes, all that's true, and it happened," said Dan'l Webster. "But what's to come in the future?"

The stranger grinned, kind of happily, and shook his head. "The future's not as you think it," he said. "It's dark. You have a great ambition, Mr. Webster."

"I have," said Dan'l firmly, for everybody knew he wanted to be President.

"It seems almost within your grasp," said the stranger, "but you will not attain it. Lesser men will be made President and you will be passed over."

"And, if I am, I'll still be Daniel Webster," said Dan'l. "Say on."

"You have two strong sons," said the stranger, shaking his head. "You look to found a line. But each will die in war and neither reach greatness."

"Live or die, they are still my sons," said Dan'l Webster. "Say on."

"You have made great speeches," said the stranger. "You will make more."

"Ah," said Dan'l Webster.

"But the last great speech you make will turn many of your own against you," said the stranger. "They will call you Ichabod; they will call you by other names. Even in New England some will say you have turned your coat and sold your country, and their voices will be loud against you till you die."

"So it is an honest speech, it does not matter what men say," said Dan'l Webster. Then he looked at the stranger and their glances locked.

"One question," he said. "I have fought for the Union all my life. Will I see that fight won against those who would tear it apart?"

"Not while you live," said the stranger, grimly, "but it will be won. And after you are dead, there are thousands who will fight for your cause, because of words that you spoke."

"Why, then, you long-barreled, slab-sided, lantern-jawed, fortune-telling note shaver!" said Dan'l Webster, with a great roar of laughter, "be off with you to your own place before I put my mark on you! For, by the thirteen original colonies, I'd go to the Pit itself to save the Union!"

And with that he drew back his foot for a kick that would have stunned a horse. It was only the tip of his shoe that caught the stranger, but he went flying out of the door with his collecting box under his arm.

"And now," said Dan'l Webster, seeing Jabez Stone beginning to rouse from his swoon, "let's see what's left in the jug, for it's dry work talking all night. I hope there's pie for breakfast, Neighbor Stone."

But they say that whenever the devil comes near Marshfield, even now, he gives it a wide berth. And he hasn't been seen in the state of New Hampshire from that day to this. I'm not talking about Massachusetts or Vermont.

Willa Cather

THE SCULPTOR'S FUNERAL

A GROUP of the townspeople stood on the station siding of a little Kansas town, awaiting the coming of the night train, which was already twenty minutes overdue. The snow had fallen thick over everything; in the pale starlight the line of bluffs across the wide, white meadows south of the town made soft, smoke-coloured curves against the clear sky. The men on the siding stood first on one foot and then on the other, their hands thrust deep into their trousers pockets, their overcoats open, their shoulders screwed up with the cold; and they glanced from time to time toward the southeast, where the railroad track wound along the river shore. They conversed in low tones and moved about restlessly, seeming uncertain as to what was expected of them. There was but one of the company who looked as if he knew exactly why he was there, and he kept conspicuously apart; walking to the far end of the platform, returning to the station door, then pacing up the track again, his chin sunk in the high collar of his overcoat, his burly shoulders drooping forward, his gait heavy and dogged. Presently he was approached by a tall, spare, grizzled man clad in a faded Grand Army suit, who shuffled out from the group and advanced with a certain deference, craning his neck forward until his back made the angle of a jack-knife three-quarters open.

"I reckon she's a-goin' to be pretty late agin tonight, Jim," he remarked in a squeaky falsetto. "S'pose it's the snow?"

"I don't know," responded the other man with a shade of annoyance, speaking from out an astonishing cataract of red beard that grew fiercely and thickly in all directions.

The spare man shifted the quill toothpick he was chewing to the other side of his mouth. "It ain't likely that anybody from the East will come with the corpse, I s'pose," he went on reflectively.

"I don't know," responded the other, more curtly than before.

"It's too bad he didn't belong to some lodge or other. I like an order funeral myself. They seem more appropriate for people of some repytation," the spare man continued, with an ingratiating concession in his shrill voice, as he carefully placed his toothpick in his vest pocket. He always carried the flag at the G. A. R. funerals in the town.

The heavy man turned on his heel, without replying, and walked up the siding. The spare man rejoined the uneasy group. "Jim's ez full ez a tick, ez ushel," he commented commiseratingly.

Just then a distant whistle sounded, and there was a shuffling of feet on the platform. A number of lanky boys, of all ages, appeared as suddenly and slimily as eels wakened by the crack of thunder; some came from the waiting-room, where they had been warming themselves by the red stove, or half asleep on the slat benches; others uncoiled themselves from baggage trucks or slid out of express wagons. Two clambered down from the driver's seat of a hearse that stood backed up against the siding. They straightened their stooping shoulders and lifted their heads, and a flash of momentary animation kindled their dull eyes at that cold, vibrant scream,

78

the world-wide call for men. It stirred them like the note of a trumpet; just as it had often stirred the man who was coming home tonight, in his boyhood.

The night express shot, red as a rocket, from out the eastward marsh lands and wound along the river shore under the long lines of shivering poplars that sentinelled the meadows, the escaping steam hanging in grey masses against the pale sky and blotting out the Milky Way. In a moment the red glare from the headlight streamed up the snow-covered track before the siding and glittered on the wet, black rails. The burly man with the dishevelled red beard walked swiftly up the platform toward the approaching train, uncovering his head as he went. The group of men behind him hesitated, glanced questioningly at one another, and awkwardly followed his example. The train stopped, and the crowd shuffled up to the express car just as the door was thrown open, the man in the G. A. R. suit thrusting his head forward with curiosity. The express messenger appeared in the doorway, accompanied by a young man in a long ulster and travelling cap.

"Are Mr. Merrick's friends here?" inquired the young man.

The group on the platform swayed uneasily. Philip Phelps, the banker, responded with dignity: "We have come to take charge of the body. Mr. Merrick's father is very feeble and can't be about."

"Send the agent out here," growled the express messenger, "and tell the operator to lend a hand."

The coffin was got out of its rough-box and down on the snowy platform. The townspeople drew back enough to make room for it and then formed a close semicircle about it, looking curiously at the palm leaf which lay across the black cover. No one said anything. The baggage man stood by his truck, waiting to get at the trunks. The engine panted heavily, and the fireman dodged in and out among the wheels with his yellow torch and long oil-can, snapping the spindle

79

boxes. The young Bostonian, one of the dead sculptor's pupils who had come with the body, looked about him helplessly. He turned to the banker, the only one of that black, uneasy, stoop-shouldered group who seemed enough of an individual to be addressed.

"None of Mr. Merrick's brothers are here?" he asked uncertainly.

The man with the red beard for the first time stepped up and joined the others. "No, they have not come yet; the family is scattered. The body will be taken directly to the house." He stooped and took hold of one of the handles of the coffin.

"Take the long hill road up, Thompson, it will be easier on the horses," called the liveryman as the undertaker snapped the door of the hearse and prepared to mount to the driver's seat.

Laird, the red-bearded lawyer, turned again to the stranger: "We didn't know whether there would be any one with him or not," he explained. "It's a long walk, so you'd better go up in the hack." He pointed to a single battered conveyance, but the young man replied stiffly: "Thank you, but I think I will go up with the hearse. If you don't object," turning to the undertaker, "I'll ride with you."

They clambered up over the wheels and drove off in the starlight up the long, white hill toward the town. The lamps in the still village were shining from under the low, snow-burdened roofs; and beyond, on every side, the plains reached out into emptiness, peaceful and wide as the soft sky itself, and wrapped in a tangible, white silence.

When the hearse backed up to a wooden sidewalk before a naked, weather-beaten frame house, the same composite, ill-defined group that had stood upon the station siding was huddled about the gate. The front yard was an icy-swamp, and a couple of warped planks, extending from the sidewalk to the door, made a sort of rickety footbridge. The gate hung on one hinge, and was opened wide with difficulty.

Steavens, the young stranger, noticed that something black was tied to the knob of the front door.

The grating sound made by the casket, as it was drawn from the hearse, was answered by a scream from the house; the front door was wrenched open, and a tall, corpulent woman rushed out bareheaded into the snow and flung herself upon the coffin, shrieking: "My boy, my boy! And this is how you've come home to me!"

As Steavens turned away and closed his eyes with a shudder of unutterable repulsion, another woman, also tall, but flat and angular, dressed entirely in black, darted out of the house and caught Mrs. Merrick by the shoulders, crying sharply: "Come, come, mother; you mustn't go on like this!" Her tone changed to one of obsequious solemnity as she turned to the banker: "The parlour is ready, Mr. Phelps."

The bearers carried the coffin along the narrow boards, while the undertaker ran ahead with the coffin-rests. They bore it into a large, unheated room that smelled of dampness and disuse and furniture polish, and set it down under a hanging lamp ornamented with jingling glass prisms and before a "Rogers group" of John Alden and Priscilla, wreathed with smilax. Henry Steavens stared about him with the sickening conviction that there had been a mistake, and that he had somehow arrived at the wrong destination. He looked at the clover-green Brussels, the fat plush upholstery, among the hand-painted china placques and panels and vases, for some mark of identification,—for something that might once conceivably have belonged to Harvey Merrick. It was not until he recognized his friend in the crayon portrait of a little boy in kilts and curls, hanging above the piano, that he felt willing to let any of these people approach the coffin.

"Take the lid off, Mr. Thompson; let me see my boy's face," wailed the elder woman between her sobs. This time Steavens looked fearfully, almost beseechingly into her face, red and swollen under its masses of strong, black, shiny hair. He flushed, dropped his eyes, and then, almost incredulously, looked again. There was a kind of power about her face—a kind of brutal handsomeness, even; but it was scarred and furrowed by violence, and so coloured and coarsened by fiercer passions that grief seemed never to have laid a gentle finger there. The long nose was distended and knobbed at the end, and there were deep lines on either side of it; her heavy, black brows almost met across her forehead, her teeth were large and square, and set far apart—teeth that could tear. She filled the room; the men were obliterated, seemed tossed about like twigs in an angry water, and even Steavens felt himself being drawn into the whirlpool.

The daughter—the tall, raw-boned woman in crêpe, with a mourning comb in her hair which curiously lengthened her long face—sat stiffly upon the sofa, her hands, conspicuous for their large knuckles, folded in her lap, her mouth and eyes drawn down, solemnly awaiting the opening of the coffin. Near the door stood a mulatto woman, evidently a servant in the house, with a timid bearing and an emaciated face pitifully sad and gentle. She was weeping silently, the corner of her calico apron lifted to her eyes, occasionally suppressing a long, quivering sob. Steavens walked over and stood beside her.

Feeble steps were heard on the stairs, and an old man, tall and frail, odorous of pipe smoke, with shaggy, unkept grey hair and a dingy beard, tobacco stained about the mouth, entered uncertainly. He went slowly up to the coffin and stood rolling a blue cotton handkerchief between his hands, seeming so pained and embarrassed by his wife's orgy of grief that he had no consciousness of anything else.

"There, there, Annie, dear, don't take on so," he quavered timidly, putting out a shaking hand and awkwardly patting her elbow. She turned and sank upon his shoulder with such violence that he tottered a little. He did not even glance toward the coffin, but continued to look at her with a dull, frightened, appealing expression, as a spaniel looks at the whip. His sunken cheeks slowly reddened and burned with miserable shame. When his wife rushed from the room, her daughter strode after her with set lips. The servant stole up to the coffin, bent over it for a moment, and then slipped away to the kitchen, leaving Steavens, the lawyer, and the father to themselves. The old man stood looking down at his dead son's face. The sculptor's splendid head seemed even more noble in its rigid stillness than in life. The dark hair had crept down upon the wide forehead; the face seemed strangely long, but in it there was not that repose we expect to find in the faces of the dead. The brows were so drawn that there were two deep lines above the beaked nose, and the chin was thrust forward defiantly. It was as though the strain of life had been so sharp and bitter that death could not at once relax the tension and smooth the countenance into perfect peace—as though he were still guarding something precious, which might even yet be wrested from him.

The old man's lips were working under his stained beard. He turned to the lawyer with timid deference: "Phelps and the rest are comin' back to set up with Harve, ain't they?" he asked. "Thank 'ee, Jim, thank 'ee." He brushed the hair back gently from his son's forehead. "He was a good boy, Jim; always a good boy. He was ez gentle ez a child and the kindest of 'em all—only we didn't none of us ever onderstand him." The tears trickled slowly down his beard and dropped upon the sculptor's coat.

"Martin, Martin! Oh, Martin! come here," his wife wailed from the top of the stairs. The old man started timorously: "Yes, Annie, I'm coming." He turned away, hesitated, stood for a moment in miserable indecision; then reached back and patted the dead man's hair softly, and stumbled from the room.

"Poor old man, I didn't think he had any tears left. Seems as if his eyes would have gone dry long ago. At his age nothing cuts very deep," remarked the lawyer.

Something in his tone made Steavens glance up. While the mother had been in the room, the young man had scarcely seen any one else; but now, from the moment he first glanced into Jim Laird's florid face and blood-shot eyes, he knew that he had found what he had been heartsick at not finding before—the feeling, the understanding, that must exist in some one, even here.

The man was red as his beard, with features swollen and blurred by dissipation, and a hot, blazing blue eye. His face was strained—that of a man who is controlling himself with difficulty—and he kept plucking at his beard with a sort of fierce resentment. Steavens, sitting by the window, watched him turn down the glaring lamp, still its jangling pendants with an angry gesture, and then stand with his hands locked behind him, staring down into the master's face. He could not help wondering what link there had been between the porcelain vessel and so sooty a lump of potter's clay.

From the kitchen an uproar was sounding; when the dining-room door opened, the import of it was clear. The mother was abusing the maid for having forgotten to make the dressing for the chicken salad which had been prepared for the watchers. Steavens had never heard anything in the least like it; it was injured, emotional, dramatic abuse, unique and masterly in its excruciating cruelty, as violent and unrestrained as had been her grief of twenty minutes before. With a shudder of disgust the lawyer went into the dining-room and closed the door into the kitchen.

"Poor Roxy's getting it now," he remarked when he came back. "The Merricks took her out of the poor-house years ago; and if her loyalty would let her, I guess the poor old thing could tell tales that would curdle your blood. She's the mulatto woman who was standing in here a while ago, with her apron to her eyes. The old woman is a fury; there never was anybody like her. She made Harvey's life a hell for him when he lived at home; he was so sick ashamed of it. I never could see how he kept himself sweet."

"He was wonderful," said Steavens slowly, "wonderful; but until tonight I have never known how wonderful."

"That is the eternal wonder of it, anyway; that it can come even from such a dung heap as this," the lawyer cried, with a sweeping gesture which seemed to indicate much more than the four walls within which they stood.

"I think I'll see whether I can get a little air. The room is so close I am beginning to feel rather faint," murmured Steavens, struggling with one of the windows. The sash was stuck, however, and would not yield, so he sat down dejectedly and began pulling at his collar. The lawyer came over, loosened the sash with one blow of his red fist and sent the window up a few inches. Steavens thanked him, but the nausea which had been gradually climbing into his throat for the last half hour left him with but one desire—a desperate feeling that he must get away from this place with what was left of Harvey Merrick. Oh, he comprehended well enough now the quiet bitterness of the smile that he had seen so often on his master's lips!

Once when Merrick returned from a visit home, he brought with him a singularly feeling and suggestive bas-relief of a thin, faded old woman, sitting and sewing something pinned to her knee; while a full-lipped, full-blooded little urchin, his trousers held up by a single gallows, stood beside her, impatiently twitching her gown to call her attention to a butterfly he had caught. Steavens, impressed by the tender and delicate modelling of the thin, tired face, had asked him if it were his mother. He remembered the dull flush that had burned up in the sculptor's face.

The lawyer was sitting in a rocking-chair beside the coffin, his head thrown back and his eyes closed. Steavens looked at him earnestly, puzzled at the line of the chin, and wondering why a man should conceal a feature of such distinction under that disfiguring shock of beard. Suddenly, as though he felt the young sculptor's keen glance, Jim Laird opened his eyes.

"Was he always a good deal of an oyster?" he asked abruptly. "He was terribly shy as a boy."

"Yes, he was an oyster, since you put it so," rejoined Steavens. "Although he could be very fond of people, he always gave one the impression of being detached. He disliked violent emotion; he was reflective, and rather distrustful of himself—except, of course, as regarded his work. He was sure enough there. He distrusted men pretty thoroughly and women even more, yet somehow without believing ill of them. He was determined, indeed, to believe the best; but he seemed afraid to investigate."

"A burnt dog dreads the fire," said the lawyer grimly, and closed his eyes.

Steavens went on and on, reconstructing that whole miserable boyhood. All this raw, biting ugliness had been the portion of the man whose mind was to become an exhaustless gallery of beautiful impressions—so sensitive that the mere shadow of a poplar leaf flickering against a sunny wall would be etched and held there for ever. Surely, if ever a man had the magic word in his finger tips, it was Merrick. Whatever he touched, he revealed its holiest secret; liberated it from enchantment and restored it to its pristine loveliness. Upon whatever he had come in contact with, he had left a beautiful record of the experience—a sort of ethereal signature; a scent, a sound, a colour that was his own.

Steavens understood now the real tragedy of his master's life; neither love nor wine, as many had conjectured; but a blow which had fallen earlier and cut deeper than anything else could have done—a shame not his, and yet so unescapably his, to hide in his heart from his very boyhood. And without—the frontier warfare; the yearning of a boy, cast ashore upon a desert of newness and ugliness and sordidness, for all that is chastened and old, and noble with traditions.

At eleven o'clock the tall, flat woman in black announced that the watchers were arriving, and asked them to "step into the dining-room." As Steavens rose, the lawyer said dryly: "You go on—it'll be a good experience for you. I'm

86

not equal to that crowd tonight; I've had twenty years of them."

As Steavens closed the door after him he glanced back at the lawyer, sitting by the coffin in the dim light, with his chin resting on his hand.

The same misty group that had stood before the door of the express car shuffled into the dining-room. In the light of the kerosene lamp they separated and became individuals. The minister, a pale, feeble-looking man with white hair and blond chin-whiskers, took his seat beside a small side table and placed his Bible upon it. The Grand Army man sat down behind the stove and tilted his chair back comfortably against the wall, fishing his quill toothpick from his waistcoat pocket. The two bankers, Phelps and Elder, sat off in a corner behind the dinner-table, where they could finish their discussion of the new usury law and its effect on chattel security loans. The real estate agent, an old man with a smiling, hypocritical face, soon joined them. The coal and lumber dealer and the cattle shipper sat on opposite sides of the hard coal-burner, their feet on the nickel-work. Steavens took a book from his pocket and began to read. The talk around him ranged through various topics of local interest while the house was quieting down. When it was clear that the members of the family were in bed, the Grand Army man hitched his shoulders and, untangling his long legs, caught his heels on the rounds of his chair.

"S'pose there'll be a will, Phelps?" he queried in his weak falsetto.

The banker laughed disagreeably, and began trimming his nails with a pearl-handled pocket-knife.

"There'll scarcely be any need for one, will there?" he queried in his turn.

The restless Grand Army man shifted his position again, getting his knees still nearer his chin. "Why, the ole man says Harve's done right well lately," he chirped.

The other banker spoke up. "I reckon he means by that

87

Harve ain't asked him to mortgage any more farms lately, so as he could go on with his education."

"Seems like my mind don't reach back to a time when Harve wasn't bein' edycated," tittered the Grand Army man.

There was a general chuckle. The minister took out his handkerchief and blew his nose sonorously. Banker Phelps closed his knife with a snap. "It's too bad the old man's sons didn't turn out better," he remarked with reflective authority. "They never hung together. He spent money enough on Harve to stock a dozen cattle-farms, and he might as well have poured it into Sand Creek. If Harve had stayed at home and helped nurse what little they had, and gone into stock on the old man's bottom farm, they might all have been well fixed. But the old man had to trust everything to tenants and was cheated right and left."

"Harve never could have handled stock none," interposed the cattleman. "He hadn't it in him to be sharp. Do you remember when he bought Sander's mules for eight-year olds, when everybody in town knew that Sander's father-in-law give 'em to his wife for a wedding present eighteen years before, an' they was full-grown mules then?"

The company laughed discreetly, and the Grand Army man rubbed his knees with a spasm of childish delight.

"Harve never was much account for anything practical, and he shore was never fond of work," began the coal and lumber dealer. "I mind the last time he was home; the day he left, when the old man was out to the barn helpin' his hand hitch up to take Harve to the train, and Cal Moots was patchin' up the fence; Harve, he come out on the step and sings out, in his ladylike voice: 'Cal Moots, Cal Moots! please come cord my trunk.'"

"That's Harve for you," approved the Grand Army man. "I kin hear him howlin' yet, when he was a big feller in long pants and his mother used to whale him with a rawhide in the barn for lettin' the cows git foundered in the cornfield

88

when he was drivin' 'em home from pasture. He killed a cow of mine that-a-way onct—a pure Jersey and the best milker I had, an' the ole man had to put up for her. Harve, he was watchin' the sun set acrost the marshes when the anamile got away."

"Where the old man made his mistake was in sending the boy East to school," said Phelps, stroking his goatee and speaking in a deliberate, judicial tone. "There was where he got his head full of nonsense. What Harve needed, of all people, was a course in some first-class Kansas City business college."

The letters were swimming before Steavens's eyes. Was it possible that these men did not understand, that the palm on the coffin meant nothing to them? The very name of their town would have remained for ever buried in the postal guide had it not been now and again mentioned in the world in connection with Harvey Merrick's. He remembered what his master had said to him on the day of his death, after the congestion of both lungs had shut off any probability of recovery, and the sculptor had asked his pupil to send his body home. "It's not a pleasant place to be lying while the world is moving and doing and bettering," he had said with a feeble smile, "but it rather seems as though we ought to go back to the place we came from, in the end. The townspeople will come in for a look at me; and after they have had their say, I shan't have much to fear from the judgment of God!"

The cattleman took up the comment. "Forty's young for a Merrick to cash in; they usually hang on pretty well. Probably he helped it along with whisky."

"His mother's people were not long lived, and Harvey never had a robust constitution," said the minister mildly. He would have liked to say more. He had been the boy's Sunday-school teacher, and had been fond of him; but he felt that he was not in a position to speak. His own sons had turned out badly, and it was not a year since one of them

89

had made his last trip home in the express car, shot in a gambling-house in the Black Hills.

"Nevertheless, there is no disputin' that Harve frequently looked upon the wine when it was red, also variegated, and it shore made an oncommon fool of him," moralized the cattleman.

Just then the door leading into the parlour rattled loudly and every one started involuntarily, looking relieved when only Jim Laird came out. The Grand Army man ducked his head when he saw the spark in his blue, blood-shot eye. They were all afraid of Jim; he was a drunkard, but he could twist the law to suit his client's needs as no other man in all western Kansas could do, and there were many who tried. The lawyer closed the door behind him, leaned back against it and folded his arms, cocking his head a little to one side. When he assumed this attitude in the court-room, ears were always pricked up, as it usually foretold a flood of withering sarcasm.

"I've been with you gentlemen before," he began in a dry, even tone, "when you've sat by the coffins of boys born and raised in this town; and, if I remember rightly, you were never any too well satisfied when you checked them up. What's the matter, anyhow? Why is it that reputable young men are as scarce as millionaires in Sand City? It might almost seem to a stranger that there was some way something the matter with your progressive town. Why did Reuben Sayer, the brightest young lawyer you ever turned out, after he had come home from the university as straight as a die, take to drinking and forge a check and shoot himself? Why did Bill Merrit's son die of the shakes in a saloon in Omaha? Why was Mr. Thomas's son, here, shot in a gambling-house? Why did young Adams burn his mill to beat the insurance companies and go to the pen?"

The lawyer paused and unfolded his arms, laying one clenched fist quietly on the table. "I'll tell you why. Because you drummed nothing but money and knavery into their

90

ears from the time they wore knickerbockers; because you carped away at them as you've been carping here tonight, holding our friends Phelps and Elder up to them for their models, as our grandfathers held up George Washington and John Adams. But the boys were young, and raw at the business you put them to, and how could they match coppers with such artists as Phelps and Elder? You wanted them to be successful rascals; they were only unsuccessful ones—that's all the difference. There was only one boy ever raised in this borderland between ruffianism and civilization who didn't come to grief, and you hated Harvey Merrick more for winning out than you hated all the other boys who got under the wheels. Lord, Lord, how you did hate him! Phelps, here, is fond of saying that he could buy and sell us all out any time he's a mind to; but he knew Harve wouldn't have given a tinker's damn for his bank and all his cattlefarms put together; and a lack of appreciation, that way, goes hard with Phelps.

"Old Nimrod thinks Harve drank too much; and this from such as Nimrod and me!

"Brother Elder says Harve was too free with the old man's money—fell short in filial consideration, maybe. Well, we can all remember the very tone in which brother Elder swore his own father was a liar, in the county court; and we all know that the old man came out of that partnership with his son as bare as a sheared lamb. But maybe I'm getting personal, and I'd better be driving ahead at what I want to say."

The lawyer paused a moment, squared his heavy shoulders, and went on: "Harvey Merrick and I went to school together, back East. We were dead in earnest, and we wanted you all to be proud of us some day. We meant to be great men. Even I, and I haven't lost my sense of humour, gentlemen, I meant to be a great man. I came back here to practise, and I found you didn't in the least want me to be a great man. You wanted me to be a shrewd lawyer—oh, yes! Our veteran here wanted me to get him an increase of pension, because he had dyspepsia; Phelps wanted a new county survey that would put the widow Wilson's little bottom farm inside his south line; Elder wanted to lend money at 5 per cent. a month, and get it collected; and Stark here wanted to wheedle old women up in Vermont into investing their annuities in real-estate mortgages that are not worth the paper they are written on. Oh, you needed me hard enough, and you'll go on needing me!

"Well, I came back here and became the damned shyster you wanted me to be. You pretend to have some sort of respect for me; and yet you'll stand up and throw mud at Harvey Merrick, whose soul you couldn't dirty and whose hands you couldn't tie. Oh, you're a discriminating lot of Christians! There have been times when the sight of Harvey's name in some Eastern paper has made me hang my head like a whipped dog; and, again, times when I liked to think of him off there in the world, away from all this hog-wallow, climbing the big, clean up-grade he'd set for himself.

"And we? Now that we've fought and lied and sweated and stolen, and hated as only the disappointed strugglers in a bitter, dead little Western town know how to do, what have we got to show for it? Harvey Merrick wouldn't have given one sunset over your marshes for all you've got put together, and you know it. It's not for me to say why, in the inscrutable wisdom of God, a genius should ever have been called from this place of hatred and bitter waters; but I want this Boston man to know that the drivel he's been hearing here tonight is the only tribute any truly great man could have from such a lot of sick, side-tracked, burnt-dog, land-poor sharks as the here-present financiers of Sand City—upon which town may God have mercy!"

The lawyer thrust out his hand to Steavens as he passed him, caught up his overcoat in the hall, and had left the house before the Grand Army man had had time to lift his ducked head and crane his long neck about at his fellows.

Next day Jim Laird was drunk and unable to attend the

funeral services. Steavens called twice at his office, but was compelled to start East without seeing him. He had a presentiment that he would hear from him again, and left his address on the lawyer's table; but if Laird found it, he never acknowledged it. The thing in him that Harvey Merrick had loved must have gone under ground with Harvey Merrick's coffin; for it never spoke again, and Jim got the cold he died of driving across the Colorado mountains to defend one of Phelps's sons who had got into trouble out there by cutting government timber.

Ring Lardner

HAIRCUT

I GOT another barber that comes over from Carterville and helps me out Saturdays, but the rest of the time I can get along all right alone. You can see for yourself that this ain't no New York City and besides that, the most of the boys works all day and don't have no leisure to drop in here and get themselves prettied up.

You're a newcomer, ain't you? I thought I hadn't seen you round before. I hope you like it good enough to stay. As I say, we ain't no New York City or Chicago, but we have pretty good times. Not as good, though, since Jim Kendall got killed. When he was alive, him and Hod Meyers used to keep this town in an uproar. I bet they was more laughin' done here than any town its size in America.

Jim was comical, and Hod was pretty near a match for him. Since Jim's gone, Hod tries to hold his end up just the same as ever, but it's tough goin' when you ain't got nobody to kind of work with.

They used to be plenty fun in here Saturdays. This place is jam-packed Saturdays, from four o'clock on. Jim and Hod would show up right after their supper, round six o'clock. Jim would set himself down in that big chair, nearest the blue spittoon. Whoever had been settin' in that chair, why they'd get up when Jim come in and give it to him.

You'd of thought it was a reserved seat like they have sometimes in a theayter. Hod would generally always stand or walk up and down, or some Saturdays, of course, he'd be settin' in this chair part of the time, gettin' a haircut.

Well, Jim would set there a w'ile without openin' his mouth only to spit, and then finally he'd say to me, "Whitey,"—my right name, that is, my right first name, is Dick, but everybody round here calls me Whitey—Jim would say, "Whitey, your nose looks like a rosebud tonight. You must of been drinkin' some of your aw de cologne."

So I'd say, "No, Jim, but you look like you'd been drinkin' somethin' of that kind or somethin' worse."

Jim would have to laugh at that, but then he'd speak up and say, "No, I ain't had nothin' to drink, but that ain't sayin' I wouldn't like somethin'. I wouldn't even mind if it was wood alcohol."

Then Hod Meyers would say, "Neither would your wife." That would set everybody to laughin' because Jim and his wife wasn't on very good terms. She'd of divorced him only they wasn't no chance to get alimony and she didn't have no way to take care of herself and the kids. She couldn't never understand Jim. He *was* kind of rough, but a good fella at heart.

Him and Hod had all kinds of sport with Milt Sheppard. I don't suppose you've seen Milt. Well, he's got an Adam's apple that looks more like a mushmelon. So I'd be shavin' Milt and when I'd start to shave down here on his neck, Hod would holler, "Hey, Whitey, wait a minute! Before you cut

94

into it, let's make up a pool and see who can guess closest to the number of seeds."

And Jim would say, "If Milt hadn't of been so hoggish, he'd of ordered a half a cantaloupe instead of a whole one and it might not of stuck in his throat."

All the boys would roar at this and Milt himself would force a smile, though the joke was on him. Jim certainly was a card!

There's his shavin' mug, settin' on the shelf, right next to Charley Vail's. "Charles M. Vail." That's the druggist. He comes in regular for his shave, three times a week. And Jim's is the cup next to Charley's. "James H. Kendall." Jim won't need no shavin' mug no more, but I'll leave it there just the same for old time's sake. Jim certainly was a character!

Years ago, Jim used to travel for a canned goods concern over in Carterville. They sold canned goods. Jim had the whole northern half of the State and was on the road five days out of every week. He'd drop in here Saturdays and tell his experiences for that week. It was rich.

I guess he paid more attention to playin' jokes than makin' sales. Finally the concern let him out and he come right home here and told everybody he'd been fired instead of sayin' he'd resigned like most fellas would of.

It was a Saturday and the shop was full and Jim got up out of that chair and says, "Gentlemen, I got an important announcement to make. I been fired from my job."

Well, they asked him if he was in earnest and he said he was and nobody could think of nothin' to say till Jim finally broke the ice himself. He says, "I been sellin' canned goods and now I'm canned goods myself."

You see, the concern he'd been workin' for was a factory that made canned goods. Over in Carterville. And now Jim said he was canned himself. He was certainly a card!

Jim had a great trick that he used to play w'ile he was travelin'. For instance, he'd be ridin' on a train and they'd come to some little town like, well, like, we'll say, like Benton. Jim would look out the train window and read the signs on the stores.

For instance, they'd be a sign, "Henry Smith, Dry Goods." Well, Jim would write down the name and the name of the town and when he got to wherever he was goin' he'd mail back a postal card to Henry Smith at Benton and not sign no name to it, but he'd write on the card, well, somethin' like "Ask your wife about that book agent that spent the afternoon last week," or "Ask your Missus who kept her from gettin' lonesome the last time you was in Carterville." And he'd sign the card, "A Friend."

Of course, he never knew what really come of none of these jokes, but he could picture what *probably* happened and that was enough.

Jim didn't work very steady after he lost his position with the Carterville people. What he did earn, doin' odd jobs round town, why he spent pretty near all of it on gin and his family might of starved if the stores hadn't of carried them along. Jim's wife tried her hand at dressmakin', but they ain't nobody goin' to get rich makin' dresses in this town.

As I say, she'd of divorced Jim, only she seen that she couldn't support herself and the kids and she was always hopin' that some day Jim would cut out his habits and give her more than two or three dollars a week.

They was a time when she would go to whoever he was workin' for and ask them to give her his wages, but after she done this once or twice, he beat her to it by borrowin' most of his pay in advance. He told it all round town, how he had outfoxed his Missus. He certainly was a caution!

But he wasn't satisfied with just outwittin' her. He was sore the way she had acted, tryin' to grab off his pay. And he made up his mind he'd get even. Well, he waited till Evans's Circus was advertised to come to town. Then he told his wife and two kiddies that he was goin' to take them to the circus. The day of the circus, he told them he would

96

get the tickets and meet them outside the entrance to the tent.

Well, he didn't have no intentions of bein' there or buyin' tickets or nothin'. He got full of gin and laid round Wright's poolroom all day. His wife and the kids waited and waited and of course he didn't show up. His wife didn't have a dime with her, or nowhere else, I guess. So she finally had to tell the kids it was all off and they cried like they wasn't never goin' to stop.

Well, it seems, w'ile they was cryin', Doc Stair came along and he asked what was the matter, but Mrs. Kendall was stubborn and wouldn't tell him, but the kids told him and he insisted on takin' them and their mother in the show. Jim found this out afterwards and it was one reason why he had it in for Doc Stair.

Doc Stair come here about a year and a half ago. He's a mighty handsome young fella and his clothes always look like he has them made to order. He goes to Detroit two or three times a year and w'ile he's there he must have a tailor take his measure and then make him a suit to order. They cost pretty near twice as much, but they fit a whole lot better than if you just bought them in a store.

For a w'ile everybody was wonderin' why a young doctor like Doc Stair should come to a town like this where we already got old Doc Gamble and Doc Foote that's both been here for years and all the practice in town was always divided between the two of them.

Then they was a story got round that Doc Stair's gal had throwed him over, a gal up in the Northern Peninsula somewheres, and the reason he come here was to hide himself away and forget it. He said himself that he thought they wasn't nothin' like general practice in a place like ours to fit a man to be a good all round doctor. And that's why he'd came.

Anyways, it wasn't long before he was makin' enough to live on, though they tell me that he never dunned nobody for what they owed him, and the folks here certainly has

97

got the owin' habit, even in my business. If I had all that was comin' to me for just shaves alone, I could go to Carterville and put up at the Mercer for a week and see a different picture every night. For instance, they's old George Purdy —but I guess I shouldn't ought to be gossipin'.

Well, last year, our coroner died, died of the flu. Ken Beatty, that was his name. He was the coroner. So they had to choose another man to be coroner in his place and they picked Doc Stair. He laughed at first and said he didn't want it, but they made him take it. It ain't no job that anybody would fight for and what a man makes out of it in a year would just about buy seeds for their garden. Doc's the kind, though, that can't say no to nothin' if you keep at him long enough.

But I was goin' to tell you about a poor boy we got here in town—Paul Dickson. He fell out of a tree when he was about ten years old. Lit on his head and it done somethin' to him and he ain't never been right. No harm in him, but just silly. Jim Kendall used to call him cuckoo; that's a name Jim had for anybody that was off their head, only he called people's head their bean. That was another of his gags, callin' head bean and callin' crazy people cuckoo. Only poor Paul ain't crazy, but just silly.

You can imagine that Jim used to have all kinds of fun with Paul. He'd send him to the White Front Garage for a left-handed monkey wrench. Of course they ain't no such a thing as a left-handed monkey wrench.

And once we had a kind of a fair here and they was a baseball game between the fats and the leans and before the game started Jim called Paul over and sent him way down to Schrader's hardware store to get a key for the pitcher's box.

They wasn't nothin' in the way of gags that Jim couldn't think up, when he put his mind to it.

Poor Paul was always kind of suspicious of people, maybe on account of how Jim had kept foolin' him. Paul wouldn't

98

have much to do with anybody only his own mother and Doc Stair and a girl here in town named Julie Gregg. That is, she ain't a girl no more, but pretty near thirty or over.

When Doc first come to town, Paul seemed to feel like here was a real friend and he hung round Doc's office most of the w'ile; the only time he wasn't there was when he'd go home to eat or sleep or when he seen Julie Gregg doin' her shoppin'.

When he looked out Doc's window and seen her, he'd run downstairs and join her and tag along with her to the different stores. The poor boy was crazy about Julie and she always treated him mighty nice and made him feel like he was welcome, though of course it wasn't nothin' but pity on her side.

Doc done all he could to improve Paul's mind and he told me once that he really thought the boy was gettin' better, that they was times when he was as bright and sensible as anybody else.

But I was goin' to tell you about Julie Gregg. Old Man Gregg was in the lumber business, but got to drinkin' and lost the most of his money and when he died, he didn't leave nothin' but the house and just enough insurance for the girl to skimp along on.

Her mother was a kind of a half invalid and didn't hardly ever leave the house. Julie wanted to sell the place and move somewheres else after the old man died, but the mother said she was born here and would die here. It was tough on Julie, as the young people round this town—well, she's too good for them.

She's been away to school and Chicago and New York and different places and they ain't no subject she can't talk on, where you take the rest of the young folks here and you mention anything to them outside of Gloria Swanson or Tommy Meighan and they think you're delirious. Did you see Gloria in Wages of Virtue? You missed somethin'!

Well, Doc Stair hadn't been here more than a week when

he come in one day to get shaved and I recognized who he was as he had been pointed out to me, so I told him about my old lady. She's been ailin' for a couple years and either Doc Gamble or Doc Foote, neither one, seemed to be helpin' her. So he said he would come out and see her, but if she was able to get out herself, it would be better to bring her to his office where he could make a completer examination.

So I took her to his office and w'ile I was waitin' for her in the reception room, in come Julie Gregg. When somebody comes in Doc Stair's office, they's a bell that rings in his inside office so as he can tell they's somebody to see him.

So he left my old lady inside and come out to the front office and that's the first time him and Julie met and I guess it was what they call love at first sight. But it wasn't fifty-fifty. This young fella was the slickest lookin' fella she'd ever seen in this town and she went wild over him. To him she was just a young lady that wanted to see the doctor.

She'd came on about the same business I had. Her mother had been doctorin' for years with Doc Gamble and Doc Foote and without no results. So she'd heard they was a new doc in town and decided to give him a try. He promised to call and see her mother that same day.

I said a minute ago that it was love at first sight on her part. I'm not only judgin' by how she acted afterwards but how she looked at him that first day in his office. I ain't no mind reader, but it was wrote all over her face that she was gone.

Now Jim Kendall, besides bein' a jokesmith and a pretty good drinker, well, Jim was quite a lady-killer. I guess he run pretty wild durin' the time he was on the road for them Carterville people, and besides that, he'd had a couple little affairs of the heart right here in town. As I say, his wife could of divorced him, only she couldn't.

But Jim was like the majority of men, and women, too, I guess. He wanted what he couldn't get. He wanted Julie Gregg and worked his head off tryin' to land her. Only he'd of said bean instead of head.

Well, Jim's habits and his jokes didn't appeal to Julie and of course he was a married man, so he didn't have no more chance than, well, than a rabbit. That's an expression of Jim's himself. When somebody didn't have no chance to get elected or somethin', Jim would always say they didn't have no more chance than a rabbit.

He didn't make no bones about how he felt. Right in here, more than once, in front of the whole crowd, he said he was stuck on Julie and anybody that could get her for him was welcome to his house and his wife and kids included. But she wouldn't have nothin' to do with him; wouldn't even speak to him on the street. He finally seen he wasn't gettin' nowheres with his usual line so he decided to try the rough stuff. He went right up to her house one evenin' and when she opened the door he forced his way in and grabbed her. But she broke loose and before he could stop her, she run in the next room and locked the door and phoned to Joe Barnes. Joe's the marshal. Jim could hear who she was phonin' to and he beat it before Joe got there.

Joe was an old friend of Julie's pa. Joe went to Jim the next day and told him what would happen if he ever done it again.

I don't know how the news of this little affair leaked out. Chances is that Joe Barnes told his wife and she told somebody else's wife and they told their husband. Anyway, it did leak out and Hod Meyers had the nerve to kid Jim about it, right here in this shop. Jim didn't deny nothin' and kind of laughed it off and said for us all to wait; that lots of people had tried to make a monkey out of him, but he always got even.

Meanw'ile everybody in town was wise to Julie's bein' wild mad over the Doc. I don't suppose she had any idear how her face changed when him and her was together; of course she couldn't of, or she'd of kept away from him. And she didn't know that we was all noticin' how many times she made excuses to go up to his office or pass it on the other side of the street and look up in his window to see if he was there. I felt sorry for her and so did most other people.

Hod Meyers kept rubbin' it into Jim about how the Doc had cut him out. Jim didn't pay no attention to the kiddin' and you could see he was plannin' one of his jokes.

One trick Jim had was the knack of changin' his voice. He could make you think he was a girl talkin' and he could mimic any man's voice. To show you how good he was along this line, I'll tell you the joke he played on me once.

You know, in most towns of any size, when a man is dead and needs a shave, why the barber that shaves him soaks him five dollars for the job; that is, he don't soak *him*, but whoever ordered the shave. I just charge three dollars because personally I don't mind much shavin' a dead person. They lay a whole lot stiller than live customers. The only thing is that you don't feel like talkin' to them and you get kind of lonesome.

Well, about the coldest day we ever had here, two years ago last winter, the phone rung at the house w'ile I was home to dinner and I answered the phone and it was a woman's voice and she said she was Mrs. John Scott and her husband was dead and would I come out and shave him.

Old John had always been a good customer of mine. But they live seven miles out in the country, on the Streeter road. Still I didn't see how I could say no.

So I said I would be there, but would have to come in a jitney and it might cost three or four dollars besides the price of the shave. So she, or the voice, it said that was all right, so I got Frank Abbott to drive me out to the place and when I got there, who should open the door but old John himself! He wasn't no more dead than, well, than a rabbit.

It didn't take no private detective to figure out who had played me this little joke. Nobody could of thought it up but Jim Kendall. He certainly was a card!

I tell you this incident just to show you how he could disguise his voice and make you believe it was somebody else talkin'. I'd of swore it was Mrs. Scott had called me. Anyways, some woman.

Well, Jim waited till he had Doc Stair's voice down pat; then he went after revenge.

He called Julie up on a night when he knew Doc was over in Carterville. She never questioned but what it was Doc's voice. Jim said he must see her that night; he couldn't wait no longer to tell her somethin'. She was all excited and told him to come to the house. But he said he was expectin' an important long distance call and wouldn't she please forget her manners for once and come to his office. He said they couldn't nothin' hurt her and nobody would see her and he just *must* talk to her a little w'ile. Well, poor Julie fell for it.

Doc always keeps a night light in his office, so it looked to Julie like they was somebody there.

Meanw'ile Jim Kendall had went to Wright's poolroom, where they was a whole gang amusin' themselves. The most of them had drank plenty of gin, and they was a rough bunch even when sober. They was always strong for Jim's jokes and when he told them to come with him and see some fun they give up their card games and pool games and followed along.

Doc's office is on the second floor. Right outside his door they's a flight of stairs leadin' to the floor above. Jim and his gang hid in the dark behind these stairs.

Well, Julie come up to Doc's door and rung the bell and they was nothin' doin'. She rung it again and she rung it seven or eight times. Then she tried the door and found it locked. Then Jim made some kind of a noise and she heard it and waited a minute, and then she says, "Is that you, Ralph?" Ralph is Doc's first name.

They was no answer and it must of came to her all of a sudden that she'd been bunked. She pretty near fell downstairs and the whole gang after her. They chased her all the way home, hollerin', "Is that you, Ralph?" and "Oh, Ralphie, dear, is that you?" Jim says he couldn't holler it himself, as he was laughin' too hard.

Poor Julie! She didn't show up here on Main Street for a long, long time afterward.

And of course Jim and his gang told everybody in town, everybody but Doc Stair. They was scared to tell him, and he might of never knowed only for Paul Dickson. The poor cuckoo, as Jim called him, he was here in the shop one night when Jim was still gloatin' yet over what he'd done to Julie. And Paul took in as much of it as he could understand and he run to Doc with the story.

It's a cinch Doc went up in the air and swore he'd make Jim suffer. But it was a kind of a delicate thing, because if it got out that he had beat Jim up, Julie was bound to hear of it and then she'd know that Doc knew and of course knowin' that he knew would make it worse for her than ever. He was goin' to do somethin', but it took a lot of figurin'.

Well, it was a couple days later when Jim was here in the shop again, and so was the cuckoo. Jim was goin' duck-shootin' the next day and had came in lookin' for Hod Meyers to go with him. I happened to know that Hod had went over to Carterville and wouldn't be home till the end of the week. So Jim said he hated to go alone and he guessed he would call it off. Then poor Paul spoke up and said if Jim would take him he would go along. Jim thought a w'ile and then he said, well, he guessed a half-wit was better than nothin'.

I suppose he was plottin' to get Paul out in the boat and play some joke on him, like pushin' him in the water. Anyways, he said Paul could go. He asked him had he ever shot a duck and Paul said no, he'd never even had a gun in his hands. So Jim said he could set in the boat and watch him and if he behaved himself, he might lend him his gun for a couple of shots. They made a date to meet in the mornin' and that's the last I seen of Jim alive.

Next mornin', I hadn't been open more than ten minutes
104

when Doc Stair come in. He looked kind of nervous. He asked me had I seen Paul Dickson. I said no, but I knew where he was, out duck-shootin' with Jim Kendall. So Doc says that's what he had heard, and he couldn't understand it because Paul had told him he wouldn't never have no more to do with Jim as long as he lived.

He said Paul had told him about the joke Jim had played on Julie. He said Paul had asked him what he thought of the joke and the Doc had told him that anybody that would do a thing like that ought not to be let live.

I said it had been a kind of a raw thing, but Jim just couldn't resist no kind of a joke, no matter how raw. I said I thought he was all right at heart, but just bubblin' over with mischief. Doc turned and walked out.

At noon he got a phone call from old John Scott. The lake where Jim and Paul had went shootin' is on John's place. Paul had came runnin' up to the house a few minutes before and said they'd been an accident. Jim had shot a few ducks and then give the gun to Paul and told him to try his luck. Paul hadn't never handled a gun and he was nervous. He was shakin' so hard that he couldn't control the gun. He let fire and Jim sunk back in the boat, dead.

Doc Stair, bein' the coroner, jumped in Frank Abbott's flivver and rushed out to Scott's farm. Paul and old John was down on the shore of the lake. Paul had rowed the boat to shore, but they'd left the body in it, waitin' for Doc to come.

Doc examined the body and said they might as well fetch it back to town. They was no use leavin' it there or callin' a jury, as it was a plain case of accidental shootin'.

Personally I wouldn't never leave a person shoot a gun in the same boat I was in unless I was sure they knew somethin' about guns. Jim was a sucker to leave a new beginner have nis gun, let alone a half-wit. It probably served Jim right, what he got. But still we miss him round here. He certainly was a card!

Comb it wet or dry?

RED, WHITE AND BLUE

THANKSGIVING

THERE was the time Uncle Mat and Aunt Harriet came to Thanksgiving Dinner. The sizzly smell of the turkey and the spices in the stuffing filled the kitchen every time Mother opened the oven door to baste. Glenn had helped lay the table in the cramped diningroom of the little apartment and had filled the two china swans with red white and blue candies and, carefully, with only one or two smudges, had printed out the names on the placecards.

Dad had been around the house all morning getting into Mother's way in the kitchen and frowning as he sat bent almost double reading, with his green eyeshade on, at his desk in the corner of the livingroom. A letter had come from Tyler overseas that morning that had upset Dad a good deal. The letter had said that Tyler wasn't coming home with his outfit but that he had just gotten under the line with his commission at Saumur before the armistice and was going to be sent to Coblenz in the Army of Occupation. Glenn was too excited about Thanksgiving and everybody coming to dinner to pay much attention. He and Mother were attending to everything and Dad was just mooning around, now and then pulling at his sandy mustache with that worried look and taking down first one big book and then another from the top of his desk and setting them down on chairs and forgetting to put them back.

Mother, in her pink apron with her hair in curlers, was leaning over the oven of the gasstove basting the turkey. Glenn was standing beside her with his mouth watering as he watched the little splashes of juice sizzle as they trickled off the kitchen spoon onto the brown tight skin of the turkey. Mother was out of breath. He said couldn't he do that because she'd promised him and Dad she wouldn't do too much. She said never mind, darling, for him to run around the corner to get the icecream at Etienne's. It was all ordered but she was afraid they wouldn't bring it in time, and twenty-five cents' worth of salted almonds, and to be sure to wear his muffler because it was a terribly raw day.

Glenn ran down the three flights of steps two at a time and almost fell on his neck in the lower hall. Outside, in the broad streets, behind the trees rusty with fall, the waving flags and the bunting showed up bright and candystriped under the gray blustery sky. Down at the end of the street there must have been a parade or something because a marching band was playing "Over There."

In the French candy store on the avenue it was warm and smelt of chocolate and baking cake. The fat lady behind the counter gave Glenn the icecream and the salted nuts in a little fancy pink carton tied with ribbons at the top and, first thing he knew, he'd bought a plaster turkey with little tiny gumdrops in it for seventyfive cents out of his own money. That sort of thing helped to garnish the table, the fat lady agreed in her wheedling French accent. When he got home he ran up the three steep flights of the back stairs and broke breathless into the apartment through the back kitchen door.

Dad was in his shirtsleeves mashing the potatoes and saying, Ada, he couldn't help feeling bad about the thought of our boy in a uniform strutting around lording it over those miserable defeated Germans. "I'm afraid he'll never be good for anything again." Mother was whispering she could only feel thankful that he was safe.

Yes, indeed, Dad intoned in a loud false voice that made nothing seem fun any more to Glenn, it was a real Thanksgiving day for the Spotswood family all right, wasn't it, my boy; and then he said for him to help his mother beat the potatoes, because he had to change his clothes; the family

107

would soon be coming and it would never do for them to find him like this; they had a poor enough opinion of him as it was. And Glenn set to beating the mashed potatoes with all his might with a big fork while Mother poured in a little milk from a cup. Then she put the mashed potatoes on the stove in a double boiler to keep hot.

My, they looked good, he said, he was so hungry he could eat an elephant, and Mother told him to run along now and brush his hair and wash his hands, because they'd soon be there, and to tell his father to come and open the oysters.

He'd hardly gotten into his bedroom when the bell rang and he ran to the door, and there they were, Uncle Mat and Aunt Harriet and Lorna. Aunt Harriet and Lorna smelt of perfume and furs and Uncle Mat smelt of bayrum like a barbershop. They had so many coats and mufflers and furs to hang up that Glenn was still in the coatcloset when Cousin Jane and Miss Jenks arrived in tweedy outofdoorslooking wraps, and everybody was crying out, my dear, what a wonderful Thanksgiving it was, and the news about Tyler, imagine his coming back an officer and going to the Army of Occupation and maybe he'd have a career in the regular army, and when Mother came out of the kitchen in her new silkyruffly dress and with her hair all curls there was such squealing and kissing and, my dear, you look like a schoolgirl, and to think that Tyler's a second lieutenant at twenty; and out of it came Uncle Mat's voice grumbling that Tyler had ought to have gotten his commission before he went over like the other college boys did; but Miss Jenks screeched that Herbert hadn't wanted him to, he'd wanted him to rise from the ranks, it was so much more democratic, and she thought it was splendid.

Mother said for Glenn to go help Dad bring in the oysters and Uncle Mat followed into the kitchen where Dad was standing by the sink. Dad had a couple of plates of oysters ready but he'd jabbed himself with the oysterknife and was standing there looking down with that slow puzzled look he had at a little drop of dark blood swelling up in the palm of his hand.

Uncle Mat roared that it was too bad, Herbert, and that he'd ought to use a leather mit, and grabbed the oysterknife out of Dad's hand and started to open the oysters at a great rate while Dad and Glenn carried the plates into the diningroom where the table had every leaf in it and they'd hung paper festoons round the electriclightfixture that Mother always said was so ugly. Glenn went around straightening the old linen tablecloth with its stiff creases and Mother's best silver spoons and forks that had belonged to Grandmama Carroll. Uncle Mat caught him at it and slapped him on the back so hard it hurt and said he was darned if they hadn't turned little Glenn into a regular parlormaid, and Glenn felt his face getting red, and went out in the back hall and stood looking out the window at the garbage cans and the spilt ashes in the back yard, where there was still an oak all golden with fall and a scraggly privet bush with green leaves on it. Somebody had stuck a faded paper American flag at the top of the privet bush.

When Glenn got back they were all at their places and Dad was standing still with his eyes drooping, waiting to say grace. As soon as they'd sat down Aunt Harriet said, now dear Ada mustn't do another thing, she was afraid she'd overdone. Mother shook her head, but she did look pale instead of looking flushed like she had in the kitchen. Her voice sounded tired when she said she'd so looked forward to having everybody at her house this Thanksgiving so that they could be happy with her because she was so happy, and tears began to run down her cheeks.

Well, now the Huns would get what was coming to them, Uncle Mat said. He was lifting an oyster dripping with cocktail sauce into his fat mouth. He smacked his lips and said he for one hoped they'd hang the Kaiser and burn Berlin to the ground, teach 'em a lesson, that was all they understood.

Two wrongs didn't make a right; Dad was speaking his

carefully pronounced words from the end of the table, when Lorna began to kick up a row because she'd found an oyster-crab in her oyster. Uncle Mat roared that she must eat it and Glenn said he thought they were cute and Lorna screeched that they were horrid, and Dad said nothing that was Nature was horrid, they were just cute little pink crabs that lived in the oysters. Lorna dared Glenn and doubledared him to eat it and poked it across the table at him on her spoon. The tiny crab crawled a little on his tongue but he crunched it up and swallowed it. Then Lorna kicked him in the shins under the table and said now she thought he was horrid.

Uncle Mat got red in the face laughing and spilt cocktail sauce on his chin gulping down his oysters, so that he looked like he'd cut himself shaving. He said he didn't think the younger generation appreciated oysters, so he distributed Lorna's oysters among the grownups and Glenn lost some of his too, though he liked them fine. When Uncle Mat had eaten his last oyster he pushed back his chair a little and Aunt Harriet made him wipe the cocktail sauce off his chin and he declared that nothing in the world could beat a Potomac oyster. But now that we'd won the war the Huns would have to pay for it, he said looking straight at Dad. Mother and Cousin Jane were fluttering around taking away the plates.

Dad got that cornered look on his face. He took off his glasses and rubbed his gray bulging eyes and leaned forward across his plate before he spoke. He hoped that those really responsible for the war would be made to pay for it, instead of the poor people of Germany who were its first victims, he said, his voice trembling a little; he had confidence that the President . . . Cousin Jane came to the door and said in her businesslike way that Herbert must come help them with the turkey, they were afraid they'd drop it, it was so heavy, and wasn't little Glenn coming to act as headwaiter, so that his poor mother could sit down and entertain her guests a little.

When Glenn was through passing the vegetables with a napkin on his arm like a real waiter, he sat down and began to eat. Oh, she hoped the turkey wasn't dry, Mother kept saying as she watched Dad shakily carving. Everybody was eating the turkey and saying how good the stuffing was and please pass the cranberry sauce or the piccalilli, and it wasn't until the second helpings had gone around that Uncle Mat started to argue with Dad some more. Of course, Uncle Mat said, he was for backing the President but he thought the leniency shown to conscientious objectors and disloyal elements in this country was a scandal. Dad flared up and said did he call twenty years in jail lenient when the Constitution . . . Uncle Mat interrupted that that kind of talk was disloyal at a time like this when our boys were giving their lives to defend the very principles . . . "After all, Brother Matthew, Tyler's our son," Mother said with a shy smile, "and we ought to know about sacrifice." Then she told little Glenn to clear the table and bring in the icecream. She said for Lorna to help him but Lorna didn't move.

When Glenn brought out the icecream it slithered back and forth on the platter. Cousin Jane, who was following with a silver sauceboat of chocolate sauce, cried, "Whoops, my boy," in her jolly way that made him feel good again. But Uncle Mat was still talking about how pacifism was giving aid and comfort to the enemy and at a time like this. . . . Dad looked very pale and stern and was spacing his words slowly and saying that he realized that a great deal of dogma was out of date and rather obscured the gospels than clarified them but that he could find no justification for a Christian to take part in war and that he thought the application of Christianity to war was not only spiritual but practical.

Uncle Mat pushed back his chair and got very red and said he hadn't come to listen to a sermon but in his opinion all pacifists were yellow. "Mat, now you promised me you wouldn't," Aunt Harriet was whining in a singsong voice. Cousin Jane added in her snappy cheerful tone that this was Thanksgiving dinner and that arguing at meals gave people indigestion.

"Herbert, don't argue with him please," Mother whispered down the table, and made Glenn get Uncle Mat's plate and gave him another helping of icecream. It made Glenn feel awful to see how her hand was trembling when she poured out the bitter fudge sauce. "I should think his own sons would be ashamed," Uncle Mat muttered as he helped himself to another piece of fruit cake.

Lorna started giggling. Aunt Harriet kept hissing hush across the table. Uncle Mat went on rumbling in his throat that it was a surprise to him Herbert hadn't been arrested before this for his disloyal utterances and us with him for listening to 'em.

Dad had gotten to his feet, leaving his icecream untouched on his plate. "After all, Matthew, you are my guest and Ada's." He walked over to the window and stood there looking out with his thin hands clasped behind his back.

"Mercy," broke out Miss Jenks, who hadn't said much during dinner because her new set of false teeth bothered her, but had sat there, with her little pursedup mouth munching fast like a rabbit's, in the middle of her bright little lined pink and white face. "You wouldn't think the war was over, would you?"

Then Aunt Harriet suggested that Glenn take his little cousin Lorna for a walk around the zoo. Lorna pushed her face out in a big pout and said she hated the old zoo but everybody thought it was a lovely idea and Uncle Mat gave them a half dollar to buy peanuts for the elephant with and they were bundled up and shooed out of the house into the chilly twilight of the streets.

"Aw, it'll be closed anyway by the time we get there," Glenn drawled out of the corner of his mouth, trying to talk tough. Lorna put her hand on his arm and said, "Let's us go downtown and go to the movies. My Uncle Herbert's a big sissy, isn't he?" That made Glenn sore and he wouldn't speak to her all the time they were in the movie.

112

Jerome Weidman

THE TUXEDOS

EVER since the time, some ten years ago, when I worked for Mr. Brunschweig on Canal Street, I have been peculiarly sensitive to the half-hour of the day that comes between five-thirty and six o'clock in the late afternoon. Mr. Brunschweig was an excellent boss, as bosses go, except for one lamentable defect: he was a minute-pincher. He carried two large pocket watches and spent a good part of each day comparing them with each other and with the huge Seth Thomas on the wall. I am certain that he was a little terrified by the inexorableness of time and that his sensitivity to it was a direct result of the way he earned his living. Mr. Brunschweig rented tuxedos.

The tuxedo-renting business, as I knew it, was distinguished by two cardinal rules. First, the suits had to be made of the toughest and heaviest materials available. And second, it was necessary to deliver them as close to the moment of wearing as possible and even more imperative to pick them up as soon after they were taken off as the wearer would permit. Mr. Brunschweig's timing in this respect was so good and I was so nimble as a delivery boy that while many of his customers cursed him roundly for having delayed them in getting to a wedding, not one of them could say with honesty that he had worn a Brunschweig tuxedo to more than one affair for the price of a single renting.

My relations with Mr. Brunschweig were amicable if somewhat exhausting, but every day, as the hands of the clock crept around to half-past five, a definite tension would come into the atmosphere. My quitting time was six o'clock. As a general rule, Mr. Brunschweig arranged deliveries in such fashion that the last one carried me up to, or past, that hour. We had an understanding to the effect that if I took out a delivery at any time after five-thirty and could not get to my destination until six o'clock or a few minutes before, I did not have to return to the Canal Street store that night and was at liberty to go directly home. However, the possibility of his only employee departing for home five or ten minutes ahead of quitting time was so disturbing to Mr. Brunschweig that very often he would detain me in the store before I went out on my final delivery, talking about the weather or discussing the baseball scores, just to make sure that I could not possibly complete the delivery before six o'clock.

Strangely enough, I did not resent these obvious subterfuges, because I sensed that Mr. Brunschweig was a little ashamed of them. What I did resent was that unconsciously I was being forced into practices I didn't approve of to combat him.

For instance, I would instinctively stall on any delivery after five-fifteen to make certain that I would not get back to the store in time to make another delivery before quitting. Or I would rush through a four-o'clock delivery to make sure that there would be ample time for still another one before six o'clock. In either case it was very unsettling, and scarcely a day went by that I didn't have a struggle with my conscience or the clock.

There were times, of course, when my energy overcame my caution. One day, in an industrious mood, I returned from an uptown delivery at twenty minutes to six. It had been a long trip and I could have stretched it for another twenty minutes with ease, but I had temporarily forgotten Mr. Brunschweig's vice and I did not realize my mistake until I came into the store. He was boxing an unusually large order, and I could tell from his cheery greeting that this one would carry me well past six o'clock. I was about to dismiss the occurrence as simply another occasion on which I had been outmaneuvered by Mr. Brunschweig when I saw that he had stacked six boxes, one on top of the other.

"Is that *one* delivery?" I asked in amazement.

The average delivery weighed well over ten pounds and consisted of a tuxedo, a shirt, a tie, studs, and a pair of patent-leather pumps, packed neatly into a heavy cardboard box. Two or three of these boxes were a load. Six of them were an incredible amount.

"Yeah," he said cheerfully. "Italian wedding. It all goes to one family. I'll give you a help to the subway."

I should have been grateful to him for this offer, I suppose, since it was an unusual move, but all I could think of was the prospect of juggling sixty pounds of tuxedos through the subway in the rush hour.

"Where's it going?" I asked.

"Brooklyn," he said. "It's just over the bridge. Won't take you long."

The boxes weighed so much I could scarcely raise them from the floor.

"Here," he said. "You take the hats. I'll take the suits till we get to the train."

I hadn't even thought about top hats. They were not very heavy, but they were the most perishable items in Mr. Brunschweig's stock and consequently were always packed with great care in individual boxes.

"We gotta hurry," Mr. Brunschweig said, handing me a slip of paper with an address on it. "It's the bride's family and I promised them early. Name is Lasquadro."

He took the lashed tuxedo boxes and I took the pile of hatboxes, tied one on top of another so that they resembled a small steamship funnel. In the street we paused for a moment while he locked the store, and then we started off down Canal Street to the subway station.

The only satisfactory recollection I have of that evening is the brief memory of Mr. Brunschweig tottering along in front of me under the weight of six boxes of tuxedos and accessories. The rest was a nightmare. I remember being on the subway platform, between my two huge bundles, trying to get into train after train. I had to let seven or eight go by before I could wedge my way into one of them. Then I remember standing, perspiring and exhausted, outside the subway station in Brooklyn, looking at the two bundles and realizing that I could carry them no further. It had grown quite dark and I began to be worried, too, about being late with the delivery. Finally I worked out a plan. I dragged the tuxedos along the ground for a short distance, then went back for the hats, dragged them up to the tuxedos, and then repeated the process. It was an effective method but an extremely slow one. Though the address Mr. Brunschweig had given me was only three blocks from the Brooklyn subway station, it was almost twenty minutes later that I stopped, breathless, in front of the correct house number.

The street was deserted and dark; the house was a two-story brownstone affair and only the basement windows showed lights from behind drawn shades. As I wiped the perspiration from my face and tried to think of an excuse for being so late, I heard noises coming from the basement. Figures kept passing the windows quickly and the sounds of scuffling and angry voices reached me clearly. I was frightened and spent another precious minute trying to puzzle out a way of leaving my bundles without having to face the people inside the house.

Then, in a burst of nervous courage, I tumbled the bulky bundles down the steps that led to the basement door and knocked gently. There was no answer. The angry noises inside continued, and I knocked again. Still no answer. Then I discovered a push button on the wall beside the door, jabbed at it hastily, and a bell pealed shrilly somewhere inside the house. At once the door was pulled open and a small young man in shirtsleeves, with a tight, dark, scowling face, shot his head out and glared at me.

"What the hella *you* want?" he demanded harshly.

"The—the tuxedos," I said awkwardly. "I brought the tuxedos."

The young man turned his head and yelled at someone in the room behind him. "He brought the tuxedos! You hear that? He brought the tuxedos!"

He laughed unpleasantly and a man's voice replied from inside the room, "Tell him he knows what he can do with them!"

The young man in front of me reached for the door and started to slam it shut. The thought that I might have to drag those two bundles back to Canal Street that night was enough to make me forget my fright. I braced my shoulder against the door and held it open.

"I have to leave these here," I said quickly. "I have to— I have to get the receipt signed."

The little dark face glared at me and the hand on the door drew back threateningly. "Aah," he started to say, and then stopped. "O.K., O.K., come on. Bring 'em in and beat it."

He dragged the bundles in and the door swung shut behind me. As I began to fumble in my pocket for the receipt book, I stole a scared look at the scene in the room. It was a large, shabbily furnished living room, with a new radio in one corner, a huge potted rubber plant in another, and embroidered mottoes on the wall. A pretty, dark-haired girl in a white wedding gown was sitting at a table in the middle of the room. Five men, all in vests and shirtsleeves and all looking as if they must be brothers of the young man who had opened the door for me, were standing over her. One of the men held the girl and was twisting her arm behind her, and she was sobbing violently. A tiny old woman, with white hair in a knot at the back of her head and wearing a black alpaca apron, hovered on the outskirts of the group around the table, jabbering shrilly in Italian. The young man who had let me in joined his brothers. Nobody paid any attention to me.

"Come on," one of the men said, leaning over the girl. "What's his address? Give us that address!"

The girl shook her head and the man who was holding her arm gave it another twist. She screamed and dropped her head forward. Another man pushed his face down close to hers.

"Come on!" he yelled. "Give it to us. We're doing this for the family, ain't we? What's his address?"

The girl shook her head again; the little old lady chattered away. One of the brothers reached over and slapped the girl's face.

"Where was he when he called up?" he said. "Come on, tell us. We ain't gonna hurt him. We'll just murder the louse, that's all. Where was he?"

She didn't answer.

"Come on, you damn fool," the man who held her arm said. "Talk! You want him to go spreading it to the whole world he walked out on you an hour before the wedding?" He shook her angrily. "Where was he when he called up? Where does he live? We'll fix him so he won't talk. What's his address?"

The girl did not answer. He started to shake her again, then he saw me standing near the door. "Get that guy out of here," he said. The brother who had let me in came across the room in three steps and grabbed my shoulder. "Come on, kid," he said. "Beat it!"

I lifted my receipt book in front of his face. "The receipt," I said. "I must get my receipt signed. I can't leave the—" He snatched the book from me and fumbled in his vest pocket for a pencil. He couldn't find one. I held my own out to him and he scribbled his name in my receipt book.

"O.K., kid," he said sharply. "Outside!" and he shoved the receipt book and pencil at me. I took them and started toward the door. Suddenly the little old lady grabbed my arm and pulled me back.

"What the hellsa matter?" the young man asked angrily.

She gestured violently toward me and poured a stream of Italian at him.

"All right, all right," he said, and reached into his pocket, pulled out a coin, and tossed the tip to me. I caught it and turned toward the door again.

"Thanks," I said quickly. But before I could open the door the old lady was on me. She clawed at my hand until I opened it so she could see the coin. It was a quarter. She swung around to the young man and clutched his coat.

"What the hellsa matter now?" he cried. "I gave him the tip, didn't I?"

Again she started talking in Italian, pointing at the bundle of tuxedos and tapping off the boxes with her finger—one, two, three, four, five, six. She waved six fingers in his face and yelled at him. He bit his lip, dug into his pocket again, and slapped some more coins into my palm. At once the little old lady seized my hand again. Now there were two quarters, a dime, and a nickel in it. She counted them quickly, snatched up the nickel, and counted again. Sixty cents remained. Another glance at the tuxedos and another glance at the two quarters and dime in my hand. Six tuxedos. Sixty cents. She nodded sharply to herself. Now it was all right.

"Give us that address!" shouted one of the brothers. There was the sound of a slap and the girl screamed again. "Where was he when he called up?"

The little old lady pulled open the door, pushed me out roughly, and slammed it shut behind me.

James Thurber

THE SECRET LIFE OF WALTER MITTY

"We're going through!" The Commander's voice was like thin ice breaking. He wore his full-dress uniform, with the heavily braided white cap pulled down rakishly over one cold gray eye. "We can't make it, sir. It's spoiling for a hurricane, if you ask me." "I'm not asking you, Lieutenant Berg," said the Commander. "Throw on the power lights! Rev her up to 8,500! We're going through!" The pounding of the cylinders increased: ta-pocketa-pocketa-pocketa-*pocketa-pocketa*. The Commander stared at the ice forming on the pilot window. He walked over and twisted a row of complicated dials. "Switch on No. 8 auxiliary!" he shouted. "Switch on No. 8 auxiliary!" repeated Lieutenant Berg. "Full strength in No. 3 turret!" shouted the Commander. "Full strength in No. 3 turret!" The crew, bending to their various tasks in the huge, hurtling eight-engined Navy hydroplane, looked at each other and grinned. "The Old Man'll get us through," they said to one another. "The Old Man ain't afraid of Hell!". . .

"Not so fast! You're driving too fast!" said Mrs. Mitty. "What are you driving so fast for?"

"Hmm?" said Walter Mitty. He looked at his wife, in the seat beside him, with shocked astonishment. She seemed grossly unfamiliar, like a strange woman who had yelled at him in a crowd. "You were up to fifty-five," she said. "You know I don't like to go more than forty. You were up to fifty-five." Walter Mitty drove on toward Waterbury in silence, the roaring of the SN202 through the worst storm in twenty years of Navy flying fading in the remote, intimate airways of his mind. "You're tensed up again," said Mrs.

120

Mitty. "It's one of your days. I wish you'd let Dr. Renshaw look you over."

Walter Mitty stopped the car in front of the building where his wife went to have her hair done. "Remember to get those overshoes while I'm having my hair done," she said. "I don't need overshoes," said Mitty. She put her mirror back into her bag. "We've been all through that," she said, getting out of the car. "You're not a young man any longer." He raced the engine a little. "Why don't you wear your gloves? Have you lost your gloves?" Walter Mitty reached in a pocket and brought out the gloves. He put them on, but after she had turned and gone into the building and he had driven on to a red light, he took them off again. "Pick it up, brother!" snapped a cop as the light changed, and Mitty hastily pulled on his gloves and lurched ahead. He drove around the streets aimlessly for a time, and then he drove past the hospital on his way to the parking lot.

. . ."It's the millionaire banker, Wellington McMillan," said the pretty nurse. "Yes?" said Walter Mitty, removing his gloves slowly. "Who has the case?" "Dr. Renshaw and Dr. Benbow, but there are two specialists here, Dr. Remington from New York and Dr. Pritchard-Mitford from London. He flew over." A door opened down a long, cool corridor and Dr. Renshaw came out. He looked distraught and haggard. "Hello, Mitty," he said. "We're having the devil's own time with McMillan, the millionaire banker and close personal friend of Roosevelt. Obstreosis of the ductal tract. Tertiary. Wish you'd take a look at him." "Glad to," said Mitty.

In the operating room there were whispered introductions: "Dr. Remington, Dr. Mitty. Dr. Pritchard-Mitford, Dr. Mitty." "I've read your book on streptothricosis," said Pritchard-Mitford, shaking hands. "A brilliant performance, sir." "Thank you," said Walter Mitty. "Didn't know you were in the States, Mitty," grumbled Remington. "Coals to Newcastle, bringing Mitford and me up here for a tertiary."

"You are very kind," said Mitty. A huge, complicated machine, connected to the operating table, with many tubes and wires, began at this moment to go pocketa-pocketa-pocketa. "The new anaesthetizer is giving away!" shouted an interne. "There is no one in the East who knows how to fix it!" "Quiet, man!" said Mitty, in a low, cool voice. He sprang to the machine, which was now going pocketa-pocketa-queep-pocketa-queep. He began fingering delicately a row of glistening dials. "Give me a fountain pen!" he snapped. Someone handed him a fountain pen. He pulled a faulty piston out of the machine and inserted the pen in its place. "That will hold for ten minutes," he said. "Get on with the operation." A nurse hurried over and whispered to Renshaw, and Mitty saw the man turn pale. "Coreopsis has set in," said Renshaw nervously. "If you would take over, Mitty?" Mitty looked at him and at the craven figure of Benbow, who drank, and at the grave, uncertain faces of the two great specialists. "If you wish," he said. They slipped a white gown on him; he adjusted a mask and drew on thin gloves; nurses handed him shining . . .

"Back it up, Mac! Look out for that Buick!" Walter Mitty jammed on the brakes. "Wrong lane, Mac," said the parking-lot attendant, looking at Mitty closely. "Gee. Yeh," muttered Mitty. He began cautiously to back out of the lane marked "Exit Only." "Leave her sit there," said the attendant. "I'll put her away." Mitty got out of the car. "Hey, better leave the key." "Oh," said Mitty, handing the man the ignition key. The attendant vaulted into the car, backed it up with insolent skill, and put it where it belonged.

They're so damn cocky, thought Walter Mitty, walking along Main Street; they think they know everything. Once he had tried to take his chains off, outside New Milford, and he had got them wound around the axles. A man had had to come out in a wrecking car and unwind them, a young, grinning garageman. Since then Mrs. Mitty always made him drive to a garage to have the chains taken off. The next time, he thought, I'll wear my right arm in a sling; they won't grin at me then. I'll have my right arm in a sling and they'll see I couldn't possibly take the chains off myself. He kicked at the slush on the sidewalk. "Overshoes," he said to himself, and he began looking for a shoe store.

When he came out into the street again, with the overshoes in a box under his arm, Walter Mitty began to wonder what the other thing was his wife had told him to get. She had told him, twice before they set out from their house for Waterbury. In a way he hated these weekly trips to town—he was always getting something wrong. Kleenex, he thought, Squibb's, razor blades? No. Toothpaste, toothbrush, bicarbonate, carborundum, initiative and referendum? He gave it up. But she would remember it. "Where's the what's-its-name?" she would ask. "Don't tell me you forgot the what's-its-name." A newsboy went by shouting something about the Waterbury trial.

. . . "Perhaps this will refresh your memory." The District Attorney suddenly thrust a heavy automatic at the quiet figure on the witness stand. "Have you ever seen this before?" Walter Mitty took the gun and examined it expertly. "This is my Webley-Vickers 50.80," he said calmly. An excited buzz ran around the courtroom. The Judge rapped for order. "You are a crack shot with any sort of firearms, I believe?" said the District Attorney, insinuatingly. "Objection!" shouted Mitty's attorney. "We have shown that the defendant could not have fired the shot. We have shown that he wore his right arm in a sling on the night of the fourteenth of July." Walter Mitty raised his hand briefly and the bickering attorneys were stilled. "With any known make of gun," he said evenly, "I could have killed Gregory Fitzhurst at three hundred feet *with my left hand*." Pandemonium broke loose in the courtroom. A woman's scream rose above the bedlam and suddenly a lovely, dark-haired girl was in Walter Mitty's arms. The District Attorney struck at her savagely. Without rising from his chair, Mitty

123

let the man have it on the point of the chin. "You miserable cur!" . . .

"Puppy biscuit," said Walter Mitty. He stopped walking and the buildings of Waterbury rose up out of the misty courtroom and surrounded him again. A woman who was passing laughed. "He said 'Puppy biscuit,'" she said to her companion. "That man said 'Puppy biscuit' to himself." Walter Mitty hurried on. He went into an A. & P., not the first one he came to but a smaller one farther up the street. "I want some biscuit for small, young dogs," he said to the clerk. "Any special brand, sir?" The greatest pistol shot in the world thought a moment. "It says 'Puppies Bark for It' on the box," said Walter Mitty.

His wife would be through at the hairdresser's in fifteen minutes, Mitty saw in looking at his watch, unless they had trouble drying it; sometimes they had trouble drying it. She didn't like to get to the hotel first; she would want him to be there waiting for her as usual. He found a big leather chair in the lobby, facing a window, and he put the overshoes and the puppy biscuit on the floor beside it. He picked up an old copy of *Liberty* and sank down into the chair. "Can Germany Conquer the World Through the Air?" Walter Mitty looked at the pictures of bombing planes and of ruined streets.

. . ."The cannonading has got the wind up in young Raleigh, sir," said the sergeant. Captain Mitty looked up at him through tousled hair. "Get him to bed," he said wearily, "with the others. I'll fly alone." "But you can't, sir," said the sergeant anxiously. "It takes two men to handle that bomber and the Archies are pounding hell out of the air. Von Richtman's circus is between here and Saulier." "Somebody's got to get that ammunition dump," said Mitty. "I'm going over. Spot of brandy?" He poured a drink for the sergeant and one for himself. War thundered and whined around the dugout and battered at the door. There was a rending of wood and splinters flew through the room. "A bit of a near thing," said Captain Mitty carelessly. "The box barrage is closing in," said he sergeant. "We only live once, Sergeant," said Mitty, with his faint, fleeting smile. "Or do we?" He poured another brandy and tossed it off. "I never see a man could hold his brandy like you, sir," said the sergeant. "Begging your pardon, sir." Captain Mitty stood up and strapped on his huge Webley-Vickers automatic. "It's forty kilometres through hell, sir," said the sergeant. Mitty finished one last brandy. "After all," he said softly, "what isn't?" The pounding of the cannon increased; there was the rat-tat-tatting of machine guns, and from somewhere came the menacing pocketa-pocketa-pocketa of the new flame-throwers. Walter Mitty walked to the door of the dugout humming "Auprès de Ma Blonde." He turned and waved to the sergeant. "Cheerio!" he said. . . .

Something struck his shoulder. "I've been looking all over this hotel for you," said Mrs. Mitty. "Why do you have to hide in this old chair? How did you expect me to find you?" "Things close in," said Walter Mitty vaguely. "What?" Mrs. Mitty said. "Did you get the what's-its-name? The puppy biscuit? What's in that box?" "Overshoes," said Mitty. "Couldn't you have put them on in the store?" "I was think-ing," said Walter Mitty. "Does it ever occur to you that I am sometimes thinking?" She looked at him. "I'm going to take your temperature when I get you home," she said.

They went out through the revolving doors that made a faintly derisive whistling sound when you pushed them. It was two blocks to the parking lot. At the drugstore on the corner she said, "Wait here for me. I forgot something. I won't be a minute." She was more than a minute. Walter Mitty lighted a cigarette. It began to rain, rain with sleet in it. He stood up against the wall of the drugstore, smok-ing. . . . He put his shoulders back and his heels together. "To hell with the handkerchief," said Walter Mitty scorn-fully. He took one last drag on his cigarette and snapped it away. Then, with that faint, fleeting smile playing about his lips, he faced the firing squad; erect and motionless, proud and disdainful, Walter Mitty the Undefeated, inscrutable to the last.

Robert Penn Warren

WHEN THE LIGHT GETS GREEN

MY GRANDFATHER had a long white beard and sat under the cedar tree. The beard, as a matter of fact, was not very long and not white, only grey, but when I was a child and was away from him at school during the winter, I would think of him, not seeing him in my mind's eye, and say, he has a long white beard. Therefore it was a shock to me, on the first morning back home, to watch him lean over the dresser toward the wavy green mirror, which in his always shadowy room reflected things like deep water riffled by a little wind, and clip his grey beard to a point. It is grey and pointed, I would say then, remembering what I had thought before.

He turned his face to the green wavy glass, first one side and then the other in quarter profile, and lifted the long shears, which trembled a little, up to cut the beard. His face being turned like that, with his good nose and pointed grey beard, he looked like General Robert E. Lee without any white horse to ride. My grandfather had been a soldier too, but now he wore blue jean pants and when he leaned over like that toward the mirror I couldn't help but notice how small his hips and backsides were. Only they weren't just small, they were shrunken. I noticed how the blue jeans hung loose from his suspenders and loose off his legs and down around his shoes. And in the morning when I noticed all this about his legs and backsides, I felt a tight feeling in my stomach like when you walk behind a woman and see the high heel of her shoe is worn and twisted and jerks her ankle every time she takes a step.

Always before my grandfather had finished clipping his beard, my Uncle Kirby came to the door and beat on it for breakfast. "I'll be down in just a minute, thank you sir," my grandfather said. My uncle called him Mr. Barden. "Mr. Barden, breakfast is ready." It was because my Uncle Kirby was not my real uncle, having married my Aunt Lucy, who lived with my grandfather. Then my grandfather put on a black vest and put his gold watch and chain in the vest and picked up his cob pipe from the marble dresser top, and he and I went down to breakfast, after Uncle Kirby was already downstairs.

When we came into the dining room, Aunt Lucy was sitting at the foot of the table with the iron coffee pot on a plate beside her. She said, "Good morning, Papa."

"Good morning, Lucy," he said, and sat down at the head of the table, taking one more big puff off his pipe before laying it beside his plate.

"You've brought that old pipe down to breakfast again," my aunt said, while she poured the bright-looking coffee into the cups.

"Don't it stink," he always said . . .

After we ate, my uncle got up, and said, "I got to get going," and went out through the kitchen where the cook was knocking and sloshing around. If it had rained right and was a good tobacco setting season, my grandfather went off with me down to the stable to get his mare, for he had to see the setting. We saddled up the mare and went across the lot, where limestone bunched out of the ground and cedar trees and blue grass grew out of the split rock. A branch of cold water with minnows in it went through the lot between the rocks and under the cedar trees; it was where I used to play before I got big enough to go to the river with the niggers to swim.

My grandfather rode across the lot and over the rise back of the house. He sat up pretty straight for an old man, holding the bridle in his left hand, and in his right hand a long hickory tobacco stick whittled down to make a walking cane. I walked behind him, and watched the big straw hat he wore waggle a little above his narrow neck, or how he held the stick in the middle, firm and straight up like something carried in a parade, or how smooth and slow the muscles in the mare's flanks worked as she put each hoof down on the ground going up the hill. Sassafrass bushes and blackberry bushes grew thick along the lane over the rise. In summer tufts of hay would catch and hang on the dry bushes, and showed that the hay wagons had been that way; but when we went that way in setting time, just after breakfast, the blackberry blooms were hardly gone, only a few rusty patches of white left, and the sassafrass leaves showed still wet with dew or maybe the rain.

From the rise we could look back on the house. The shingles were black with damp, and the whitewash greyish, except in spots where the sun already struck it and it was drying. The tops of the cedar trees, too, were below us, very dark green and quiet. When we crossed the rise, there were the fields going down toward the river, all checked off and ready for setting, very even, only for the gullies where brush was piled to stop the washing. The fields were reddish from the wet, not yet steaming. Across them, the green woods and the sycamores showing white far off told where the river was.

The hands were standing at the edge of the field under the trees when we got there. The little niggers were filling their baskets with the wet plants to drop, and I got me a basket and filled it. My Uncle Kirby gave me fifty cents for dropping plants, but he didn't give the little niggers that much, I remember. The hands and the women stood around waiting a minute, watching Uncle Kirby, who always fumed around,

128

waving his dibble, his blue shirt already sticking to his arms with sweat . . .

Then, of a sudden, they all moved out into the field, scattering out down the rows, the droppers first, and after a minute, the setters, who lurched along, never straightening up, down the rows toward the river. I walked down my row, separating out the plants and dropping them at the hills, while it got hotter and the ground steamed. The sun broke out now and then, making my shadow on the ground, then the cloud would come again, and I could see its shadow on the red field drifting at me.

My grandfather rode very slow along the edge of the field to watch the setting, or stayed still under the trees. After a while, maybe about ten o'clock, he would leave and go home. I could see him riding the mare up the rise and then go over the rise; or if I was working the other way toward the river, when I turned round at the end, the lane would be empty and nothing on top the rise, with the cloudy blue-grey sky low behind it.

The tobacco was all he cared about now, now we didn't have any horses that were any real good. He had some silver cups, only one real silver one though, that his horses won at fairs, but all that was before I was born. The real silver one, the one he kept on his dresser and kept string and old minie balls and pins and things in, had 1859 on it because his horse won it then before the War, when he was a young man. Uncle Kirby said horses were foolishness, and my grandfather said, yes, he reckoned horses were foolishness all right. So what he cared about now was the tobacco. One time he was a tobacco buyer for three years, but after he bought a lot of tobacco and had it in his sheds, the sheds burned up on him. He didn't have enough insurance to do any good and he was a ruined man. After that all his children, he had all girls and his money was gone, said about him, "Papa's just visionary, he tried to be a tobacco buyer but he's too visionary and not practical." Now he was old the corn could get the rust or the hay could get rained on for all he cared, it was Uncle Kirby's worry, but all summer off and on he had to go down to the tobacco field to watch them sucker or plow or worm, and sometimes he pulled a few suckers himself. And when a cloud would blow up black in summer, he got nervous as a cat, not knowing whether it was the rain they needed or maybe a hail storm coming that would cut the tobacco up bad.

Mornings he didn't go down to the field he went out under the cedar tree where his chair was. Most of the time he took a book with him along with his pipe, for he was an inveterate reader. His being an inveterate reader was one of the things made his children say he was visionary. He read a lot until his eyes went bad the summer before he had his stroke, then after that I read to him some, but not as much as I ought. He used to read out loud some from Macaulay's *History of England* or Gibbon's *Decline and Fall:* about Flodden Field or about how the Janizaries took Constantinople amid great slaughter and how the Turk surveyed the carnage and quoted from the Persian poet about the lizard keeping the courts of the mighty. My grandfather knew some poetry too, and he said it to himself when he didn't have anything else to do. I lay on my back on the ground, feeling the grass cool and tickly on the back of my neck, and looked upsidedown into the cedar tree where the limbs were tangled and black-green like big hairy fern fronds with the sky blue all around, while he said some poetry. Like the "Isles of Greece, the Isles of Greece, where burning Sappho loved and sung"; or like, "Roll on thou deep and dark blue ocean, roll."

But he never read poetry, he just said what he already knew. He only read history and *Napoleon and his Marshals*, having been a soldier and fought in the War himself. He rode off and joined the cavalry, but he never told me whether he took the horse that won the real silver cup or not. He was with Forrest before Forrest was a general. He said Forrest was a great general, and if they had done what Forrest wanted and cleaned the country ahead of the Yankees, like the Russians beat Napoleon, they'd whipped the Yankees sure. He told me about Donelson, how they fought in the winter woods, and how they got away with Forrest at night, splashing through the cold water. And how the dead men looked in the river bottoms in winter, and I lay on my back on the grass, looking up in the thick cedar limbs, and thought how it was to be dead.

After Shiloh was fought and they pushed the Yankees down in the river, my grandfather was a captain, for he raised a cavalry company of his own out of West Tennessee. He was a captain, but he never got promoted after the War; when I was a little boy everybody still called him Captain Barden, though they called lots of other people in our section Colonel and Major. One time I said to him: "Grandpa, did you ever kill any Yankees?" He said: "God-er-mighty, how do I know?" So, being little, I thought he was just a captain because he never killed anybody; and I was ashamed. He talked about Fort Pillow, and the drunk niggers under the bluff. And one time he said niggers couldn't stand a charge or stand the cold steel, so I thought maybe he killed some of them. But then I thought, niggers don't count, maybe.

He only talked much in the morning. Almost every afternoon right after dinner, he went to sleep in his chair, with his hands curled up in his lap, one of them holding the pipe that still sent up a little smoke in the shadow, and his head propped back on the tree trunk. His mouth hung open, and under the hairs of his mustache, all yellow with nicotine, you could see his black teeth and his lips that were wet and pink like a baby's. Usually I remember him that way, asleep.

I remember him that way, or else trampling up and down the front porch, nervous as a cat, while a cloud blew up and the trees began to rustle. He tapped his walking cane on the boards and whistled through his teeth with his breath and kept looking off at the sky where the cloud and sometimes the lightning was. Then of a sudden it came, and if it was rain he used to go up to his room and lie down; but if it came hail on the tobacco, he stayed on the front porch, not trampling any more, and watched the hail rattle off the roof and bounce soft on the grass. "God-er-mighty," he always said, "bigger'n minie balls"; even when it wasn't so big.

In 1914, just before the War began, it was a hot summer with the tobacco mighty good but needing rain. And when the dry spell broke and a cloud blew up, my grandfather came out on the front porch, watching it like that. It was mighty still, with lightning way off, so far you couldn't hardly hear the thunder. Then the leaves began to ruffle like they do when the light gets green, and my grandfather said to me, "Son, it's gonna hail." And he stood still. Down in the pasture, little that far off, you could see the cattle bunching up and the white horse charging across the pasture, looking bright, for the sun was shining bright before the cloud struck it all at once. "It's gonna hail," my grandfather said. It was dark, with jagged lightning and the thunder high and steady. And there the hail was.

He just turned around and went in the house. I watched the hail bouncing, then I heard a noise and my aunt yelled. I ran back in the dining room where the noise was, and my grandfather was lying on the floor with the old silver pitcher he dropped and dented and the glass he had started to drink out of broken. We tried to drag him, but he was too heavy, then my Uncle Kirby came up wet from the stable, so we carried my grandfather upstairs and put him on his bed. My aunt tried to call the doctor even if the lightning might hit the telephone. I stayed back in the dining room and picked up the broken glass and the pitcher and wiped up the floor with a rag. After a while Dr. Blake came from town, then he went away.

When Dr. Blake was gone I went upstairs to see my grandfather. I shut the door and went in his room, which was almost dark, like always, and quiet because the hail didn't beat on the roof any more. He was lying on his back in the feather-bed, with a sheet pulled up over him, lying there in the dark. He had his hands curled loose on his stomach, like when he went to sleep in his chair holding the pipe. I sat on a split-bottom chair by the bed and looked at him: he had his eyes shut and his mouth hung loose, but you couldn't hear his breathing. Then I quit looking at him and looked round the room, my eyes getting used to the shadow. I could see his pants on the floor, and the silver cup on the dresser by the mirror, which was green and wavy like water.

When he said something I almost jumped out of my skin, hearing his voice like that. He said: "Son, I'm gonna die." I tried to say something, but I couldn't. And he waited, then he said: "I'm on borrowed time, it's time to die." I said "No!" so sudden and loud I jumped. He waited a long time and said: "It's time to die. Nobody loves me." I tried to say, "Grandpa, I love you." And then I did say it all right, feeling like it hadn't been me said it, and knowing all of a sudden it was a lie, because I didn't feel anything. He just lay there; and I went downstairs.

It was sunshiny in the yard, the clouds gone, but the grass was wet. I walked down toward the gate, rubbing my bare feet over the slick cold grass. A hen was in the yard and she kept trying to peck up a piece of hail, like a fool chicken will do after it hails; but every time she pecked, it bounced away from her over the green grass. I leaned against the gate, noticing the ground on one side the posts close up was still dry and dusty. I wondered if the tobacco was cut up bad, because Uncle Kirby had gone to see. And while I looked through the gate down across the pasture where everything in the sun was green and shiny with wet and the cattle grazed, I thought about my grandfather, not feeling anything. But I said out loud anyway: "Grandpa, I love you."

My grandfather lived four more years. The year after his stroke they sold the farm and moved away, so I didn't stay with them any more. My grandfather died in 1918, just before the news came my Uncle Kirby was killed in France, and my aunt had to go to work in a store. I got the letter about my grandfather, who died of flu, but I thought about four years back, and it didn't matter much.

Erskine Caldwell

PRIMING THE WELL

WHEN I was a little fellow my mother, who was half dam-yankee, used to tell me the story about wooden nutmegs. Even now I can clearly remember her picturing the early peddlers with pouches of painted nutmegs going from farm to farm along the Potomac, selling the spice with all the solemnity of a Methodist circuit-rider. That the nutmegs were easily sold and eagerly bought is beside the story; the wonder is that we Southerners were so dumb we did not know the difference.

For some reason I never fully understood, my mother and father, when I was still quite young, went Down East and bought a farm in the Kennebec River Valley. Then, when I was eleven years old and my sister nine, they decided that they would sell the farm and move back to Virginia. This was the easiest phase of the decision, because finding somebody who wanted to invest six thousand dollars in a Maine farm was a problem difficult to solve. Even when we did find a purchaser it was by mere accident that the sale was so easily made.

It was a three-months' drought that finally brought a buyer to us. And that was chance, too; because droughts for more

134

than three or four weeks were uncommon where we were.

In the late spring, about four months before the drought came to an end,—the last rain fell on the first day of June—there were two men who were very anxious to buy our farm. The price either of them was willing to pay at that time, however, was not much more than one half the figure my father had placed on it. Mr. Geroux, a Frenchman, was one of the prospective purchasers, and Elisha Goodwin the other. Mr. Geroux was a native of New Brunswick, but he had lived in Maine thirty years or longer. He had become unusually prosperous in recent years because of the rising market for seed potatoes, and during all that time he had been acquiring that same cautious mind Elisha Goodwin had inherited from six generations of forefathers. Both of these men, however, realized the value of our farm and both knew it was worth every dollar of six thousand. Neither of them was willing, though, to pay the price asked until he was sure it could not be bought for less. And, as we were told afterwards, Mr. Geroux would have paid almost anything up to ten thousand for the farm, because its improvements, fertility, and location were making it increasingly valuable.

In the month of August, the beginning of the last month of the terrible drought, both Mr. Geroux and Elisha Goodwin came to see my father in regard to purchasing our farm. They did not come together, of course, because each of them wanted to buy it before the other did. At the same time, each of them wanted to close the deal before he was forced to bid against the other. The month of August was the dryest ever to be recorded in the State of Maine. Everyone was certain of that. No rain had fallen since the first of June. The Kennebec River was so low that it was out of the question for the paper-mills to float pulpwood, and all of those which were not importing Scandinavian baled pulp had to close down. Even the lakes in the back-country were so low that at least fifty per cent of the fish had already died. There was nothing that could be done about the weather, though, and everybody just had to wait for fall to come, bringing rain or snow. Towards the end of the month the water famine was becoming dangerous. The farmers, whose wells had gone dry and who had been drawing water from the river and lakes, were faced with additional danger when the river went completely dry along with most of the lakes. The stock on every farm was dropping dead day and night. There had been no milk in the valley for nearly a month, and the horses, steers, and sheep were hungry and thirsty. The month of August was without exception the most damaging month in the history of the entire Kennebec River Valley.

There was a deep lake on our farm about a mile and a half from the buildings and we were fortunate in having some water for our stock and ourselves. We drew water to the house every day from the lake. Our well had gone dry just as quickly as all the other wells in the valley.

We had been drawing water in three barrels every day from the lake. After six weeks of this my father became tired of having to go to the lake every day. He decided that we would draw twenty-five or thirty barrels one day a week and store it on the farm. This would save us the trouble of having to go every day and give us time to do some other work that was needed. The real problem, however, was where and how to store a week's supply of water. It would have been foolish to buy twenty-five or thirty barrels, or even half that many, when we could use them at the most only two or three weeks longer. Then they would have to be stored away and they would dry and warp until they were valueless. I believe it was my mother who made the suggestion of storing the water in the well. At least, it was she who said it was the only place she knew about. At first my father was of the opinion that the water would run or seep out of the well faster than we could haul it, but he was willing to try it, anyway. The plan worked, much to my mother's joy. All of us—my father, my sister, and myself—congratulated her on making such a wise suggestion.

136

We went to work at once and all that day we drew water from the lake and poured it into the well. By late afternoon we had transferred about thirty or thirty-five barrels of lake water to the well. That evening all we had to do was to lower the bucket and bring up as much water as we needed for the stock. The next day it was the same. The water was still there and apparently none had seeped away. It was a great improvement over the way we had been doing before.

It was by accident that Elisha Goodwin stopped at our house that afternoon. His horse had thrown a shoe and he came up to the barn to draw out the nails so the hoof would not be injured. He came up to the barn where we were at the time.

"Well, Mr. Langley," he said to my father, "what are we going to do about this here drought? The whole State of Maine will be ruined if this keeps up another two weeks. There ain't a drop of water on my whole farm."

"The drought is terrible," my father said. "I won't have even a peck of potatoes out of the whole farm to sell this year. But, strange to say, I've got plenty of water in my well."

"What?" Mr. Goodwin shouted unbelievingly. "You say you got water in your well?"

"Plenty of it."

"Well, I don't believe it. Nobody else has got any water in their wells. How comes it you got water in your'n?"

"I water my stock from it twice a day and we have plenty of water for the kitchen besides. It's just as full as it's ever been."

Elisha Goodwin thought we were joking with him about having plenty of water in the well, but he went over to see for himself just the same.

My father sent my sister into the house.

Elisha Goodwin picked up three or four pebbles and leaned far over the well looking down into it and trying to see the water. He dropped one of the pebbles into the well and cocked his head sideways, listening for the *ker-plunk*

137

the stone made when it struck the water. He repeated this as long as his pebbles lasted. Then he stood up and looked at us. By watching his face we could tell that he was getting ready to say something important.

He stood up looking at us and scratching the top of his head with three of his fingers while his hatbrim was held tightly by the other two. His chin-whiskers moved up and down faster than I could count.

"How much is it you're asking for this place of your'n?"

My father told him how much we were holding it for.

"You haven't closed a deal with anybody yet, have you?"

"Well, not exactly," my father stated. "Though Mr. Geroux has asked me to give him a two-months' option on the place."

"Did you let him have it?" Elisha Goodwin asked hurriedly.

"I'm to let him know tomorrow about it," my father said.

"You come with me to the village," Elisha Goodwin said. "We'll fix up a sale before sundown. I'm going to buy your place. It's the only farm in the whole gol-darned State that's got any well-water on it."

"Are you sure you want to buy it, Mr. Goodwin?" my father asked him. "You know the price and terms. It's six thousand dollars cash."

"I don't give a gol-darn what your terms are. I'm going to pay you six thousand dollars in cash for it as soon as you go to the village with me and draw up a bill of sale and turn over the deed. I ain't going to let that good-for-nothing Canuck get his hands on the best farm in the whole gol-darned country. Come on to the village and get it settled right away."

Instead of driving to the village in the buggy, he and my father went in our automobile. He left his horse and buggy hitched at our barn. They were gone about two hours.

When they came back, they shook hands with each other

138

and Elisha Goodwin drove home at a fast clip. He must have forgotten about his horse throwing a shoe.

My mother came out with my sister and asked us what agreement had been made. My father told her all about it. She smiled a little but did not say anything just then. While I carried water to the stock and while my sister went down into the cellar to get some potatoes for supper, they walked across the pasture talking to themselves about something they did not want us to overhear. When they came back, we all went into the kitchen while supper was cooking.

"Well, we are moving back to Virginia next week," my father told us, smiling at my mother. "As soon as we can pack everything we want to take with us we're leaving."

He called my sister to him and lifted her on his knee. He stroked her curls absent-mindedly several times.

"Louise," he smiled at her, "tell me: are you a little Virginia girl, or are you a little New Englander?"

My sister answered without a moment's hesitation.

"I'd rather be a little Virginia lady."

"But your mother is a damyankee—don't you want to be like her?"

He always smiled to himself when he called my mother a damyankee.

Before my sister could reply, my mother came over where we were and lifted her to the floor from my father's lap.

"Louise, you and Tommy run out into the yard and play until supper is ready. Run along, now."

We left the kitchen and went out on the porch. Hardly before we were down the front steps, we heard two people laughing as though they had just seen the funniest thing in the world. We tiptoed to the kitchen window and looked in to see what was so funny. Both my mother and father were standing in the middle of the kitchen floor holding on to each other and laughing so hard I thought they would burst open if they kept it up much longer.

My sister pulled me by the arm and pointed down the

139

river. The sky down there was the blackest I have ever seen. The black clouds were coming closer and closer all the time, like somebody covering you with a big black blanket at night. Away down the valley we could see the tops of trees bending over so far that many of them broke off and fell to the ground.

"Look!" my sister said, clutching my arm. She was trembling all over. "Look!"

Holding each other tightly by the hand, we ran into the house as fast as we could.

❧

Andrew Nelson Lytle

JERICHO, JERICHO, JERICHO

SHE OPENED her eyes. She must have been asleep for hours or months. She could not reckon; she could only feel the steady silence of time. She had been Joshua and made it swing suspended in her room. Forever she had floated above the counterpane; between the tester and the counterpane she had floated until her hand, long and bony, its speckled-dried skin drawing away from the bulging blue veins, had reached and drawn her body under the covers. And now she was resting, clear-headed and quiet, her thoughts clicking like a new-greased mower. All creation could not make her lift her thumb or cross it over her finger. She looked at the bed, the bed her mother had died in, the bed her children had been born in, her marriage bed, the bed the General had drenched with his blood. Here it stood where it had stood for seventy years, square and firm on the floor, wide enough for three people to lie comfortable in, if they didn't sleep restless; but not wide enough for her nor long enough when her conscience scorched the cool wrinkles in the sheets. The two footposts, octagonal-shaped and mounted by carved pieces that looked like absurd flowers, stood up to comfort her when the world began to crumble. Her eyes followed down the posts and along the basket-quilt. She had made it before her marriage to the General, only he wasn't a general then. He was a slight, tall young man with a rolling mustache and perfume in his hair. A many a time she had seen her young love's locks dripping with scented oil, down upon his collar . . . She had cut the squares for the baskets in January, and for stuffing had used the letters of old lovers, fragments of passion cut to warm her of a winter's night. The General would have his fun. *Miss Kate, I didn't sleep well last night. I heard Sam Buchanan make love to you out of that farthest basket. If I hear him again, I mean to toss this piece of quilt in the fire.* Then he would chuckle in his round, soft voice; reach under the covers and pull her over to his side of the bed. On a cold and frosting night he would sleep with his nose against her neck. His nose was so quick to turn cold, he said, and her neck was so warm. Sometimes her hair, the loose unruly strands at the nape, would tickle his nostrils and he would wake up with a sneeze. This had been so long ago, and there had been so many years of trouble and worry. Her eyes, as apart from her as the mirror on the bureau, rested upon the half-tester, upon the enormous button that caught the rose-colored canopy and shot its folds out like the rays of the morning sun. She could not see but she could feel the heavy cluster of mahogany grapes that tumbled from the center of the headboard—out of its vines curling down the sides it tumbled. How much longer would these never-picked grapes hang above her head? How much longer would she, rather, hang to the vine of this world, she who lay beneath as dry as any raisin. Then she remembered. She looked at the blinds. They were closed.

141

"You, Ants, where's my stick? I'm a great mind to break it over your trifling back."

"Awake? What a nice long nap you've had," said Doctor Ed.

"The boy? Where's my grandson? Has he come?"

"I'll say he's come. What do you mean taking to your bed like this? Do you realize, beautiful lady, that this is the first time I ever saw you in bed in my whole life? I believe you've taken to bed on purpose. I don't believe you want to see me."

"Go long, boy, with your foolishness."

That's all she could say, and she blushed as she said it—she blushing at the words of a snip of a boy, whom she had diapered a hundred times and had washed as he stood before the fire in the round tin tub, his little back swayed and his little belly sticking out in front, rosy from the scrubbing he had gotten. *Mammy, what for I've got a hole in my stummick; what for, Mammy?* Now he was sitting on the edge of the bed calling her beautiful lady, an old hag like her, beautiful lady. A good-looker the girls would call him, with his bold, careless face and his hands with their fine, long fingers. Soft, how soft they were, running over her rough, skinny bones. He looked a little like his grandpa, but somehow there was something missing . . .

"Well, boy, it took you a time to come home to see me die."

"Nonsense. Cousin Edwin, I wouldn't wait on a woman who had so little faith in my healing powers."

"There an't nothing strange about dying. But I an't in such an all-fired hurry. I've got a heap to tell you about before I go."

The boy leaned over and touched her gently. "Not even death would dispute you here, on Long Gourd, Mammy."

He was trying to put her at her ease in his carefree way. It was so obvious a pretending, but she loved him for it. There was something nice in its awkwardness, the charm of

142

the young's blundering and of their efforts to get along in the world. Their pretty arrogance, their patronizing airs, their colossal unknowing of what was to come. It was a quenching drink to a sin-thirsty old woman. Somehow his vitality had got crossed in her blood and made a dry heart leap, her blood that was almost water. Soon now she would be all water, water and dust, lying in the burying ground between the cedar—and fire. She could smell her soul burning and see it. What a fire it would make below, dripping with sin, like a rag soaked in kerosene. But she had known what she was doing. And here was Long Gourd, all its fields intact, ready to be handed on, in better shape than when she took it over. Yes, she had known what she was doing. How long, she wondered, would his spirit hold up under the trials of planting, of cultivating, and of the gathering time, year in and year out—how would he hold up before so many springs and so many autumns. The thought of him giving orders, riding over the place, or rocking on the piazza, and a great pain would pin her heart to her backbone. She wanted him by her to train—there was so much for him to know: how the south field was cold and must be planted late, and where the orchards would best hold their fruit, and where the frosts crept soonest—that now could never be. She turned her head—who was that woman, that strange woman standing by the bed as if she owned it, as if . . .

"This is Eva, Mammy."

"Eva?"

"We are going to be married."

"I wanted to come and see—to meet Dick's grandmother . . ."

I wanted to come see her die. That's what she meant. Why didn't she finish and say it out. She had come to lick her chops and see what she would enjoy. That's what she had come for, the lying little slut. The richest acres in Long Gourd valley, so rich hit'd make yer feet greasy to walk over'm, Saul Oberly at the first tollgate had told the peddler once, and the peddler had told it to her, knowing it would please and make her trade. *Before you die.* Well, why didn't you finish it out? You might as well. You've given yourself away.

Her fierce thoughts dried up the water in her eyes, tired and resting far back in their sockets. They burned like a smothered fire stirred up by the wind as they traveled over the woman who would lie in her bed, eat with her silver, and caress her flesh and blood. The woman's body was soft enough to melt and pour about him. She could see that; and her firm, round breasts, too firm and round for any good to come from them. And her lips, full and red, her eyes bright and cunning. The heavy hair crawled about her head to tangle the poor, foolish boy in its ropes. She might have known he would do something foolish like this. He had a foolish mother. There warn't any way to avoid it. But look at her belly, small and no-count. There wasn't a muscle the size of a worm as she could see. And those hips—

And then she heard her voice: "What did you say her name was, son? Eva? Eva Callahan, I'm glad to meet you, Eva. Where'd your folks come from, Eva? I knew some Callahans who lived in the Goosepad settlement. They couldn't be any of your kin, could they?"

"Oh, no, indeed. My people . . ."

"Right clever people they were. And good farmers, too. Worked hard. Honest—that is, most of 'em. As honest as that run of people go. We always gave them a good name."

"My father and mother live in Birmingham. Have always lived there."

"Birmingham," she heard herself say with contempt. They could have lived there all their lives and still come from somewhere. I've got a mule older'n Birmingham. "What's your pa's name?"

"Her father is Mister E. L. Callahan, Mammy."

"First name not Elijah by any chance? Lige they called him."

144

"No. Elmore, Mammy."

"Old Mason Callahan had a son they called Lige. Somebody told me he moved to Elyton. So you think you're going to live with the boy here."

"We're to be married . . . that is, if Eva doesn't change her mind."

And she saw his arm slip possessively about the woman's waist. "Well, take care of him, young woman, or I'll come back and han't you. I'll come back and claw your eyes out."

"I'll take very good care of him, Mrs. McCowan."

"I can see that." She could hear the threat in her voice, and Eva heard it.

"Young man," spoke up Doctor Edwin, "you should feel powerful set up, two such women pestering each other about you."

The boy kept an embarrassed silence.

"All of you get out now. I want to talk to him by himself. I've got a lot to say and precious little time to say it in. And he's mighty young and helpless and ignorant."

"Why, Mammy, you forget I'm a man now. Twenty-six. All teeth cut. Long trousers."

"It takes a heap more than pants to make a man. Throw open them blinds, Ants."

"Yes'm."

"You don't have to close the door so all-fired soft. Close it naturally. And you can tip about all you want to—later. I won't be hurried to the burying ground. And keep your head away from that door. What I've got to say to your new master is private."

"Listen at you, Mistiss."

"You listen to me. That's all. No, wait. I had something else on my mind—what is it? Yes. How many hens has Melissy set? You don't know. Find out. A few of the old hens ought to be setting. Tell her to be careful to turn the turkey eggs every day. No, you bring them and set them under my bed. I'll make sure. We got a mighty pore hatch last year.

145

You may go now. I'm plumb worn out, boy, worn out thinking for these people. It's that that worries a body down. But you'll know all about it in good time. Stand out there and let me look at you good. You don't let me see enough of you, and I almost forget how you look. Not really, you understand. Just a little. It's your own fault. I've got so much to trouble me that you, when you're not here, naturally slip back in my mind. But that's all over now. You are here to stay, and I'm here to go. There will always be Long Gourd, and there must always be a McCowan on it. I had hoped to have you by me for several years, but you would have your fling in town. I thought it best to clear your blood of it, but as God is hard, I can't see what you find to do in town. And now you've gone and gotten you a woman. Well, they all have to do it. But do you reckon you've picked the right one —you must forgive the frankness of an old lady who can see the bottom of her grave—I had in mind one of the Carlisle girls. The Carlisle place lies so handy to Long Gourd and would give me a landing on the river. Have you seen Anna Belle since she's grown to be a woman? I'm told there's not a better housekeeper in the valley."

"I'm sure Anna Belle is a fine girl. But Mammy, I love Eva."

"She'll wrinkle up on you, Son; and the only wrinkles land gets can be smoothed out by the harrow. And she looks sort of puny to me, Son. She's powerful small in the waist and walks about like she had worms."

"Gee, Mammy, you're not jealous are you? That waist is in style."

"You want to look for the right kind of style in a woman. Old Mrs. Penter Matchem had two daughters with just such waists, but 'twarnt natural. She would tie their corset strings to the bed posts and whip'm out with a buggy whip. The poor girls never drew a hearty breath. Just to please that old woman's vanity. She got paid in kind. It did something to Eliza's bowels and she died before she was twenty. The other

146

one never had any children. She used to whip'm out until they cried. I never liked that woman. She thought a whip could do anything."

"Well, anyway, Eva's small waist wasn't made by any corset strings. She doesn't wear any."

"How do you know, sir?"

"Well . . . I . . . What a question for a respectable woman to ask."

"I'm not a respectable woman. No woman can be respectable and run four thousand acres of land. Well, you'll have it your own way. I suppose the safest place for a man to take his folly is to bed."

"Mammy!"

"You must be lenient with your Cousin George. He wanders about night times talking about the War. I put him off in the west wing where he won't keep people awake, but sometimes he gets in the yard and gives orders to his troops. 'I will sweep that hill, General'—and many's the time he's done it when the battle was doubtful—'I'll sweep it with my iron brooms'; then he shouts out his orders, and pretty soon the dogs commence to barking. But he's been a heap of company for me. You must see that your wife humors him. It won't be for long. He's mighty feeble."

"Eva's not my wife yet, Mammy."

"You won't be free much longer—the way she looks at you, like a hungry hound."

"I was just wondering," he said hurriedly. "I hate to talk about anything like this . . ."

"Everybody has a time to die, and I'll have no maudlin nonsense about mine."

"I was wondering about Cousin George . . . if I could get somebody to keep him. You see, it will be difficult in the winters. Eva will want to spend the winters in town . . ."

He paused, startled, before the great bulk of his grandmother rising from her pillows, and in the silence that frightened the air, his unfinished words hung suspended about them.

After a moment he asked if he should call the doctor.

It was some time before she could find words to speak.

"Get out of the room."

"Forgive me, Mammy. You must be tired."

"I'll send for you," sounded the dead voice in the still room, "when I want to see you again. I'll send for you and—the woman."

She watched the door close quietly on his neat square back. Her head whirled and turned like a flying jennet. She lowered and steadied it on the pillows. Four thousand acres of the richest land in the valley he would sell and squander on that slut, and he didn't even know it and there was no way to warn him. This terrifying thought rushed through her mind, and she felt the bed shake with her pain, while before the footboard the spectre of an old sin rose up to mock her. How she had struggled to get this land and keep it together—through the War, the Reconstruction, and the pleasanter after days. For eighty-seven years she had suffered and slept and planned and rested and had pleasure in this valley, seventy of it, almost a turning century, on this place; and now that she must leave it . . .

The things she had done to keep it together. No. The one thing . . . From the dusty stacks the musty odor drifted through the room, met the tobacco smoke over the long table piled high with records, reports. Iva Louise stood at one end, her hat clinging perilously to the heavy auburn hair, the hard blue eyes and the voice:

"You promised Pa to look after me"—she had waited for the voice to break and scream—"and you have stolen my land!"

"Now, Miss Iva Louise," the lawyer dropped his empty eyes along the floor, "you don't mean . . ."

"Yes. I do mean it."

148

Her own voice had restored calm to the room: "I promised your pa his land would not be squandered."

"My husband won't squander my property. You just want it for yourself."

She cut through the scream with the sharp edge of her scorn: "What about that weakling's farm in Madison? Who pays the taxes now?"

The girl had no answer to that. Desperate, she faced the lawyer: "Is there no way, sir, I can get my land from the clutches of this unnatural woman?"

The man coughed; the red rim of his eyes watered with embarrassment. "I'm afraid," he cleared his throat, "you say you can't raise the money . . . I'm afraid—"

That trapped look as the girl turned away. It had come back to her, now trapped in her bed. As a swoon spreads, she felt the desperate terror of weakness, more desperate where there has been strength. Did the girl see right? Has she stolen the land because she wanted it?

Suddenly, like the popping of a thread in a loom, the struggles of the flesh stopped, and the years backed up and covered her thoughts like the spring freshet she had seen so many times creep over the dark soil. Not in order, but as if they were stragglers trying to catch up, the events of her life passed before her sight that had never been so clear. Sweeping over the mounds of her body rising beneath the quilts came the old familiar odors—the damp, strong, penetrating smell of new-turned ground; the rank, clinging, resistless odor of green-picked feathers stuffed in a pillow by Guinea Nell, thirty-odd years ago; tobacco on the mantel, clean and sharp like smelling salts; her father's sweat, sweet like stale oil; the powerful ammonia of manure turned over in a stall; curing hay in the wind; the polecat's stink on the night air, almost pleasant, a sort of commingled scent of all the animals, man and beast; the dry smell of dust under a rug; the overstrong scent of too-sweet fruit trees blooming; the inhospitable wet ashes of a dead fire in a poor white's cabin;

black Rebeccah in the kitchen; a wet hound steaming before a fire. There were other odors she could not identify, overwhelming her, making her weak, taking her body and drawing out of it a choking longing to hover over all that she must leave, the animals, the fences, the crops growing in the fields, the houses, the people in them . . .

It was early summer, and she was standing in the garden after dark—she had heard something after the small chickens. Mericy and Yellow Jane passed beyond the paling fence. Dark shadows—gay, full voices. *Where you gwine, gal? I dunno. Jest a-gwine. Where you? To the frolic, do I live. Well, stay off'n yoe back tonight.* Then out of the rich, gushing laughter: *All right, you stay off'n yourn. I done caught de stumbles.* More laughter.

The face of Uncle Ike, head man in slavery days, rose up. A tall Senegalese, he was standing in the crib of the barn unmoved before the bush-whackers. *Nigger, whar is that gold hid? You better tell us, nigger. Down in the well; in the far-place. By God, you black son of a bitch, we'll roast ye alive if you air too contrary to tell. Now, listen ole nigger, Miss McCowan ain't nothen to you no more. You been set free. We'll give ye some of it, a whole sack. Come on, now—* out of the dribbling, leering mouth—*whar air it?* Ike's tall form loomed towards the shadows. In the lamp flame his forehead shone like the point, the core of night. He stood there with no word for answer. As she saw the few white beads of sweat on his forehead, she spoke.

She heard her voice reach through the dark—*I know your kind. In better days you'd slip around and set people's barns afire. You shirked the War to live off the old and weak. You don't spare me because I'm a woman. You'd shoot a woman quicker because she has the name of being frail. Well, I'm not frail, and my Navy Six an't frail. Ike, take their guns.* Ike moved and one of them raised his pistol arm. He dropped it, and the acrid smoke stung her nostrils. *Now, Ike, get the rest*

150

*of their weapons. Their knives, too. One of us might turn our
backs.*

On top of the shot she heard the soft pat of her servants' feet. White eyeballs shining through the cracks in the barn. Then: *Caesar, Al, Zebedee, step in here and lend a hand to Ike.* By sun the people had gathered in the yard. Uneasy, silent, they watched her on the porch. She gave the word, and the whips cracked. The mules strained, trotted off, skittish and afraid, dragging the white naked bodies bouncing and cursing over the sod: *Turn us loose. We'll not bother ye no more, lady. You ain't no woman, you're a devil.* She turned and went into the house. It is strange how a woman gets hard when trouble comes a-gobbling after her people.

Worn from memory, she closed her eyes to stop the whirl, but closing her eyes did no good. She released the lids and did not resist. Brother Jack stood before her, handsome and shy, but ruined from his cradle by a cleft palate, until he came to live only in the fire of spirits. And she understood, so clear was life, down to the smallest things. She had often heard tell of this clarity that took a body whose time was spending on the earth. Poor Brother Jack, the gentlest of men, but because of his mark, made the butt and wit of the valley. She saw him leave for school, where he was sent to separate him from his drinking companions, to a church school where the boys buried their liquor in the ground and sipped it up through straws. His letters: *Dear Ma, quit offering so much advice and send me more money. You send barely enough to keep me from stealing.* His buggy wheels scraping the gravel, driving up as the first roosters crowed. *Katharine, Malcolm, I thought you might want to have a little conversation.* Conversation two hours before sun! And down she would come and let him in, and the General would get up, stir the fire, and they would sit down and smoke. Jack would drink and sing, *If the Little Brown Jug was mine, I'd be drunk all the time and I'd never be sob-er a-gin*—or, *Hog drovers, hog drovers, hog drovers we air, a-courting your darter so sweet and so fair*. They would sit and smoke and drink until she got up to ring the bell.

He stayed as long as the whiskey held out, growing more violent towards the end. She watered his bottles; begged whiskey to make camphor—*Gre't God, Sis Kate, do you sell camphor? I gave you a pint this morning*. Poor Brother Jack, killed in Breckinridge's charge at Murfreesboro, cut in two by a chain shot from an enemy gun. All night long she had sat up after the message came. His body scattered about a splintered black gum tree. She had seen that night, as if she had been on the field, the parties moving over the dark field hunting the wounded and dead. Clyde Bascom had fallen near Jack with a bad hurt. They were messmates. He had to tell somebody; and somehow she was the one he must talk to. The spectral lanterns, swinging towards the dirge of pain and the monotonous cries of *Water*, caught by the river dew on the before-morning air and held suspended over the fields in its acrid quilt. There death dripped to mildew the noisy throats . . . and all the while relief parties, moving, blots of night, sullenly moving in the viscous blackness.

Her eyes widened, and she looked across the foot posts into the room. There was some mistake, some cruel blunder; for there now, tipping about the carpet, hunting in her wardrobe, under the bed, blowing down the fire to its ashes until they glowed in their dryness, stalked the burial parties. They stepped out of the ashes in twos and threes, hunting, hunting, and shaking their heads. Whom were they searching for? Jack had long been buried. They moved more rapidly; looked angry. They crowded the room until she gasped for breath. One, gaunt and haggard, jumped on the foot of her bed; rose to the ceiling; gesticulated; argued in animated silence. He leaned forward; pressed his hand upon her leg. She tried to tell him to take it off. Cold and crushing heavy, it pressed her down to the bowels of the earth. Her lips trembled, but no sound came forth. Now the hand moved up to her stomach; and the haggard eyes looked gravely at her,

152

alert, as if they were waiting for something. Her head turned giddy. She called to Dick, to Ants, to Doctor Ed; but the words struck her teeth and fell back in her throat. She concentrated on lifting the words, and the burial parties sadly shook their heads. Always the cries struck her teeth and fell back down. She strained to hear the silence they made. At last from a great distance she thought she heard . . . *too late* . . . *too late.* How exquisite the sound, like a bell swinging without ringing. Suddenly it came to her. She was dying.

How slyly death slipped up on a body, like sleep moving over the vague boundary. How many times she had laid awake to trick the unconscious there. At last she would know . . . But she wasn't ready. She must first do something about Long Gourd. That slut must not eat it up. She would give it to the hands first. He must be brought to understand this. But the spectres shook their heads. Well let them shake. She'd be damned if she would go until she was ready to go. She'd be damned all right, and she smiled at the meaning the word took on now. She gathered together all the particles of her will; the spectres faded; and there about her were the anxious faces of kin and servants. Edwin had his hands under the cover feeling her legs. She made to raise her own hand to the boy. It did not go up. Her eyes wanted to roll upward and look behind her forehead, but she pinched them down and looked at her grandson.

"You want to say something, Mammy?"—she saw his lips move.

She had aplenty to say, but her tongue had somehow got glued to her lips. Truly it was now too late. Her will left her. Life withdrawing gathered like a frosty dew on her skin. The last breath blew gently past her nose. The dusty nostrils tingled. She felt a great sneeze coming. There was a roaring; the wind blew through her head once, and a great cotton field bent before it, growing and spreading, the bolls swelling as big as cotton sacks and bursting white as thunderheads. From a distance, out of the far end of the field, under a sky so blue that it was painful-bright, voices came singing, *Joshua fit the battle of Jericho, Jericho, Jericho—Joshua fit the battle of Jericho, and the walls come a-tumbling down.*

𝄞

Thomas Wolfe

IN THE SLEEPER

"WHERE shall I go now? What shall I do?" A dozen times that year he made these tormented journeys of desire. Why did he make them? What did he expect to find? He did not know: he only knew that at night he would feel again the huge and secret quickening of desire to which all life in the city moved, that he would be drawn again, past hope and past belief, to the huge glare, the swarming avenues of night, with their great tides of livid night-time faces. He only knew that he would prowl again, again, each night, the thronging passages of rat's alley where the dead men were, that the million faces, forms and shapes of ungraspable desire would pass, would weave and throng and vanish from his grasp like evil figures in a dream, and that the old unanswered questions which have foiled so many million lives lost there in the labyrinthine maze and fury of the city's life, would come back again, and that he never found an answer to them.

"What shall I do now? Where shall I go?" They returned to mock his furious prowling of kaleidoscopic night with their unsearchable enigmas and when this happened, instant, mad, and overwhelming the desire to burst out of these can-yoned walls that held him in, this Tantalus mocker of a city

154

that duped his hunger with a thousand phantom shapes of impossible desire. And when this blind and furious impulse came to him, he knew only one desire—to escape, to escape instantly from the great well and prison of the city; and he had only one conviction—wild, mad, overmastering in its huge unreason—that escape, fulfilment, a fortunate and impossibly happy fruition lay somewhere out across the dark and lonely continent—was somewhere there in any of its thousand silent sleeping little towns—could be found anywhere, certainly, instantly, by the divining rod of miraculous chance, upon the pounding wheels of a great train, at any random halt made in the night.

Thus, by an ironic twist which at the time he did not see or understand, this youth, who in his childhood, like a million other boys, had dreamed and visioned in the darkness of the shining city, and of the fortunate good and happy life that he would find there was now fleeing from it to find in unknown little towns the thing that he had come to the great city to possess.

A dozen times that year he made these mad and sudden journeys: to New England many times, to Pennsylvania, or Virginia; and more than once at night up the great river towards the secret North.

One night that year, in the month of March he was returning from the wintry North—from one of those sudden and furious journeys of caprice, which were decided on the impulse of the moment, towards which he was driven by the goadings of desire, and from which he would return, as now, weary, famished, unassuaged, and driven to seek anew in the city's life for some appeasement.

Under an immense, stormy, and tempestuous sky the train was rushing across the country with a powerful unperturbed movement; it seemed in this dark and wintry firmament of earth and sky that the train was the only fixed and timeless object—the land swept past the windows of the train in a level and powerful tide of white fields, clumped woodland, and the solid, dark, and warmly grouped buildings of a farm, pierced scarcely by a light. High up, in the immense and tempestuous skies the clouds were driving at furious speed, in an inexhaustible processional, across the visage of a wild and desolate moon, which broke through momently with a kind of savage and beleaguered reprisal to cast upon the waste below a shattered, lost and fiercely ragged light. Here then, in this storm-lost desolation of earth and sky the train hung poised as the only motionless and unchanging object, and all things else—the driving and beleaguered moon, the fiercely scudding clouds, the immense regimentation of heaven which stormed onward with the fury of a gigantic and demoniacal cavalry, and the lonely and immortal earth below sweeping past with a vast fan-shaped stroke of field and wood and house—had in them a kind of unchanging changefulness, a spoke-like recurrence which, sweeping past into oblivion, would return as on the upstroke of a wheel to repeat itself with an immutable precision, an unvarying repetition.

And under the spell of this lonely processional of white field, dark wood and wild driven sky, he fell into a state of strange waking-sleepfulness, a kind of comatose perceptiveness that the motion of the train at night had always induced in him. In this weary world of sleep and wakefulness and all the flooding visions of old time and memory, he was conscious of the grand enchantments of the landscape which is at all times one of the most beautiful and lovely on the continent, and which now, under this wild spell of moon and scudding cloud and moving fields and wintry woods, forever stroking past the windows of the train, evoked that wild and solemn joy—the sense of nameless hope, impossible desire, and man's tragic brevity—which only the wildness, the cruel and savage loveliness of the American earth can give.

Thus, as he lay in his berth, in this strange state of comatose perceptiveness he was conscious first of the vast level snowclad fields of the Canadian boundaries, the lights of farms, the whipping past of darkened little stations; then of a wooded land, the foothills of the Adirondacks, dark with their wintry foresting, wild with snow; the haunting vistas of the Champlain country, strange as time, the noble music of Ticonderoga, with its tread of Indians and old wars, and then the pleasant swelling earth and fields and woods and lonely little towns set darkly in the night with a few spare lights; and pauses in the night at Saratoga, and for a moment the casual and familiar voices of America, and people crowding in the windows of the train, and old familiar words and quiet greetings, the sudden thrum and starting of a motor car, and then dark misty woods, white fields, a few spare lights and houses, all sweeping past beneath the wild beleaguered moon with the fan-like stroke of the immortal and imperturbable earth, with a wild and haunting loneliness, with tragic brevity and strong joy.

Suddenly, in the middle of the night, he started up into sharp wakefulness. The train had slackened in its speed, it was slowing for a halt at the outskirts of a town: in the distance upon the flanks of low sweeping hills he could see a bracelet of hard bright lights, and presently the outposts of the town appeared. And now he saw the spokes of empty wintry streets, and hard street lamps that cast a barren light upon the grimy façades of old houses; and now old grimy blocks of buildings of brown stone and brick, all strange and close and near and as familiar as a dream.

And now the train was slowing to its halt; the old red brick of station warehouses, the worn rust and grime of factory walls abutting on the tracks with startling nearness, and all of it was as it had always been, as he had always known it, and yet he had not seen the place before.

And now the train had slowed to a full halt; he found himself looking at a wall of old red brick at one of the station's corners. It was one of the old brick buildings that one sees in the station section of almost any town: in the wall beside the tracks, there was a dingy-looking door and above the door a red electric bulb was burning with a dim but sinister invitation. Even as he looked, the door opened, a man stepped quickly out, looked quickly to both sides with the furtive and uneasy look men have when they come out of a brothel, and then, turning up the collar of his overcoat, he walked rapidly away.

And at the corner, in the first floor of the old brick building, he could see a disreputable old barroom, and this, too, had this dream-like, stage-like immediacy, it was so near to him that he could almost have touched the building with his hand, a kind of gigantic theatrical setting, overpowering in its immediacy, as strange and as familiar as a dream.

Without moving in his berth he could look through the windows of the bar, which were glazed or painted half way up, and see everything that was going on inside. Despite the lateness of the hour—the round visage of a clock above the bar told him it was just four o'clock—there were several people in the place, and it was doing an open thriving business. Several men, who by their look were probably railway workers, taxi drivers, and night-time prowlers of the station district—(one even wore black leather leggings, and had the fresh red complexion and healthy robust look of a country man)—were standing at the old dark walnut bar and drinking beer. The bartender stood behind the bar with his thick hands stretched out and resting on the bar, and with a wet cloth in one hand. He wore an apron and was in his shirtsleeves; he had the dead eyes and heavy sagging night-time face that some bartenders have, but he could be seen talking to the men, responding to their jests, with a ready professional cordiality that was nevertheless warily ready for any situation that might come up. And further down the bar, another man was drinking beer and with him was a woman. She was one of the heavy coarsely friendly and experienced whores that one also finds in railway sections, she was drinking beer, talking to the man amiably and with coarse persuasiveness, and presently she took his arm with a rude persuasive gesture, and jerking her head towards the stairs, pulled him towards her. Grinning rather sheepishly, with a pleased but foolish look, he went along with her, and they could be seen going up-stairs. When they were gone, the other men drinking at the bar spoke quietly to the bartender, and in a moment he could see them shaking with coarse guffawing laughter. Behind the bar, in old ornately carved walnut frames, there were big mirrors, and at the top of the central mirror there was an American flag, fluted and spread fan-wise, and below this there was a picture of the beetling eyebrows and nobly Roman features of the President of the United States, War-ren G. Harding. The whole place looked very old and shabby, and yet somehow warm; dingy with old lights, and stained with drink and worn with countless elbows, and weary and worn and brutal with its memories of ten thou-sand nights of brawls and lust and drunkenness—its immeas-urable age and dateless weariness of violence and desire.

Then the train moved slowly on, and left this scene for-ever; it passed the street, and there were lights here, taxis, rows of silent buildings, and then the station, the sight of the baggage room big with trunks, piled with mail sacks, crates and boxes, and there were also a few people, a yardman with a lantern, a conductor waiting with a small case in his hand, a few passengers, the brick sides of the station, and the con-crete quays.

Then the train stopped again, and this time it stopped across the street at the other end of the station. And again, from his dark berth, he could see without moving this whole immense and immediate theatre of human event, and again it gripped and held him with its dream-like magic, its unbeliev-able familiarity. At the corner, in another old brick building there was a little lunchroom of the kind he had seen ten thou-sand times before. Several taxicabs were drawn up along the curb, and from the lunchroom he could hear the hoarse wrangling voices of the taxi drivers, joined in their incessant and trivial debate, and through the misted window he could see the counterman, young, thin, sallow, wearily attentive, wearing a dirty apron, and in his shirtsleeves, leaning back, his thin white arms humbly folded as he listened.

And on the corner, just below the window of his berth there stood a boy of eighteen or twenty years. The boy was tall, thin, and rather fragile-looking, his face had the sullen, scowling almost feverish intensity that boys have on such occasions, he stood there indecisively, as if trying to make up his mind, resolve himself, towards his next action; he put a cigarette into his mouth and lighted it and as he did so, his hands trembled. He turned up the collar of his overcoat impatiently, glanced grudgingly and nervously about him and stood there smoking.

Meanwhile a young prostitute, still slender and good-looking, came out of the back room, strolled over to the corner and stood there indolently, looking around with an innocent and yet impudent look, appearing not to look directly at the boy, or openly to invite him, but plainly waiting for him to speak to her.

And all the time his efforts to make up his mind, to come to a decision, were comically evident. He kept puffing nervously and rapidly at his cigarette, glancing at the girl out of the corner of his eye from time to time, pretending not to notice her, and all the time steeling himself to a decisive action.

But even as he stood there in this temper, trying to focus his wavering decision on a conclusive act, another man came up and took the girl away from him. The other man was much older than the boy; he was in his middle thirties, he was powerfully built and well, though somewhat flashily dressed. He wore a gray felt hat, set at a smart angle on his head, a well-fitting and expensive-looking overcoat cut in at the waist in the "snappy" Broadway fashion, and he looked like a prosperous Greek; he had a strong, swarthy, brutal face, full of sensual assurance, he came walking along the narrow sidewalk beside the tracks, and when he saw the girl, he

160

approached her instantly, with a swaggering assurance, began to talk to her, and in a moment walked away with her.

And again, the effect of this incident upon the boy was comically, pathetically, apparent. He did not appear to notice the girl and the Greek as they walked off together, but when they had gone, his lean young face hardened suddenly, the scowl deepened, and with a sudden angry movement he flung his cigarette into the gutter, turned, and with the sudden resolution of a man who is ashamed of his cowardly procrastination and indecision, he began to walk rapidly along the dark and narrow little sidewalk that ran down beside the tracks and along a row of shabby station tenements.

And again, that strange and stage-like panorama of human comedy was fantastically repeated: the train began to move, and the boy kept pace with it, below the windows of the berth. Immediately they began to pass the row of shabby old wooden brothels that bordered on the tracks; the windows were closely shuttered, but through the shutters there flamed hot exciting bars of reddish light, and in the doorway entrances the small red lights were burning. At the third house, the boy paused, turned, ran swiftly up the wooden steps and rang the bell, almost instantly a small slot-like peep-hole in the door was opened, an inquiring beak-like nose, a wisp of blondined hair peered out, the door was opened, the boy entered in a glow of reddish light, the door was closed behind him, and the train, gathering rapidly in speed now, went on, past the police station where the night-time cops were sitting, past spokes of brown streets, old buildings, warehouses, factories, station tenements, the sudden barren glare of corner lamps—the grimy façade of old rusty buildings—the single substance and the million patterns of America!

And now the train had left the town, and now there was a vast and distant flare, incredible in loveliness, the enormous train yards of the night, great dings and knellings on the tracks, the flare and sweep of mighty rails, the huge and sudden stirrings of the terrific locomotives.

And then there was just loneliness and earth and night, and presently the river, the great and silent river, the noble, spacious, kingly river sweeping on forever through the land at night to wash the basal cliffs and ramparts of the terrific city, to flow forever round its million-celled and prisoned sleepers, and in the night-time, in the dark, in all the sleeping silence of our lives to go flowing by us, by us, by us, to the sea.

That vision haunted him. He could not forget it. That boy who stood there on the corner in that lonely little town at night became the image of his own desire, of the desire of every youth that ever lived, of all the lonely, secret, and unsleeping desire of America, that lives forever in the little towns at night, that wakes at times, a lively, small, and savage flame, while all the sleepers sleep, that burns there, unimprisoned and alone, beneath immense and timeless skies, upon the dark and secret visage of the continent, that prowls forever past the shuttered façades of the night, and furious, famished, unassuaged and driven as it is, lives alone in darkness and will not die.

That urge held and drew him with a magnetic power. Eight times that spring he made that wild journey of impulse and desire up the river. Eight times in darkness over pounding wheel and rod, he saw the wild and secret continent of night, the nocturnal sweep and flow of the great river, and felt the swelling of the old, impossible and savage joy within him. That little town, seen first with such a charm and dreamlike casualness out of the windows of a passing train, became part of the structure of his life, carved upon the tablets of his brain indelibly.

Eight times that year he saw it in every light and weather: in blown drifts of sleeting snow, in spouting rain, in bleak and wintry darkness, and when the first gray light of day was breaking haggardly against its ridge of eastern hills. And its whole design—each grimy brick and edge and corner of its shabby pattern—became familiar to him as something he had known all his life.

He came to know its times, its movements, and its people: its station workers, railway men, and porters; the night-time litter of the station derelicts and vagabonds themselves, as he was blown past this little town in darkness.

And he came to know all the prowlers of the night that walk and wait and wear the slow gray ash of time away in little towns—and this too was like something he had known forever. He came to know them all by sight and word and name: the taxi drivers, lunchroom countermen, the soiled and weary-looking night-time Greeks, and all the others who inhabit the great shambles of the night.

Finally, and as a consequence of these blind voyages, he came to know all the whores that lived there in that little row of wooden tenements beside the tracks. Eight times, at the end of night, he came again into the last commerce of their fagged embrace; eight times he left those shabby, shuttered little houses in gray haggard light; and eight times that year, as morning came, he again made the journey down the river.

And later he could forget none of it. It became part of a whole design—all of its horror and its beauty, its grime and rustiness of stark red brick, its dark and secret loneliness of earth, the thrill and magic of its casual friendly voices, and the fagged yet friendly commerce of the whores, the haggard light of morning at the ridges of the hills, and that great enchanted river greening into May—all this was one and single, woven of the same pattern, and coherent to the same design—and that design was somehow beautiful.

That spring, along the noble sweep of the great river he returned at morning to the city many times. He saw April come, with all its sudden patches of shrewd green, and May, with all its bloom, its lights of flowers, its purity of first light and the bird-song waking in young feathered trees, its joy of morning-gold on the great river's tide.

Eight times that spring, after all the fury, wildness and debauch of night, he rode back at morning towards the city

in a world of waking men: they were for the most part railroad men—engineers, firemen, brakemen, switchmen, and
train conductors, on their way to work. And their homely,
seamed and pungent comradeship filled him with the health
of morning and with joy.

And his memory of these journeys of the night, and these
wonderful returns at morning, was haunted always by the
vision of a single house. It was a great white house, set delicate and gleaming in frail morning light upon a noble hill
that swept back from the river, and it was shaded by the
silent stature of great trees, and vast swards of velvet lawn
swept round it, and morning was always there and the tender
purity of light.

That house haunted his memory like a dream: he could not
forget it. But he did not know, he could not have foreseen,
by what strange and dreamlike chance he would later come
to it.

§

Conrad Aiken

SILENT SNOW, SECRET SNOW

JUST why it should have happened, or why it should have
happened just when it did, he could not, of course, possibly
have said; nor perhaps would it even have occurred to him
to ask. The thing was above all a secret, something to be
preciously concealed from Mother and Father; and to that
very fact it owed an enormous part of its deliciousness. It
was like a peculiarly beautiful trinket to be carried unmen-
tioned in one's trouser-pocket—a rare stamp, an old coin, a
few tiny gold links found trodden out of shape on the path

in the park, a pebble of carnelian, a seashell distinguishable from all others by an unusual spot or stripe—and, as if it were any one of these, he carried around with him everywhere a warm and persistent and increasingly beautiful sense of possession. Nor was it only a sense of possession—it was also a sense of protection. It was as if, in some delightful way, his secret gave him a fortress, a wall behind which he could retreat into heavenly seclusion. This was almost the first thing he had noticed about it—apart from the oddness of the thing itself—and it was this that now again, for the fiftieth time, occurred to him, as he sat in the little schoolroom. It was the half-hour for geography. Miss Buell was revolving with one finger, slowly, a huge terrestrial globe which had been placed on her desk. The green and yellow continents passed and repassed, questions were asked and answered, and now the little girl in front of him, Deirdre, who had a funny little constellation of freckles on the back of her neck, exactly like the Big Dipper, was standing up and telling Miss Buell that the equator was the line that ran round the middle.

Miss Buell's face, which was old and grayish and kindly, with gray stiff curls beside the cheeks, and eyes that swam very brightly, like little minnows, behind thick glasses, wrinkled itself into a complication of amusements.

"Ah! I see. The earth is wearing a belt, or a sash. Or some one drew a line round it!"

"Oh no—not that—I mean——"

In the general laughter, he did not share, or only a very little. He was thinking about the Arctic and Antarctic regions, which of course, on the globe, were white. Miss Buell was now telling them about the tropics, the jungles, the steamy heat of equatorial swamps, where the birds and butterflies, and even the snakes, were like living jewels. As he listened to these things, he was already, with a pleasant sense of half-effort, putting his secret between himself and the words. Was it really an effort at all? For effort implied something voluntary, and perhaps even something one did not

165

especially want; whereas this was distinctly pleasant, and came almost of its own accord. All he needed to do was to think of that morning, the first one, and then of all the others——

But it was all so absurdly simple! It had amounted to so little. It was nothing, just an idea—and just why it should have become so wonderful, so permanent, was a mystery—a very pleasant one, to be sure, but also, in an amusing way, foolish. However, without ceasing to listen to Miss Buell, who had now moved up to the north temperate zones, he deliberately invited his memory of the first morning. It was only a moment or two after he had waked up—or perhaps the moment itself. But was there, to be exact, an exact moment? Was one awake all at once? or was it gradual? Anyway, it was after he had stretched a lazy hand up toward the headrail, and yawned, and then relaxed again among his warm covers, all the more grateful on a December morning, that the thing had happened. Suddenly, for no reason, he had thought of the postman, he remembered the postman. Perhaps there was nothing so odd in that. After all, he heard the postman almost every morning in his life—his heavy boots could be heard clumping round the corner at the top of the little cobbled hill-street, and then, progressively nearer, progressively louder, the double knock at each door, the crossings and re-crossings of the street, till finally the clumsy steps came stumbling across to the very door, and the tremendous knock came which shook the house itself.

(Miss Buell was saying "Vast wheat-growing areas in North America and Siberia."

Deirdre had for the moment placed her left hand across the back of her neck.)

But on this particular morning, the first morning, as he lay there with his eyes closed, he had for some reason *waited* for the postman. He wanted to hear him come round the corner. And that was precisely the joke—he never did. He never came. He never had come—*round the corner*—again.

166

For when at last the steps *were* heard, they had already, he was quite sure, come a little down the hill, to the first house; and even so, the steps were curiously different—they were softer, they had a new secrecy about them, they were muffled and indistinct; and while the rhythm of them was the same, it now said a new thing—it said peace, it said remoteness, it said cold, it said sleep. And he had understood the situation at once—nothing could have seemed simpler—there had been snow in the night, such as all winter he had been longing for; and it was this which had rendered the postman's first footsteps inaudible, and the later ones faint. Of course! How lovely! And even now it must be snowing—it was going to be a snowy day—the long white ragged lines were drifting and sifting across the street, across the faces of the old houses, whispering and hushing, making little triangles of white in the corners between cobblestones, seething a little when the wind blew them over the ground to a drifted corner; and so it would be all day, getting deeper and deeper and silenter and silenter.

(Miss Buell was saying "Land of perpetual snow.")

All this time, of course (while he lay in bed), he had kept his eyes closed, listening to the nearer progress of the postman, the muffled footsteps thumping and slipping on the snow-sheathed cobbles; and all the other sounds—the double knocks, a frosty far-off voice or two, a bell ringing thinly and softly as if under a sheet of ice—had the same slightly abstracted quality, as if removed by one degree from actuality—as if everything in the world had been insulated by snow. But when at last, pleased, he opened his eyes, and turned them toward the window, to see for himself this long-desired and now so clearly imagined miracle—what he saw instead was brilliant sunlight on a roof; and when, astonished, he jumped out of bed and stared down into the street, expecting to see the cobbles obliterated by the snow, he saw nothing but the bare bright cobbles themselves.

Queer, the effect this extraordinary surprise had had upon

167

him—all the following morning he had kept with him a sense as of snow falling about him, a secret screen of new snow between himself and the world. If he had not dreamed such a thing—and how could he have dreamed it while awake?— how else could one explain it? In any case, the delusion had been so vivid as to affect his entire behavior. He could not now remember whether it was on the first or the second morning—or was it even the third?—that his mother had drawn attention to some oddness in his manner.

"But my darling—" she had said at the breakfast table— "what has come over you? You don't seem to be listening. . . ."

And how often that very thing had happened since!

(Miss Buell was now asking if any one knew the difference between the North Pole and the Magnetic Pole. Deirdre was holding up her flickering brown hand, and he could see the four white dimples that marked the knuckles.)

Perhaps it hadn't been either the second or third morning —or even the fourth or fifth. How could he be sure? How could he be sure just when the delicious *progress* had become clear? Just when it had really *begun?* the intervals weren't very precise. . . . All he now knew was, that at some point or other—perhaps the second day, perhaps the sixth—he had noticed that the presence of the snow was a little more insistent, the sound of it clearer; and, conversely, the sound of the postman's footsteps more indistinct. Not only could he not hear the steps come round the corner, he could not even hear them at the first house. It was below the first house that he heard them; and then, a few days later, it was below the second house that he heard them; and a few days later again, below the third. Gradually, gradually, the snow was becoming heavier, the sound of its seething louder, the cobblestones more and more muffled. When he found, each morning, on going to the window, after the ritual of listening, that the roofs and cobbles were as bare as ever, it made no difference. This was, after all, only what he had expected.

168

It was even what pleased him, what rewarded him: the thing was his own, belonged to no one else. No one else knew about it, not even his mother and father. There, outside, were the bare cobbles; and here, inside, was the snow. Snow growing heavier each day, muffling the world, hiding the ugly, and deadening increasingly—above all—the steps of the postman.

"But my darling—" she had said at the luncheon table— "what has come over you? You don't seem to listen when people speak to you. That's the third time I've asked you to pass your plate. . . ."

How was one to explain this to Mother? or to Father? There was, of course, nothing to be done about it: nothing. All one could do was to laugh embarrassedly, pretend to be a little ashamed, apologize, and take a sudden and somewhat disingenuous interest in what was being done or said. The cat had stayed out all night. He had a curious swelling on his left cheek—perhaps somebody had kicked him, or a stone had struck him. Mrs. Kempton was or was not coming to tea. The house was going to be housecleaned, or "turned out," on Wednesday instead of Friday. A new lamp was provided for his evening work—perhaps it was eyestrain which accounted for this new and so peculiar vagueness of his— Mother was looking at him with amusement as she said this, but with something else as well. A new lamp? A new lamp. Yes, Mother, No, Mother, Yes, Mother. School is going very well. The geometry is very easy. The history is very dull. The geography is very interesting—particularly when it takes one to the North Pole. Why the North Pole? Oh, well, it would be fun to be an explorer. Another Peary or Scott or Shackleton. And then abruptly he found his interest in the talk at an end, stared at the pudding on his plate, listened, waited, and began once more—ah, how heavenly, too, the first beginnings—to hear or feel—for could he actually hear it?—the silent snow, the secret snow.

(Miss Buell was telling them about the search for the

Northwest Passage, about Hendrik Hudson, the *Half Moon*.)

This had been, indeed, the only distressing feature of the new experience; the fact that it so increasingly had brought him into a kind of mute misunderstanding, or even conflict, with his father and mother. It was as if he were trying to lead a double life. On the one hand, he had to be Paul Hasleman, and keep up the appearance of being that person—dress, wash, and answer intelligently when spoken to—; on the other, he had to explore this new world which had been opened to him. Nor could there be the slightest doubt—not the slightest—that the new world was the profounder and more wonderful of the two. It was irresistible. It was miraculous. Its beauty was simply beyond anything—beyond speech as beyond thought—utterly incommunicable. But how then, between the two worlds, of which he was thus constantly aware, was he to keep a balance? One must get up, one must go to breakfast, one must talk with Mother, go to school, do one's lessons—and, in all this, try not to appear too much of a fool. But if all the while one was also trying to extract the full deliciousness of another and quite separate existence, one which could not easily (if at all) be spoken of—how was one to manage? How was one to explain? Would it be safe to explain? Would it be absurd? Would it merely mean that he would get into some obscure kind of trouble?

These thoughts came and went, came and went, as softly and secretly as the snow; they were not precisely a disturbance, perhaps they were even a pleasure; he liked to have them; their presence was something almost palpable, something he could stroke with his hand, without closing his eyes, and without ceasing to see Miss Buell and the schoolroom and the globe and the freckles on Deirdre's neck; nevertheless he did in a sense cease to see, or to see the obvious external world, and substituted for this vision the vision of snow, the sound of snow, and the slow, almost soundless, approach of the postman. Yesterday, it had been only at the sixth house that the postman had become audible; the snow was much deeper now, it was falling more swiftly and heavily, the sound of its seething was more distinct, more soothing, more persistent. And this morning, it had been—as nearly as he could figure—just above the seventh house—perhaps only a step or two above: at most, he had heard two or three footsteps before the knock had sounded. . . . And with each such narrowing of the sphere, each nearer approach of the limit at which the postman was first audible, it was odd how sharply was increased the amount of illusion which had to be carried into the ordinary business of daily life. Each day, it was harder to get out of bed, to go to the window, to look out at the—as always—perfectly empty and snowless street. Each day it was more difficult to go through the perfunctory motions of greeting Mother and Father at breakfast, to reply to their questions, to put his books together and go to school. And at school, how extraordinarily hard to conduct with success simultaneously the public life and the life that was secret! There were times when he longed—positively ached —to tell every one about it—to burst out with it—only to be checked almost at once by a far-off feeling as of some faint absurdity which was inherent in it—but *was* it absurd?—and more importantly by a sense of mysterious power in his very secrecy. Yes: it must be kept secret. That, more and more, became clear. At whatever cost to himself, whatever pain to others——

(Miss Buell looked straight at him, smiling, and said, "Perhaps we'll ask Paul. I'm sure Paul will come out of his daydream long enough to be able to tell us. Won't you, Paul." He rose slowly from his chair, resting one hand on the brightly varnished desk, and deliberately stared through the snow toward the blackboard. It was an effort, but it was amusing to make it. "Yes," he said slowly, "it was what we now call the Hudson River. This he thought to be the Northwest Passage. He was disappointed." He sat down again, and

171

as he did so Deirdre half turned in her chair and gave him a shy smile, of approval and admiration.)

At whatever pain to others.

This part of it was very puzzling, very puzzling. Mother was very nice, and so was Father. Yes, that was all true enough. He wanted to be nice to them, to tell them everything—and yet, was it really wrong of him to want to have a secret place of his own?

At bed-time, the night before, Mother had said, "If this goes on, my lad, we'll have to see a doctor, we will! We can't have our boy—" But what was it she had said? "Live in another world"? "Live so far away"? The word "far" had been in it, he was sure, and then Mother had taken up a magazine again and laughed a little, but with an expression which wasn't mirthful. He had felt sorry for her. . . .

The bell rang for dismissal. The sound came to him through long curved parallels of falling snow. He saw Deirdre rise, and had himself risen almost as soon—but not quite as soon—as she.

II

On the walk homeward, which was timeless, it pleased him to see through the accompaniment, or counterpoint, of snow, the items of mere externality on his way. There were many kinds of brick in the sidewalks, and laid in many kinds of pattern. The garden walls too were various, some of wooden palings, some of plaster, some of stone. Twigs of bushes leaned over the walls: the little hard green winter-buds of lilac, on gray stems, sheathed and fat; other branches very thin and fine and black and desiccated. Dirty sparrows huddled in the bushes, as dull in color as dead fruit left in leafless trees. A single starling creaked on a weather vane. In the gutter, beside a drain, was a scrap of torn and dirty newspaper, caught in a little delta of filth: the word ECZEMA appeared in large capitals, and below it was a letter from Mrs. Amelia D. Cravath, 2100 Pine Street, Fort Worth,

Texas, to the effect that after being a sufferer for years she had been cured by Caley's Ointment. In the little delta, beside the fan-shaped and deeply runnelled continent of brown mud, were lost twigs, descended from their parent trees, dead matches, a rusty horse-chestnut burr, a small concentration of eggshell, a streak of yellow sawdust which had been wet and now was dry and congealed, a brown pebble, and a broken feather. Farther on was a cement sidewalk, ruled into geometrical parallelograms, with a brass inlay at one end commemorating the contractors who had laid it, and, halfway across, an irregular and random series of dog-tracks, immortalized in synthetic stone. He knew these well, and always stepped on them; to cover the little hollows with his own foot had always been a queer pleasure; to-day he did it once more, but perfunctorily and detachedly, all the while thinking of something else. That was a dog, a long time ago, who had made a mistake and walked on the cement while it was still wet. He had probably wagged his tail, but that hadn't been recorded. Now, Paul Hasleman, aged twelve, on his way home from school, crossed the same river, which in the meantime had frozen into rock. Homeward through the snow, the snow falling in bright sunshine. Homeward?

Then came the gateway with the two posts surmounted by egg-shaped stones which had been cunningly balanced on their ends, as if by Columbus, and mortared in the very act of balance: a source of perpetual wonder. On the brick wall just beyond, the letter H had been stenciled, presumably for some purpose. H? H.

The green hydrant, with a little green-painted chain attached to the brass screw-cap.

The elm tree, with the great gray wound in the bark, kidney-shaped, into which he always put his hand—to feel the cold but living wood. The injury, he had been sure, was due to the gnawings of a tethered horse. But now it deserved only a passing palm, a merely tolerant eye. There were more important things. Miracles. Beyond the thoughts of trees, mere elms. Beyond the thoughts of sidewalks, mere stone, mere brick, mere cement. Beyond the thoughts even of his own shoes, which trod these sidewalks obediently, bearing a burden—far above—of elaborate mystery. He watched them. They were not very well polished; he had neglected them, for a very good reason: they were one of the many parts of the increasing difficulty of the daily return to daily life, the morning struggle. To get up, having at last opened one's eyes, to go to the window, and discover no snow, to wash, to dress, to descend the curving stairs to breakfast——

At whatever pain to others, nevertheless, one must persevere in severance, since the incommunicability of the experience demanded it. It was desirable of course to be kind to Mother and Father, especially as they seemed to be worried, but it was also desirable to be resolute. If they should decide—as appeared likely—to consult the doctor, Doctor Howells, and have Paul inspected, his heart listened to through a kind of dictaphone, his lungs, his stomach—well, that was all right. He would go through with it. He would give them answer for question, too—perhaps such answers as they hadn't expected? No. That would never do. For the secret world must, at all costs, be preserved.

The bird-house in the apple tree was empty—it was the wrong time of year for wrens. The little round black door had lost its pleasure. The wrens were enjoying other houses, other nests, remoter trees. But this too was a notion which he only vaguely and grazingly entertained—as if, for the moment, he merely touched an edge of it; there was something further on, which was already assuming a sharper importance; something which already teased at the corners of his eyes, teasing also at the corner of his mind. It was funny to think that he so wanted this, so awaited it—and yet found himself enjoying this momentary dalliance with the bird-house, as if for a quite deliberate postponement and enhancement of the approaching pleasure. He was aware of his de-

174

lay, of his smiling and detached and now almost uncomprehending gaze at the little bird-house; he knew what he was going to look at next: it was his own little cobbled hill-street, his own house, the little river at the bottom of the hill, the grocer's shop with the cardboard man in the window—and now, thinking of all this, he turned his head, still smiling, and looking quickly right and left through the snow-laden sunlight.

And the mist of snow, as he had foreseen, was still on it—a ghost of snow falling in the bright sunlight, softly and steadily floating and turning and pausing, soundlessly meeting the snow that covered, as with a transparent mirage, the bare bright cobbles. He loved it—he stood still and loved it. Its beauty was paralyzing—beyond all words, all experience, all dream. No fairy-story he had ever read could be compared with it—none had ever given him this extraordinary combination of ethereal loveliness with a something else, unnameable, which was just faintly and deliciously terrifying. What was this thing? As he thought of it, he looked upward toward his own bedroom window, which was open—and it was as if he looked straight into the room and saw himself lying half awake in his bed. There he was—at this very instant he was still perhaps actually there—more truly there than standing here at the edge of the cobbled hill-street, with one hand lifted to shade his eyes against the snow-sun. Had he indeed ever left his room, in all this time? since that very first morning? Was the whole progress still being enacted there, was it still the same morning, and himself not yet wholly awake? And even now, had the postman not yet come round the corner? . . .

This idea amused him, and automatically, as he thought of it, he turned his head and looked toward the top of the hill. There was, of course, nothing there—nothing and no one. The street was empty and quiet. And all the more because of its emptiness it occurred to him to count the houses—a thing which, oddly enough, he hadn't before thought of doing. Of course, he had known there weren't many—many, that is, on his own side of the street, which were the ones that figured in the postman's progress—but nevertheless it came as something of a shock to find that there were precisely *six*, above his own house—his own house was the seventh.

Six!

Astonished, he looked at his own house—looked at the door, on which was the number thirteen—and then realized that the whole thing was exactly and logically and absurdly what he ought to have known. Just the same, the realization gave him abruptly, and even a little frighteningly, a sense of hurry. He was being hurried—he was being rushed. For— he knit his brows—he couldn't be mistaken—it was just above the *seventh* house, his *own* house, that the postman had first been audible this very morning. But in that case—in that case—did it mean that to-morrow he would hear nothing? The knock he had heard must have been the knock of their own door. Did it mean—and this was an idea which gave him a really extraordinary feeling of surprise—that he would never hear the postman again?—that to-morrow morning the postman would already have passed the house, in a snow so deep as to render his footsteps completely inaudible? That he would have made his approach down the snow-filled street so soundlessly, so secretly, that he, Paul Hasleman, there lying in bed, would not have waked in time, or waking, would have heard nothing?

But how could that be? Unless even the knocker should be muffled in the snow—frozen tight perhaps? . . . But in that case——

A vague feeling of disappointment came over him; a vague sadness as if he felt himself deprived of something which he had long looked forward to, something much prized. After all this, all this beautiful progress, the slow delicious advance of the postman through the silent and secret snow, the knock creeping closer each day, and the footsteps nearer, the audible compass of the world thus daily narrowed, narrowed, narrowed, as the snow soothingly and beautifully encroached and deepened, after all this, was he to be defrauded of the one thing he had so wanted—to be able to count, as it were, the last two or three solemn footsteps, as they finally approached his own door? Was it all going to happen, at the end, so suddenly? or indeed, had it already happened? with no slow and subtle gradations of menace, in which he could luxuriate?

He gazed upward again, toward his own window which flashed in the sun: and this time almost with a feeling that it would be better if he *were* still in bed, in that room; for in that case this must still be the first morning, and there would be six more mornings to come—or, for that matter, seven or eight or nine—how could he be sure?—or even more.

III

After supper, the inquisition began. He stood before the doctor, under the lamp, and submitted silently to the usual thumpings and tappings.

"Now will you please say 'Ah!'?"

"Ah!"

"Now again please, if you don't mind."

"Ah."

"Say it slowly, and hold it if you can——"

"Ah-h-h-h-h-h——"

"Good."

How silly all this was. As if it had anything to do with his throat! Or his heart or lungs!

Relaxing his mouth, of which the corners, after all this absurd stretching, felt uncomfortable, he avoided the doctor's eyes, and stared toward the fireplace, past his mother's feet (in gray slippers) which projected from the green chair, and his father's feet (in brown slippers) which stood neatly side by side on the hearth rug.

"Hm. There is certainly nothing wrong there . . . ?"

He felt the doctor's eyes fixed upon him, and, as if merely

177

to be polite, returned the look, but with a feeling of justifiable evasiveness.

"Now, young man, tell me—do you feel all right?"

"Yes, sir, quite all right."

"No headaches? no dizziness?"

"No, I don't think so."

"Let me see. Let's get a book, if you don't mind—yes, thank you, that will do splendidly—and now, Paul, if you'll just read it, holding it as you would normally hold it——"

He took the book and read:

"And another praise have I to tell for this the city our mother, the gift of a great god, a glory of the land most high; the might of horses, the might of young horses, the might of the sea. . . . For thou, son of Cronus, our lord Poseidon, hath throned herein this pride, since in these roads first thou didst show forth the curb that cures the rage of steeds. And the shapely oar, apt to men's hands, hath a wondrous speed on the brine, following the hundred-footed Nereids. . . . O land that art praised above all lands, now is it for thee to make those bright praises seen in deeds."

He stopped, tentatively, and lowered the heavy book.

"No—as I thought—there is certainly no superficial sign of eyestrain."

Silence thronged the room, and he was aware of the focussed scrutiny of the three people who confronted him. . . .

"We could have his eyes examined—but I believe it is something else."

"What could it be?" That was his father's voice.

"It's only this curious absent-mindedness—" This was his mother's voice.

In the presence of the doctor, they both seemed irritatingly apologetic.

"I believe it is something else. Now Paul—I would like very much to ask you a question or two. You will answer them, won't you—you know I'm an old, old friend of yours, eh? That's right! . . ."

178

His back was thumped twice by the doctor's fat fist—then the doctor was grinning at him with false amiability, while with one fingernail he was scratching the top button of his waistcoat. Beyond the doctor's shoulder was the fire, the fingers of flame making light prestidigitation against the sooty fireback, the soft sound of their random flutter the only sound.

"I would like to know—is there anything that worries you?"

The doctor was again smiling, his eyelids low against the little black pupils, in each of which was a tiny white bead of light. Why answer him? why answer him at all? "At whatever pain to others"—but it was all a nuisance, this necessity for resistance, this necessity for attention: it was as if one had been stood up on a brilliantly lighted stage, under a great round blaze of spotlight; as if one were merely a trained seal, or a performing dog, or a fish, dipped out of an aquarium and held up by the tail. It would serve them right if he were merely to bark or growl. And meanwhile, to miss these last few precious hours, these hours of which each minute was more beautiful than the last, more menacing—! He still looked, as if from a great distance, at the beads of light in the doctor's eyes, at the fixed false smile, and then, beyond, once more at his mother's slippers, his father's slippers, the soft flutter of the fire. Even here, even amongst these hostile presences, and in this arranged light, he could see the snow, he could hear it—it was in the corners of the room, where the shadow was deepest, under the sofa, behind the half-opened door which led to the dining room. It was gentler here, softer, its seethe the quietest of whispers, as if, in deference to a drawing-room, it had quite deliberately put on its "manners"; it kept itself out of sight, obliterated itself, but distinctly with an air of saying, "Ah, but just wait! Wait till we are alone together! Then I will begin to tell you something new! Something white! something cold! something sleepy! something of cease, and peace, and the long bright curve of space! Tell them to go away. Banish them. Refuse to speak. Leave them, go upstairs to your room, turn out the light and get into bed—I will go with you, I will be waiting for you, I will tell you a better story than Little Kay of the Skates, or The Snow Ghost—I will surround your bed, I will close the windows, pile a deep drift against the door, so that none will ever again be able to enter. Speak to them! . . ."

It seemed as if the little hissing voice came from a slow white spiral of falling flakes in the corner by the front window—but he could not be sure. He felt himself smiling, then, and said to the doctor, but without looking at him, looking beyond him still——

"Oh no, I think not——"

"But are you sure, my boy?"

His father's voice came softly and coldly then—the familiar voice of silken warning.

"You needn't answer at once, Paul—remember we're trying to help you—think it over and be quite sure, won't you?"

He felt himself smiling again, at the notion of being quite sure. What a joke! As if he weren't so sure that reassurance was no longer necessary, and all this cross-examination a ridiculous farce, a grotesque parody! What could they know about it? these gross intelligences, these humdrum minds so bound to the usual, the ordinary? Impossible to tell them about it! Why, even now, even now, with the proof so abundant, so formidable, so imminent, so appallingly present here in this very room, could they believe it?—could even his mother believe it? No—it was only too plain that if anything were said about it, the merest hint given, they would be incredulous—they would laugh—they would say "Absurd!"—think things about him which weren't true. . . .

"Why no, I'm not worried—why should I be?"

He looked then straight at the doctor's low-lidded eyes, looked from one of them to the other, from one bead of light to the other, and gave a little laugh.

The doctor seemed to be disconcerted by this. He drew

180

back in his chair, resting a fat white hand on either knee. The smile faded slowly from his face.

"Well, Paul!" he said, and paused gravely, "I'm afraid you don't take this quite seriously enough. I think you perhaps don't quite realize—don't quite realize—" He took a deep quick breath, and turned, as if helplessly, at a loss for words, to the others. But Mother and Father were both silent—no help was forthcoming.

"You must surely know, be aware, that you have not been quite yourself, of late? don't you know that? . . ."

It was amusing to watch the doctor's renewed attempt at a smile, a queer disorganized look, as of confidential embarrassment.

"I feel all right, sir," he said, and again gave the little laugh.

"And we're trying to help you." The doctor's tone sharpened.

"Yes sir, I know. But why? I'm all right. I'm just *thinking*, that's all."

His mother made a quick movement forward, resting a hand on the back of the doctor's chair.

"Thinking?" she said. "But my dear, about what?"

This was a direct challenge—and would have to be directly met. But before he met it, he looked again into the corner by the door, as if for reassurance. He smiled again at what he saw, at what he heard. The little spiral was still there, still softly whirling, like the ghost of a white kitten chasing the ghost of a white tail, and making as it did so the faintest of whispers. It was all right! If only he could remain firm, everything was going to be all right.

"Oh, about anything, about nothing—*you* know the way you do!"

"You mean—daydreaming?"

"Oh, no—thinking!"

"But thinking about *what?*"

"Anything."

He laughed a third time—but this time, happening to

glance upward toward his mother's face, he was appalled at the effect his laughter seemed to have upon her. Her mouth had opened in an expression of horror. . . . This was too bad! Unfortunate! He had known it would cause pain, of course—but he hadn't expected it to be quite so bad as this. Perhaps—perhaps if he just gave them a tiny gleaming hint——?

"About the snow," he said.

"What on earth!" This was his father's voice. The brown slippers came a step nearer on the hearth-rug.

"But my dear, what do you mean?" This was his mother's voice.

The doctor merely stared.

"Just *snow*, that's all. I like to think about it."

"Tell us about it, my boy."

"But that's all it is. There's nothing to tell. *You* know what snow is?"

This he said almost angrily, for he felt that they were trying to corner him. He turned sideways so as no longer to face the doctor, and the better to see the inch of blackness between the window-sill and the lowered curtain—the cold inch of beckoning and delicious night. At once he felt better, more assured.

"Mother—can I go to bed, now, please? I've got a head-ache."

"But I thought you said——"

"It's just come. It's all these questions—! Can I, mother?"

"You can go as soon as the doctor has finished."

"Don't you think this thing ought to be gone into thoroughly, and *now?*" This was Father's voice. The brown slippers again came a step nearer, the voice was the well-known "punishment" voice, resonant and cruel.

"Oh, what's the use, Norman——"

Quite suddenly, every one was silent. And without precisely facing them, nevertheless he was aware that all three of them were watching him with an extraordinary intensity

182

—staring hard at him—as if he had done something monstrous, or was himself some kind of monster. He could hear the soft irregular flutter of the flames; the cluck-click-cluck-click of the clock; far and faint, two sudden spurts of laughter from the kitchen, as quickly cut off as begun; a murmur of water in the pipes; and then, the silence seemed to deepen, to spread out, to become world-long and world-wide, to become time-less and shapeless, and to center inevitably and rightly, with a slow and sleepy but enormous concentration of all power, on the beginning of a new sound. What this new sound was going to be, he knew perfectly well. It might begin with a hiss, but it would end with a roar—there was no time to lose —he must escape. It mustn't happen here——

Without another word, he turned and ran up the stairs.

IV

Not a moment too soon. The darkness was coming in long white waves. A prolonged sibilance filled the night—a great seamless seethe of wild influence went abruptly across it— a cold low humming shook the windows. He shut the door and flung off his clothes in the dark. The bare black floor was like a little raft tossed in waves of snow, almost over-whelmed, washed under whitely, up again, smothered in curled billows of feather. The snow was laughing: it spoke from all sides at once: it pressed closer to him as he ran and jumped exulting into his bed.

"Listen to us!" it said. "Listen! We have come to tell you the story we told you about. You remember? Lie down. Shut your eyes, now—you will no longer see much—in this white darkness who could see, or want to see? We will take the place of everything. . . . Listen——"

A beautiful varying dance of snow began at the front of the room, came forward and then retreated, flattened out to-ward the floor, then rose fountain-like to the ceiling, swayed, recruited itself from a new stream of flakes which poured laughing in through the humming window, advanced again,

183

lifted long white arms. It said peace, it said remoteness, it said cold—it said——

But then a gash of horrible light fell brutally across the room from the opening door—the snow drew back hissing—something alien had come into the room—something hostile. This thing rushed at him, clutched at him, shook him—and he was not merely horrified, he was filled with such a loathing as he had never known. What was this? this cruel disturbance? this act of anger and hate? It was as if he had to reach up a hand toward another world for any understanding of it —an effort of which he was only barely capable. But of that other world he still remembered just enough to know the exorcising words. They tore themselves from his other life suddenly——

"Mother! Mother! Go away! I hate you!"

And with that effort, everything was solved, everything became all right: the seamless hiss advanced once more, the long white wavering lines rose and fell like enormous whispering sea-waves, the whisper becoming louder, the laughter more numerous.

"Listen!" it said. "We'll tell you the last, the most beautiful and secret story—shut your eyes—it is a very small story —a story that gets smaller and smaller—it comes inward instead of opening like a flower—it is a flower becoming a seed —a little cold seed—do you hear? we are leaning closer to you——"

The hiss was now becoming a roar—the whole world was a vast moving screen of snow—but even now it said peace, it said remoteness, it said cold, it said sleep.

II

ACKNOWLEDGMENTS

T. S. Eliot, ASH-WEDNESDAY from "Collected Poems of T. S. Eliot," copyright 1936 by Harcourt, Brace & Co., Inc.; Marianne Moore, POETRY and THE MONKEYS from "Selected Poems," copyright 1935 by The Macmillan Co.; Edwin Arlington Robinson, EROS TURANNOS from "Collected Poems," copyright 1921 by The Macmillan Co., and LUKE HAVERGAL from "The Children of the Night," copyright 1914 by Charles Scribner's Sons; Robert Frost, STOPPING BY WOODS ON A SNOWY EVENING and MENDING WALL from "Collected Poems," copyright 1939 by Henry Holt & Co., Inc.; Edna St. Vincent Millay, THE CAMEO from "The Buck in the Snow," and SONNET LII from "Fatal Interview," copyright 1928, 1931 by Edna St. Vincent Millay (Harper & Bros.); Wallace Stevens, EMPEROR OF ICE-CREAM and SUNDAY MORNING from "Harmonium," copyright 1931 by Alfred A. Knopf, Inc.; Louise Bogan, HENCEFORTH FROM THE MIND from "Poems and New Poems," copyright 1941 by Charles Scribner's Sons; Léonie Adams, COUNTRY SUMMER and THE MOUNT from "High Falcon," copyright 1929 by the John Day Co., Inc.; Phelps Putnam, HASBROUCK AND THE ROSE from "The Five Seasons," by permission of Charles Scribner's Sons; Mark Van Doren, THIS AMBER SUNSTREAM and IT IS A MOVELESS MOMENT from "Collected Poems," copyright 1939 by Henry Holt & Co., Inc.

T. S. Eliot

ASH-WEDNESDAY

I

BECAUSE I do not hope to turn again
Because I do not hope
Because I do not hope to turn
Desiring this man's gift and that man's scope
I no longer strive to strive towards such things
(Why should the aged eagle stretch its wings?)
Why should I mourn
The vanished power of the usual reign?

Because I do not hope to know again
The infirm glory of the positive hour
Because I do not think
Because I know I shall not know
The one veritable transitory power
Because I cannot drink
There, where trees flower, and springs flow, for there is
     nothing again

Because I know that time is always time
And place is always and only place
And what is actual is actual only for one time
And only for one place
I rejoice that things are as they are and
I renounce the blessèd face
And renounce the voice

Because I cannot hope to turn again
Consequently I rejoice, having to construct something
Upon which to rejoice

And pray to God to have mercy upon us
And I pray that I may forget
These matters that with myself I too much discuss
Too much explain
Because I do not hope to turn again
Let these words answer
For what is done, not to be done again
May the judgement not be too heavy upon us

Because these wings are no longer wings to fly
But merely vans to beat the air
The air which is now thoroughly small and dry
Smaller and dryer than the will
Teach us to care and not to care
Teach us to sit still.

Pray for us sinners now and at the hour of our death
Pray for us now and at the hour of death.

II

Lady, three white leopards sat under a juniper-tree
In the cool of the day, having fed to satiety
On my legs my heart my liver and that which had been
     contained
In the hollow round of my skull. And God said
Shall these bones live? shall these
Bones live? And that which had been contained
In the bones (which were already dry) said chirping:
Because of the goodness of this Lady
And because of her loveliness, and because
She honours the Virgin in meditation,
We shine with brightness. And I who am here dissembled
Proffer my deeds to oblivion, and my love

To the posterity of the desert and the fruit of the gourd.
It is this which recovers
My guts the strings of my eyes and the indigestible portions
Which the leopards reject. The Lady is withdrawn
In a white gown, to contemplation, in a white gown.
Let the whiteness of bones atone to forgetfulness.
There is no life in them. As I am forgotten
And would be forgotten, so I would forget
Thus devoted, concentrated in purpose. And God said
Prophesy to the wind, to the wind only for only
The wind will listen. And the bones sang chirping
With the burden of the grasshopper, saying

Lady of silences
Calm and distressed
Torn and most whole
Rose of memory
Rose of forgetfulness
Exhausted and life-giving
Worried reposeful
The single Rose
Is now the Garden
Where all loves end
Terminate torment
Of love unsatisfied
The greater torment
Of love satisfied
End of the endless
Journey to no end
Conclusion of all that
Is inconclusible
Speech without word and
Word of no speech
Grace to the Mother
For the Garden
Where all love ends.

Under a juniper-tree the bones sang, scattered and shining
We are glad to be scattered, we did little good to each other,
Under a tree in the cool of the day, with the blessing of sand,
Forgetting themselves and each other, united
In the quiet of the desert. This is the land which ye
Shall divide by lot. And neither division nor unity
Matters. This is the land. We have our inheritance.

III

At the first turning of the second stair
I turned and saw below
The same shape twisted on the banister
Under the vapour in the fetid air
Struggling with the devil of the stairs who wears
The deceitful face of hope and of despair.

At the second turning of the second stair
I left them twisting, turning below;
There were no more faces and the stair was dark,
Damp, jaggèd like an old man's mouth drivelling, beyond
    repair,
Or the toothed gullet of an agèd shark.

At the first turning of the third stair
Was a slotted window bellied like the fig's fruit
And beyond the hawthorn blossom and a pasture scene
The broadbacked figure drest in blue and green
Enchanted the maytime with an antique flute.
Blown hair is sweet, brown hair over the mouth blown,
Lilac and brown hair;
Distraction, music of the flute, stops and steps of the mind
    over the third stair,
Fading, fading; strength beyond hope and despair
Climbing the third stair.

Lord, I am not worthy
Lord, I am not worthy
               but speak the word only.

IV

Who walked between the violet and the violet
Who walked between
The various ranks of varied green
Going in white and blue, in Mary's colour,
Talking of trivial things
In ignorance and in knowledge of eternal dolour
Who moved among the others as they walked,
Who then made strong the fountains and made fresh the
    springs

Made cool the dry rock and made firm the sand
In blue of larkspur, blue of Mary's colour,
Sovegna vos

Here are the years that walk between, bearing
Away the fiddles and the flutes, restoring
One who moves in the time between sleep and waking,
    wearing

White light folded, sheathed about her, folded.

The new years walk, restoring
Through a bright cloud of tears, the years, restoring
With a new verse the ancient rhyme. Redeem
The time. Redeem
The unread vision in the higher dream
While jewelled unicorns draw by the gilded hearse.

The silent sister veiled in white and blue
Between the yews, behind the garden god,
Whose flute is breathless, bent her head and signed but spoke
    no word

But the fountain sprang up and the bird sang down
Redeem the time, redeem the dream
The token of the word unheard, unspoken

Till the wind shake a thousand whispers from the yew

And after this our exile

V

If the lost word is lost, if the spent word is spent
If the unheard, unspoken
Word is unspoken, unheard;
Still is the unspoken word, the Word unheard,
The Word without a word, the Word within
The world and for the world;
And the light shone in darkness and
Against the Word the unstilled world still whirled
About the centre of the silent Word.

O my people, what have I done unto thee.

Where shall the word be found, where will the word
Resound? Not here, there is not enough silence
Not on the sea or on the islands, not
On the mainland, in the desert or the rain land,
For those who walk in darkness
Both in the day time and in the night time
The right time and the right place are not here
No place of grace for those who avoid the face
No time to rejoice for those who walk among noise and
    deny the voice

Will the veiled sister pray for
Those who walk in darkness, who chose thee and oppose thee,
Those who are torn on the horn between season and season,
    time and time, between

Hour and hour, word and word, power and power, those
    who wait
In darkness? Will the veiled sister pray
For children at the gate
Who will not go away and cannot pray:
Pray for those who chose and oppose

      O my people, what have I done unto thee.

Will the veiled sister between the slender
Yew-trees pray for those who offend her
And are terrified and cannot surrender
And affirm before the world and deny between the rocks
In the last desert between the last blue rocks
The desert in the garden the garden in the desert
Of drouth, spitting from the mouth the whithered apple-
    seed.

      O my people.

VI

Although I do not hope to turn again
Although I do not hope
Although I do not hope to turn

Wavering between the profit and the loss
In this brief transit where the dreams cross
The dreamcrossed twilight between birth and dying
(Bless me father) though I do not wish to wish these things
From the wide window towards the granite shore
The white sails still fly seaward, seaward flying
Unbroken wings

And the lost heart stiffens and rejoices
In the lost lilac and the lost sea voices
And the weak spirit quickens to rebel

For the bent golden-rod and the lost sea-smell
Quickens to recover
The cry of quail and the whirling plover
And the blind eye creates
The empty forms between the ivory gates
And smell renews the salt savour of the sandy earth

This is the time of tension between dying and birth
The place of solitude where three dreams cross
Between blue rocks
But when the voices shaken from the yew-tree drift away
Let the other yew be shaken and reply.

Blessèd sister, holy mother, spirit of the fountain, spirit of
        the garden,
Suffer us not to mock ourselves with falsehood
Teach us to care and not to care
Teach us to sit still
Even among these rocks,
Our peace in His will
And even among these rocks
Sister, mother
And spirit of the river, spirit of the sea,
Suffer me not to be separated

And let my cry come unto Thee.

Marianne Moore

POETRY

I too, dislike it: there are things that are important beyond
    all this fiddle.
Reading it, however, with a perfect contempt for it, one
    discovers that there is in
 it after all, a place for the genuine.
    Hands that can grasp, eyes
    that can dilate, hair that can rise
       if it must, these things are important not because a

high sounding interpretation can be put upon them but be-
    cause they are
    useful; when they become so derivative as to become un-
      telligible,
    the same thing may be said for all of us, that we
     do not admire what
     we cannot understand: the bat,
      holding on upside down or in quest of something to
eat, elephants pushing, a wild horse taking a roll, a tireless
    wolf under
    a tree, the immovable critic twitching his skin like a horse
          that feels a flea, the base-
    ball fan, the statistician—
    nor is it valid
      to discriminate against "business documents and
school-books"; all these phenomena are important. One must
    make a distinction
however: when dragged into prominence by half poets, the
    result is not poetry,

nor till the poets among us can be
   "literalists of
  the imagination"—above
    insolence and triviality and can present

for inspection, imaginary gardens with real toads in them,
   shall we have
it. In the meantime, if you demand on one hand,
  the raw material of poetry in
   all its rawness and
   that which is on the other hand
    genuine, then you are interested in poetry.

Marianne Moore

THE MONKEYS

winked too much and were afraid of
   snakes. The zebras, supreme
   in
their abnormality; the elephants with their fog-coloured skin
  and strictly practical appendages
   were there, the small cats; and the parrakeet—
trival and humdrum on
   examination, destroying
  bark and portions of the food it could not eat.

I recall their magnificence, now not more magnificent
than it is dim. It is difficult to recall the ornament,
  speech, and precise manner of what one might
  call the minor acquaintances twenty

years back; but I shall not forget him—that Gilgamesh
    among
the hairy carnivora—that cat with the
wedge-shaped, slate-gray marks on its forelegs and the
    resolute tail,
astringently remarking, 'They have imposed on us with
    their pale
half-fledged protestations, trembling about
in inarticulate frenzy, saying
it is not for us to understand art; finding it
all so difficult, examining the thing

as if it were inconceivably arcanic, as
      symmet-
rically frigid as if it had been carved out of chrysoprase
    or marble—strict with tension, malignant
    in its power over us and deeper
    than the sea when it proffers flattery
      in exchange for hemp,
rye, flax, horses, platinum, timber, and fur.'

1916   1921

Edwin Arlington Robinson

EROS TURANNOS

She fears him, and will always ask
What fated her to choose him;
She meets in his engaging mask
All reasons to refuse him;
But what she meets and what she fears
Are less than are the downward years,
Drawn slowly to the foamless weirs
Of age, were she to lose him.

Between a blurred sagacity
That once had power to sound him,
And Love, that will not let him be
The Judas that she found him,
Her pride assuages her almost,
As if it were alone the cost.
He sees that he will not be lost.
And waits and looks around him.

A sense of ocean and old trees
Envelops and allures him;
Tradition, touching all he sees,
Beguiles and reassures him;
And all her doubts of what he says
Are dimmed with what she knows of days—
Till even prejudice delays
And fades, and she secures him.

The falling leaf inaugurates
The reign of her confusion;
The pounding wave reverberates
The dirge of her illusion;

And home, where passion lived and died,
Becomes a place where she can hide,
While all the town and harbor-side
Vibrate with her seclusion.

We tell you, tapping on our brows,
The story as it should be,
As if the story of a house
Were told or ever could be;
We'll have no kindly veil between
Her visions and those we have seen,—
As if we guessed what hers have been,
Or what they are or would be.

Meanwhile we do no harm; for they
That with a god have striven
Not hearing much of what we say,
Take what the god has given;
Though like waves breaking it may be,
Or like a changed familiar tree,
Or like a stairway to the sea
Where down the blind are driven.

Edwin Arlington Robinson

LUKE HAVERGAL

Go to the western gate, Luke Havergal,
There where the vines cling crimson on the wall,
And in the twilight wait for what will come.
The leaves will whisper there of her, and some,
Like flying words will strike you as they fall;
But go, and if you listen, she will call.
Go to the western gate, Luke Havergal—
Luke Havergal.

No, there is not a dawn in eastern skies
To rift the fiery night that's in your eyes;
But there, where western glooms are gathering,
The dark will end the dark, if anything:
God slays himself with every leaf that flies,
And hell is more than half of paradise.
No, there is not a dawn in eastern skies—
In eastern skies.

Out of a grave I come to tell you this,
Out of a grave I come to quench the kiss
That flames upon your forehead with a glow
That blinds you to the way that you must go.
Yes, there is yet one way to where she is,
Bitter, but one that faith may never miss.
Out of a grave I come to tell you this—
To tell you this.

There is the western gate, Luke Havergal,
There are the crimson leaves upon the wall.
Go, for the winds are tearing them away,—
Nor think to riddle the dead words they say,

Nor any more to feel them as they fall;
But go, and if you trust her she will call.
There is the western gate, Luke Havergal—
Luke Havergal.

Robert Frost

STOPPING BY WOODS ON A
SNOWY EVENING

WHOSE woods these are I think I know.
His house is in the village though;
He will not see me stopping here
To watch his woods fill up with snow.

My little horse must think it queer
To stop without a farmhouse near
Between the woods and frozen lake
The darkest evening of the year.

He gives his harness bells a shake
To ask if there is some mistake.
The only other sound's the sweep
Of easy wind and downy flake.

The woods are lovely, dark and deep,
But I have promises to keep,
And miles to go before I sleep,
And miles to go before I sleep.

Robert Frost

MENDING WALL

SOMETHING there is that doesn't love a wall,
That sends the frozen-ground-swell under it,
And spills the upper bowlders in the sun;
And makes gaps even two can pass abreast.
The work of hunters is another thing:
I have come after them and made repair
Where they have left not one stone on a stone,
But they would have the rabbit out of hiding,
To please the yelping dogs. The gaps I mean,
No one has seen them made or heard them made,
But at spring mending-time we find them there.
I let my neighbor know beyond the hill;
And on a day we meet to walk the line
And set the wall between us once again.
We keep the wall between us as we go.
To each the bowlders that have fallen to each.
And some are loaves and some so nearly balls
We have to use a spell to make them balance:
"Stay where you are until our backs are turned!"
We wear our fingers rough with handling them.
Oh, just another kind of outdoor game,
One on a side. It comes to little more:
There where it is we do not need the wall:
He is all pine and I am apple-orchard.
My apple trees will never get across
And eat the cones under his pines, I tell him.
He only says, "Good fences make good neighbors."
Spring is the mischief in me, and I wonder
If I could put a notion in his head:
"*Why* do they make good neighbors? Isn't it

Where there are cows? But here there are no cows.
Before I built a wall I'd ask to know
What I was walling in or walling out,
And to whom I was like to give offense.
Something there is that doesn't love a wall,
That wants it down!" I could say "elves" to him,
But it's not elves exactly, and I'd rather
He said it for himself. I see him there,
Bringing a stone grasped firmly by the top
In each hand, like an old-stone savage armed.
He moves in darkness, as it seems to me,
Not of woods only and the shade of trees.
He will not go behind his father's saying,
And he likes having thought of it so well
He says again, "Good fences make good neighbors."

Edna St. Vincent Millay

THE CAMEO

FOREVER over now, forever, forever gone
That day. Clear and diminished like a scene
Carven in cameo, the lighthouse, and the cove between
The sandy cliffs, and the boat drawn up on the beach;
And the long skirt of a lady innocent and young,
Her hand resting on her bosom, her head hung;
And the figure of a man in earnest speech.

Clear and diminished like a scene cut in cameo
The lighthouse, and the boat on the beach, and the two shapes
Of the woman and the man; lost like the lost day

Are the words that passed, and the pain, —discarded, cut
   away
From the stone, as from the memory the heat of the tears
   escapes.

O troubled forms, O early love unfortunate and hard,
Time has estranged you into a jewel cold and pure;
From the action of the waves and from the action of sorrow
   forever secure,
White against a ruddy cliff you stand, chalcedony on sard.

Edna St. Vincent Millay

SONNET LII

OH, SLEEP forever in the Latmian cave,
Mortal Endymion, darling of the Moon!
Her silver garments by the senseless wave
Shouldered and dropped and on the shingle strewn,
Her fluttering hand against her forehead pressed,
Her scattered looks that trouble all the sky,
Her rapid footsteps running down the west—
Of all her altered state, oblivious lie!
Whom earthern you, by deathless lips adored,
Wild-eyed and stammering to the grasses thrust,
And deep into her crystal body poured
The hot and sorrowful sweetness of the dust:
Whereof she wanders mad, being all unfit
For mortal love, that might not die of it.

Wallace Stevens

THE EMPEROR OF ICE-CREAM

CALL the roller of big cigars,
The muscular one, and bid him whip
In kitchen cups concupiscent curds.
Let the wenches dawdle in such dress
As they are used to wear, and let the boys
Bring flowers in last month's newspapers.
Let be be finale of seem.
The only emperor is the emperor of ice-cream.

Take from the dresser of deal,
Lacking the three glass knobs, that sheet
On which she embroidered fantails once
And spread it so as to cover her face.
If her horny feet protrude, they come
To show how cold she is, and dumb.
Let the lamp affix its beam.
The only emperor is the emperor of ice-cream.

Wallace Stevens

SUNDAY MORNING

I

COMPLACENCIES of the peignoir, and late
Coffee and oranges in a sunny chair,
And the green freedom of a cockatoo
Upon a rug mingle to dissipate
The holy hush of ancient sacrifice.
She dreams a little, and she feels the dark
Encroachment of that old catastrophe,
As a calm darkens among water-lights.
The pungent oranges and bright, green wings
Seem things in some procession of the dead,
Winding across wide water, without sound.
The day is like wide water, without sound,
Stilled for the passing of her dreaming feet
Over the seas, to silent Palestine,
Dominion of the blood and sepulchre.

II

Why should she give her bounty to the dead?
What is divinity if it can come
Only in silent shadows and in dreams?
Shall she not find in comforts of the sun,
In pungent fruit and bright, green wings, or else
In any balm or beauty of the earth,
Things to be cherished like the thought of heaven?
Divinity must live within herself:
Passions of rain, or moods in falling snow;
Grievings in loneliness, or unsubdued
Elations when the forest blooms; gusty

Emotions on wet roads on autumn nights;
All pleasures and all pains, remembering
The bough of summer and the winter branch.
These are the measures destined for her soul.

III

Jove in the clouds had his inhuman birth.
No mother suckled him, no sweet land gave
Large-mannered motions to his mythy mind.
He moved among us, as a muttering king,
Magnificent, would move among his hinds,
Until our blood, commingling, virginal,
With heaven, brought such requital to desire
The very hinds discerned it, in a star.
Shall our blood fail? Or shall it come to be
The blood of paradise? And shall the earth
Seem all of paradise that we shall know?
The sky will be much friendlier then than now,
A part of labor and a part of pain,
And next in glory to enduring love,
Not this dividing and indifferent blue.

IV

She says, "I am content when wakened birds,
Before they fly, test the reality
Of misty fields, by their sweet questionings;
But when the birds are gone, and their warm fields
Return no more, where, then, is paradise?"
There is not any haunt of prophecy,
Nor any old chimera of the grave,
Neither the golden underground, nor isle
Melodious, where spirits gat them home,
Nor visionary south, nor cloudy palm
Remote on heaven's hill, that has endured
As April's green endures; or will endure

Like her remembrance of awakened birds,
Or her desire for June and evening, tipped
By the consummation of the swallow's wings.

V

She says, "But in contentment I still feel
The need of some imperishable bliss."
Death is the mother of beauty; hence from her,
Alone, shall come fulfilment to our dreams
And our desires. Although she strews the leaves
Of sure obliteration on our paths,
The path sick sorrow took, the many paths
Where triumph rang its brassy phrase, or love
Whispered a little out of tenderness,
She makes the willow shiver in the sun
For maidens who were wont to sit and gaze
Upon the grass, relinquished to their feet.
She causes boys to pile new plums and pears
On disregarded plate. The maidens taste
And stray impassioned in the littering leaves.

VI

Is there no change of death in paradise?
Does ripe fruit never fall? Or do the boughs
Hang always heavy in that perfect sky,
Unchanging, yet so like our perishing earth,
With rivers like our own that seek for seas
They never find, the same receding shores
That never touch with inarticulate pang?
Why set the pear upon those river-banks
Or spice the shores with odors of the plum?
Alas, that they should wear our colors there,
The silken weavings of our afternoons,
And pick the strings of our insipid lutes!

Death is the mother of beauty, mystical,
Within whose burning bosom we devise
Our earthly mothers waiting, sleeplessly.

VII

Supple and turbulent, a ring of men
Shall chant in orgy on a summer morn
Their boisterous devotion to the sun,
Not as a god, but as a god might be,
Naked among them, like a savage source.
Their chant shall be a chant of paradise,
Out of their blood, returning to the sky;
And in their chant shall enter, voice by voice,
The windy lake wherein their lord delights,
The trees, like serafin, and echoing hills,
That choir among themselves long afterward.
They shall know well the heavenly fellowship.
Of men that perish and of summer morn.
And whence they came and whither they shall go
The dew upon their feet shall manifest.

VIII

She hears, upon that water without sound,
A voice that cries, "The tomb in Palestine
Is not the porch of spirits lingering.
It is the grave of Jesus, where he lay."
We live in an old chaos of the sun,
Or old dependency of day and night,
Or island solitude, unsponsored, free,
Of that wide water, inescapable.
Deer walk upon our mountains, and the quail
Whistle about us their spontaneous cries;
Sweet berries ripen in the wilderness;
And, in the isolation of the sky,
At evening, casual flocks of pigeons make
Ambiguous undulations as they sink,
Downward to darkness, on extended wings.

Louise Bogan

HENCEFORTH, FROM THE MIND

HENCEFORTH, from the mind,
For your whole joy, must spring
Such joy as you may find
In any earthly thing,
And every time and place
Will take your thought for grace.

Henceforth, from the tongue,
From shallow speech alone,
Comes joy you thought, when young,
Would wring you to the bone,
Would pierce you to the heart
And spoil its stop and start.

Henceforward, from the shell,
Wherein you heard, and wondered
At oceans like a bell
So far from ocean sundered—
A smothered sound that sleeps
Long lost within lost deeps,

Will chime you change and hours,
The shadow of increase,
Will sound you flowers
Born under troubled peace—
Henceforth, henceforth
Will echo sea and earth.

Léonie Adams

COUNTRY SUMMER

Now THE rich cherry, whose sleek wood
And top with silver petals traced,
Like a strict box its gems encased,
Has spilt from out that cunning lid,
All in an innocent green round,
Those melting rubies which it hid;
With moss ripe-strawberry-encrusted,
So birds get half, and minds lapse merry
To taste that deep-red, lark's bite berry,
And black cap bloom is yellow dusted.

The wren that thieved it in the eaves
A trailer of the rose could catch
To her poor droopy sloven thatch,
And side by side with the wren's brood—
O lovely time of beggars' luck—
Opens the quaint and hairy bud;
And full and golden is the yield
Of cows that never have to house,
But all night nibble under boughs,
Or cool their sides in the moist field.

Into the rooms flow meadows airs,
The warm farm baking smell's blown round,
Inside and out, and sky and ground
Are much the same, the wishing star
Hesperus, kind and early born,
Is risen only finger-far;
All stars stand close in summer air,

And tremble, and look mild as amber,
When wicks are lighted in the chamber,
You might say, stars were settling there.

Now straightening from the flowery hay,
Down the still light the mowers look,
Or turn, because their dreaming shook,
And they waked half to other days,
When left alone in the yellow stubble
The rusty-coated mare would graze.
Yet thick the lazy dreams are born,
Another thought can come to mind,
But like the shivering of the wind,
Morning and evening in the corn.

Léonie Adams

THE MOUNT

No, I love tempered haste,
The joyous traveller said,
The steed has passed me now
Whose hurrying hooves I fled.
My spectre rides thereon,
I learned what mount he has,
Upon what summers fed,
And wept to know again,
Beneath the saddle swung,
Treasure for whose great theft
This breast was wrung.

His bridle bells sang out,
I could not tell their chime,
So brilliantly he rings,
But called his name as Time.
His bin was morning light,
Those straws which gild his bed
Are of the fallen West.
Although green lands consume
Beneath their burning tread,
In everlasting bright
His hooves have rest.

Phelps Putnam

HASBROUCK AND THE ROSE

HASBROUCK was there and so were Bill
And Smollet Smith the poet, and Ames was there.
After his thirteenth drink, the burning Smith,
Raising his fourteenth trembling in the air,
Said, "Drink with me, Bill, drink up to the Rose."
But Hasbrouck laughed like old men in a myth,
Inquiring, "Smollet, are you drunk? What rose?"
And Smollet said, "I drunk? It may be so;
Which comes from brooding on the flower, the flower
I mean toward which mad hour by hour
I travel brokenly; and I shall know,
With Hermes and the alchemists—but, hell,
What use is it talking that way to you?

Hard-boiled, unbroken egg, what can you care
For the enfolded passion of the Rose?"
Then Hasbrouck's voice rang like an icy bell:

"Arcane romantic flower, meaning what?
Do you know what it meant? Do I?
We do not know.
Unfolding pungent rose, the glowing bath
Of ecstasy and clear forgetfulness;
Closing and secret bud one might achieve
By long debauchery—
Except that I have eaten it, and so
There is no call for further lunacy.

In Springfield, Massachusetts, I devoured
The mystic, the improbable, the Rose.
For two nights and a day, rose and rosette,
And petal after petal and the heart,
I had my banquet by the beams
Of four electric stars which shone
Weakly into my room, for there,
Drowning their light and gleaming at my side,
Was the incarnate star
Whose body bore the stigma of the Rose.
And that is all I know about the flower;
I have eaten it—it has disappeared.
There is no Rose."

Young Smollet Smith let fall his glass; he said
"Oh Jesus, Hasbrouck, am I drunk or dead?"

Mark Van Doren

THIS AMBER SUNSTREAM

This amber sunstream, with an hour to live,
Flows carelessly, and does not save itself;
Nor recognizes any entered room—
This room; nor hears the clock upon a shelf,
Declaring the lone hour; for where it goes
All space in a great silence ever flows.

No living man may know it till this hour,
When the clear sunstream, thickening to amber,
Moves like a sea, and the sunk hulls of houses
Let it come slowly through, as divers clamber,
Feeling for gold. So now into this room
Peer the large eyes, unopen to their doom.

Another hour and nothing will be here.
Even upon themselves the eyes will close.
Nor will this bulk, withdrawing, die outdoors
In night, that from another silence flows.
No living man in any western room
But sits at amber sunset round a tomb.

Mark Van Doren

IT IS A MOVELESS MOMENT

IT IS a moveless moment, with no wings,
No feet to bring it flying. There it stays,
And there it would be always, like the dead,
But that we turn and find it on some days.
The merest turn; the neck would hardly know;
Then the sky dips, and all the landmarks go.

So is the world contracted to our eyes,
That, lacking any room for more, for less,
See all of it together, fine and small,
With no mark on it of our nothingness.
The littleness is lost that we could measure—
Knowing not then of this compacter treasure.

It is the moment when we understand,
Relaxing every effort to be wise.
It is the moment of our boundary's fall:
Proud stone, that we had armed against surprise.
It is the merest moment. Then again
We turn and are distinguished men.

III

ACKNOWLEDGMENTS

Van Wyck Brooks, CONCORD from "New England: Indian Summer," copyright 1940 by E. P. Dutton & Co.; R. P. Blackmur, EMILY DICKINSON from "The Expense of Greatness," copyright 1940 by R. P. Blackmur (Arrow Editions); Edmund Wilson, THE AMBIGUITY OF HENRY JAMES, from "The Triple Thinkers," copyright 1938 by Harcourt, Brace & Co., Inc.; T. S. Eliot, TRADITION AND THE INDIVIDUAL TALENT from "Selected Essays of T. S. Eliot," copyright 1932 by Harcourt, Brace & Co., Inc.

Van Wyck Brooks

CONCORD

If "Whittierland" was idyllic, so was Concord, though the Concord idyll had other tones. There, too, the wild grape flourished, and the hemlock and savin, the walnut, spruce and pine, and the ground was strewn in season with the kindly fruits of the earth. The quiet river, the groves and meadows, the thrifty ways of the farmer-folk, who sent their milk and firewood to Boston, suggested a tranquil happiness that knew no inordinate affections.

Concord was "without crime," in the somewhat violent phrase of one who was born there.* The only prisoner in the jail, the only one whom anyone remembered, begged, when he was released, to be allowed to live there. He sat on the steps, on summer evenings, a great pet of the Emerson household, who was hired to play the fiddle at all the dances; and as for other odd fish, when the Concord people saw one passing, they were resigned to saying, "Oh, that's a philosopher." In Concord, as in Whittier's region, they had hidden

* The painter Edward Simmons, one of the Ripley family, who was born in the Manse. He was a nephew of George P. Bradford, the old Brook Farmer who translated Fénelon and was Emerson's intimate friend. The limitations of Concord, from an artist's point of view, are suggested by Bradford's remark to Simmons, "Edward, anything but the physical or the material." The whimsical Edward Simmons was famous for his loquacity. When a lady begged his pardon once for interrupting him, he said, "Madam, no one can *speak* without interrupting me." It was in reference to this trait that his friend Oliver Herford posted a card by the fireplace in the Players' Club, New York. This card bore the words, "Exit, in case of Simmons."

219

fugitive slaves in their ovens, or built secret rooms in their attics to foil the inquisitive sheriff; and one or two Concordians had been tarred and feathered for a speech or a sermon in the South. But the tar was long since washed away, and the ovens had resumed their normal function. Bronson Alcott, building an arbour, or sitting on his rustic seat, absorbed in his Plutarch or his Plato,—or Evelyn, Donne or Cowley,—evoked the note of this later Concord. Sometimes Alcott bestirred himself to plant another row of trees, or a pleasance for his children by the brookside.

Simple as it appeared, however, Concord was very far from simple; and the wiser a visitor was the more he was puzzled. If the Sphinx was not an inhabitant, she seemed to have been a guest, at least, who had left her riddle behind her; nor had any Œdipus yet appeared, from the Theban world without, to solve or even approach the heart of the riddle. Concord was a formidable fact; and, when one tried to place one's finger on it, the fact turned out to be different from what one thought it. How was one to specify it? How was one to designate it? Most of the descriptions recoiled upon their authors. For instance, people called it the "American Weimar," as Boston had once been called the "American Athens," a singularly inept phrase. To have called Goethe's town the "German Concord" would not have been less appropriate; for nowhere were Goethe's claims more essentially challenged. Clever people had given up the attempt to classify Emerson. They never hit the nail on the head, and the reason for this was plain enough: Emerson was not for the clever. Nor was Emerson or the dead Thoreau a subject for the innocent. Whittier spoke of *Walden* as a "wicked and heathenish book," a phrase that merely described Whittier,—it did not describe Thoreau at all. There were others, like the young Henry Adams, the son of Minister Adams, who parried the riddle with irony, not attempting to meet it; * but Adams made good his position by denying the Concord premises. Idealism, for him, was a foolish thing; but if one accepted idealism, where was the force of the irony? The irony cheapened the ironist. Goodness without intellect and intellect without moral perception were helpless in the face of the Concord riddle. It was true, there were those who could read it, though they did not bear the names of Theban princes. Obscure as they often were, these were the children of light, innocent as doves but wise as serpents.

Concord was deep, in other words, deeper than any country well, and the water of life that filled it was clear to the bottom. The difficulty was that one saw the bottom only at fleeting moments, when the sun was high overhead and one's own eye was quite unclouded. Three men of genius had lived in the town, Emerson, Hawthorne, Thoreau, not to speak of the gifted Alcott and the poet Ellery Channing, —uncrystallized geniuses both, one might have called them. If the air was full of cross-vibrations, if it was opalescent, it shone with a clear white light, most of the time, that signified a harmony of all these colours; and, if there was mystery in it, the deposit of genius, there was also a singular clarity, a clarity of perception and will that sprang from older sources than Plutarch or Plato. It was this that made Goethe irrelevant in Concord. All the Concord writers knew their Goethe. Emerson had read him from end to end, though mainly to please Carlyle. *Wilhelm Meister* had gone the rounds, and all the young girls were fascinated by Goethe's correspondence with Bettina von Arnim. This appealed to their instinct of hero-worship. It led them to

* "Adams approached it [Concord] in much the same spirit as he would have entered a Gothic cathedral, for he well knew that the priests regarded him as only a worm. To the Concord church all Adamses were minds of dust and emptiness, devoid of feeling, poetry or imagination; little higher than the common scourings of State Street . . . He perpetually fell back into the heresy that if anything universal was unreal, it was himself and not the appearances; it was the poet, and not the banker; it was his own thought, not the thing that moved it."—*The Education of Henry Adams.*

221

form attachments for older men, naïvely but excessively romantic. Louisa Alcott, under the spell of Bettina, left flowers on Emerson's doorstep, as a young New Hampshire girl had laid siege to Theodore Parker. Louisa, stirred again, —she who sat in the cherry-tree, singing to the moon at midnight,—sang Mignon's song in German under Emerson's window. Emerson had written of Goethe with sympathetic comprehension, but he stood outside him and, in certain respects, behind him; for he judged him by an older and deeper standard than that of nineteenth-century culture. Mighty genius that Goethe was, mightier in genius than any American writer, he who counted his medals and used the world to promote his own vainglory and his personal ego, who vaunted egoism and made of this his message, while he bowed to the princes of the earth, was small if one measured him by the wisdom of Egypt and India; and Emerson spoke by the oldest book in the world. The tablets of the Nile were behind him; and, as for the Concord "criticism," if it was very deficient aesethetically, it possessed a more venerable sanction than any modern aesthetics. Most of the classical treatises ratified its findings. Emerson, the sage, who was only secondarily the writer, fallible in his literary judgments, uttered first and last things on the life that underlay, as it also transcended, all the expressions of life. He was often astray with "phenomena," he was seldom or never astray with "noumena,"—at least less often astray than anyone else in his time.* Kant's "two things," the "two things" of Bee-

---

* This was the point of Matthew Arnold's lecture on Emerson, in which, after saying that Emerson was "not a great writer," he observed that Emerson's essays were "the most important work done in prose . . . in our language, during the present century." This was an application of the classical law according to which the ultimate standard in writing is one that underlies the aesthetic.

It should be added that Arnold's approach to Emerson's poetry does not lead to the centre of the subject. The point is not how far Emerson fell short of Gray or Cowper, in their spheres, but how far they, in his sphere, would have fallen short of *Bacchus*, *Terminus* and *Give All to Love*.

thcven,—"the starry sky above me and the moral law within me,"—filled his soul and armed his words, as they had armed the words of all the prophets since the beginning of man.

This was the secret of Emerson's power. In a day when the greatest geniuses spoke for their time, he spoke for the timeless things, goodness, not in defence, the intellect, not with emotion, as one and the same; and he spoke with the calm clairvoyance of one who merely revealed a truth which the innermost mind of his hearers, responding, confirmed. For things were so and not otherwise. No doubt, the time had come for other teachers, who were not so fatalistically optimistic, for critical and reflective minds that grappled with secular problems. Too much of the Emersonian bred an indifference to the hard facts of American life,—which might come right in eternity but was certainly going wrong in time. This life had never gone so wrong as immediately after the war. Emerson's voice was lost in a babel of other voices, many of them prophesying doom. His words were overlaid, as the walls of a house are overlaid with fresh layers of paper. But what did the Ripleys find in Concord when they repapered the Manse? Stripping off layer after layer, till they reached the original paper, they found it was printed on old French journals of the time of the Revolution. It was covered with the speeches of Mirabeau and Danton. So Emerson's words were written on the walls of the nation. Whenever, in decades to come, the house was renovated, and the old layers of paper were stripped away, these words came to light again; and America once more saw the star of promise first seen in its early morning.

The Hawthornes had vanished from Concord. Thoreau was gone. At the Manse lived Mrs. Ripley, who was found in the attic once, rocking the cradle, with a Sanskrit book in her other hand, apologetic because she had to look a few words up and because she could not think in Sanskrit. Frank B. Sanborn, John Brown's friend and helper, who later wrote the lives of the Concord worthies, carried on the Concord school and contributed letters on books and authors to Samuel Bowles's paper, the *Springfield Republican*. These letters, with their news and gossip of the literary world, were a staple of conversation in the Berkshires. They kept Emily Dickinson well posted. Mrs. Hawthorne had taken her children to England. Julian, the son, who had lived as a boy in Liverpool, when his father was consul, was to pass many years in England; and there he began his life as a novelist. Before this, however, he had studied engineering in Dresden and worked for a while in New York as an engineer. One found a reminiscence of Dresden in his *Saxon Studies*, an acute but captious picture of German life, and in his later novel, *The Professor's Sister*, a spiritualistic romance with a German setting, involving hypnotic trances and astral forms. For a number of years, Julian Hawthorne reviewed books for the London *Spectator*, and for more than half a century he continued to write, as a novelist and a journalist, pursued by misfortune. His earlier novels, *Archibald Malmaison*, *Fortune's Fool* and *Noble Blood*, *Garth*, *Idolatry* and others suggested the later vein of the elder Hawthorne, the unfinished *Dr. Grimshawe* and *The Ancestral Footstep*. *Garth* was the tale of an old New Hampshire house with a gloomy legend. In *Idolatry*, an Egyptian palace rose on the banks of the Hudson, and the story was like the dream of an opium-eater, with hoopoe birds, enchanted rings, eccentric uncles, mysterious murders and a vague young Dane who was somehow descended from Thor. Others were tales of "American claimants" in England, of whom Nathaniel Hawthorne had met so many, in the consulate, when Julian was a child, stories of changelings, ambiguous baronets and wandering American artists, of English manor-houses with secret panels, locked doors, dusky apartments, towers with ghosts and faces at windows. These stories were heavily documented as a tribute to the realism that more and more prevailed as the years went on, but in essence they were melodramatic; and one found less and less in Julian Hawthorne's later stories that indicated a personal style and vision. One saw this writer best perhaps as a rather ineffectual link between the greater Hawthorne and Henry James.

As for the Alcotts, settled at last in Orchard House, their world was agreeably altered by Louisa's success. For the big, bouncing, ardent girl, who was almost six feet tall, with her "force and temerity of will,"—which Alcott had noted in her at the age of four, had followed her father's injunction: she was acting out her genius with a vengeance. No longer were the neighbours, asked to tea, obliged to bring their little baskets with them, to fill the pot with souchong and the bowl with sugar. "Duty's faithful child" had changed all this. Louisa had entranced her public as a chronicler of the Alcott household, which had cast its bread upon the waters and found it after many days. She published *Little Women* in 1868. In the same year appeared her father's *Tablets;* and *Concord Days* and *Table-Talk* followed, all in the train of Louisa's good fortune. Alcott's books no longer went a-begging; and, when he set out for the West, the "American Plato," with his brand-new trunk and gloves and cambric shirts, was able to count upon thousands of auditors. His "conversational tours" were prospering as far away as Iowa, where he lectured on Webster, Garrison, Greeley and Parker. He brought New England back to the homesick minds of the exiled Yankees; and those who had never understood why Emerson thought so well of Alcott had only to read his books to solve the puzzle. They had much of the charm of Whitman's *Specimen Days*. The essay on Emerson, the "favoured of the Nine," his genius and personal influence, was a moving tribute; and the papers on gardens and orchards, their poetry and philosophy, were signs that Concord well deserved its name. Not in vain had the rural muse traversed these meadows, woodlands, fields and brooksides; and, while it sounded deeper notes in others, Alcott wrote for the future as well as Thoreau. With him the American wilderness had passed its savage and animal

225

stage, and the gardener, not the hunter, was the man it called for.* It was finding this man in Olmsted, and Alcott was one of his prophets. He had led the way with his arbours and Virgilian woodpaths, which Olmsted translated into parks.

Louisa Alcott's life spanned all the great days of Concord, for she was born in 1832, a year before Emerson settled in the town of his forbears. She had witnessed, as an infant, her father's removal to Boston,—from Germantown, which happened to be her birthplace,—and the rise and fall of the Temple School and Fruitlands. She had built her first play-houses with diaries and dictionaries and had learned to use them both at four or five; for her father, a "child-psychologist," as people said in later years, analyzed and examined the minds of his daughters before they were able to speak and encouraged them to shape their thoughts in diaries and stories. At Fruitlands, reading Plato with the others, she was used to discussing such subjects as "What is Man?" She liked to watch the moon. She had good dreams. She had pleasant times with her mind.† Moreover, she was physically hardy. She liked cold baths at five in the morning, and she throve on a fare of plain boiled rice, apples and Graham meal without sugar or butter. She was a Dorian girl, if Elizabeth Peabody wished to see one, who had undergone a training as

* "I came as naturally to the spade, the plow, the scythe and sickle as to book and pen.

"The mind needs to come into tender relations with the earth and treat that most intimate of all spots with something akin to piety, since a personal pressure is diffused through every part of it, and divinity there awaits to meet us always."—*The Journals of Bronson Alcott*, edited by Odell Shepard.

† From Louisa Alcott's diary at the age of twelve:

"I wrote in my Imagination book, and enjoyed it very much. Life is pleasanter than it used to be, and I don't care about dying any more. Had a splendid run and got a box of cones to burn. Sat and heard the pines sing a long time. Read Miss Bremer's *Home* in the eve. Had good dreams, and woke now and then to think, and watch the moon. I had a pleasant time with my mind, for it was happy."

severe as a boy's, and she knew how to leap, run and wrestle. At six years old, in Boston, she had driven her hoop without stopping all round the Common, and in Concord she jumped off roofs and vaulted fences and outplayed the boys at breakneck tag. She would have nothing to do with any boy whom she had not outplayed. She thought of herself as a horse, for she liked nothing better than to race through the fields, tossing her head to sniff the morning air. She had grown up tall, thin and brown, with a yard and a half of chestnut hair, a towering, hoydenish, moody, stormy creature.

She had shared the Concord life in all its aspects. She had gathered moss for Alcott's arbours and browsed in Emerson's library, where she read Shakespeare, Dante, Carlyle and Goethe. She had roamed the fields with Thoreau, studying the birds and the flowers. She would have liked to camp out with Thoreau and Ellery Channing, like Sylvia, in her first novel, *Moods*, the restless girl who lived by "impulse,"— she had not learned to live by "principle,"—and who joined three men on an expedition, with a cockle-shell stuck in her hat. Sylvia was in love with the leader of this party, a tall, bronzed hero who suggested Thoreau, as a young girl might have seen him, although Warwick usually went to the polar regions instead of Boon's Pond and Heywood's meadow. Warwick was a master of woodcraft and Indian arts, and his grip filled everyone with life and courage. Sylvia's expedition with these companions recalled the woods of Maine and Thoreau's *Week*; and Louisa, who liked to think of "affinities," and wrote this book to express her feelings,—in a Hawthornesque style that was also Goethean,—shared all of Sylvia's impulse and indifference to trifles.* She longed to be an actress, she longed to be a novelist, and she meant to live her own life, whatever the neighbours and cousins might say. She thought nothing of walking to Boston for a play or a lecture; and, when she made a "battering-ram" of

* "I like original people who speak their minds out and don't worry about trifles."—Sylvia, in *Moods*.

her head, to force her way in the world and earn her living, she ignored the conventional notions that governed her sex. She went to the war as a nurse, or, rather, like Whitman, to amuse the wounded soldiers with games and stories; and in Boston she lived alone in boarding-houses, paying her way as a governess, a housemaid, a seamstress. Sewing sheets and pillowcases, neckties and handkerchiefs, she wrote plays and stories in her attic, lying awake and planning chapters of novels and sometimes working fourteen hours a day. One of her plays was produced at the Howard Athenæum. She was so depressed that she thought for a while of suicide. She was saved by the ministrations of Theodore Parker, who appeared as Mr. Power in her novel, *Work*.

Miss Alcott was an experienced story-teller when she finally wrote *Little Women*. Her first book was the *Flower Fables* she had told the Emerson children, in the style of Frederic Bremer or perhaps Jean Paul. But long before this she had written the melodramas and fairy-tale plays, with giants, pumpkin-coaches, harps and castles, waterfalls, thunder and armour, that she and her sisters had played in the barn at "Hillside,"—no doubt, the first of all the little theatres that rose in New England barns in days to come. As for *Little Women*, it was the author's high spirits that captivated the world in this charming book. She invested the Concord scheme of life with the gaiety and romance of a Robin Hood ballad.

R. P. Blackmur

EMILY DICKINSON

Notes on Prejudice and Fact

THE DISARRAY of Emily Dickinson's poems is the great obvious fact about them as they multiply from volume to volume—I will not say from edition to edition, for they have never been edited—just as a kind of repetitious fragmentariness is the characterizing fact of her sensibility. No poet of anything like her accomplishment has ever imposed on the reader such varied and continuous critical labor; and on few poets beyond the first bloat of reputation has so little work been done. Few poets have benefited generally, and suffered specifically, from such a handsome or fulsome set of prejudices, which, as they are expressed, seem to remove the need for any actual reading at all.

The barriers to critical labor are well known, and some of them are insuperable. No text will be certain so long as the vaults at Amherst remain closed. Without benefit of comparative scholarship it is impossible to determine whether a given item is a finished poem, an early version of a poem, a note for a poem, a part of a poem, or a prose exclamation. Worse, it is impossible to know whether what appear to be crotches in the poems as printed are correctly copied. The poet's handwriting was obscure, loose, and run-over; hence it is plain that unskilled copyists cannot be relied on in matters of punctuation, line structure, and the terminal letters of words. It is plainer still, if suspicion be in case, that many examples of merely irritating bad grammar—mistakes that merely hinder the reader—may well represent systematic bad guessing by the copyist. Perhaps it is not plain, but it is plausible, to imagine that a full and open view of the manuscripts would show the poet far less fragmentary and repetitious than the published work makes her seem. Most poets have a desk full of beginnings, a barrel of fragments and anything up to an attic full of notes. The manner of notation, if it were known, might make a beginning at the establishment of a canon. With the obvious fragments cut out, or put in an appendix, a clean, self-characterizing, responsive, and responding body of poetry, with limits and a fate and a quaking sensibility, might then be made to show itself.

Then is not now. This essay cannot enact a prophecy. This disarray of fragments, this mob of verses, this din of many motions, cannot be made to show itself in its own best order—as the strong parade we hoped it really was. This essay proposes, in lieu of adumbrating a complete criticism, first to examine a set of prejudices which are available as approaches to Emily Dickinson, and then to count—and perhaps account for—a few staring facts: obvious, animating, defacing facts about the verses as they now appear. If the essay has a good eye for the constitution of poetic facts, the affair of counting will be adventurous, a part of the great adventure of sensibility which consists, one sometimes thinks, in an arduous fealty to facts. If the fealty is sound, perhaps the vestiges of a complete criticism will be there too, or at least a bias, a prejudice, in that direction.

For it takes a strong and active prejudice to see facts at all, as any revolutionist will tell you. And just as the body must have a strong prejudice, which is its wisdom, about the nature of time in order to wake up exactly *before* the alarm goes off—an affair of counting, if ever—so the sensibility must have a pretty firm anterior conviction about the nature of poetry in order to wake up to a given body of poetry at all. We suddenly realize that we have, or have *not*—which in a very neat way comes to the same thing—counted some of these facts before. We know where we are in terms of where we thought we were, at home, lost, or shaking: which is when the alarm goes off. To depend on prejudice for the nature of time or poetry may seem a little willful and adventitiously mysterious. But it is a method that allows for mistakes, and in the present condition of Emily Dickinson's poetry, it is imperative to allow for continuous error, both in the facts and in their counting—in the prejudices by which we get at them.

Most prejudices are frivolous to the real interests concerned, which is why they are so often made to appear as facts instead of mere keys to facts. That Emily Dickinson is a great poet, "with the possible exception of Sappho, the greatest women poet of all time," or the author of poetry "perhaps the finest by a woman in the English language," or that in one of the volumes of her verse "there are no dregs, no single drop can be spared,"—these are variations upon an essentially frivolous prejudice. Only the last variation is dangerous, because by asserting perfection it makes the poet an idol and removes her from the possibility of experience. On the whole, statements of this order are seldom taken seriously, but are felt as polite salutations and farewells. The trouble is that it is hard to persuade oneself to read work towards which one has accomplished gestures so polite. If not a drop can be spared, let us not risk spilling any; let us say, rather, here is great poetry—we know what *that* is like! A chalice, a lily, a sea-change. Old memories are mulled. We have the equivalent of emotion. And equivalents, like substitutes, though not so good as what you asked for, are often, for sensibilities never exercised enough to have been starved, a full meal.

It would be unfair, though, to leave the prejudice of Emily Dickinson's magnitude so naked. Politeness may conceal a legitimate wish that dare not put itself in bald speech. I am convinced that Conrad Aiken, in referring to Emily Dickinson's poetry as "perhaps the finest by a woman in the English language," had the legitimate wish to condition the reader with a very good fundamental prejudice—which we shall come to—about Emily Dickinson to the effect that there was something exciting or vital or amusing in her work. It is a kind of flag-waving; it reminds you of what you ought to be able to feel. Most readers of poetry are flag-wavers, and in order to get them to be more, you have to begin by waving a flag. I cannot imagine Mr. Aiken, or any other reader, addressing a Dickinson poem as "perhaps the finest by a woman in the English language." That is only how he addresses other people, hoping that they will thus be prejudiced into responding to the poem as he actually does, in terms of the words and the motions of the words which make it up: which are the terms (not the thing itself) of magnitude. I too would like to begin and end with the idea that in some such sense Emily Dickinson is sometimes a great poet.

There is a more dangerous but no less frivolous type of prejudice in the following sentence. "Her revolt was absolute; she abandoned rhyme altogether when she chose, and even assonance, writing in meter alone, like a Greek." There is a Spanish proverb that if God does not bless you with children, the devil will send you nieces. As a literary critic, if not as a niece, Mme. Bianchi, who is responsible for the sentence quoted, is thoroughly diabolic; as idolaters are by rule. The idea is to make you feel that the slips and roughnesses, the truncated lines, false rhymes, the inconsistencies of every description which mar the majority of Emily Dickinson's poems are examples of a revolutionary master-craftsman. Only the idol is served here; no greater disservice could be done to the poetry the reader reads than to believe with however great sincerity that its blemishes have any closer relation than contrast to its beauty. Emily Dickinson never knew anything about the craft of verse well enough to exemplify it, let alone revolt from it. If, where you are autonomous as in the *practice* of verse, you revolt first, you only revolve in a vacuum; and you will end as Emily Dickinson did in many of her failures by producing chaotic verses which have no bearing on the proper chaos of their subject—

232

the life where precisely, as Emily Dickinson well enough knew, you are not autonomous but utterly dependent and interlocked.

As for Mme. Bianchi's specific terms: if the ear and arithmetic of this essay are right, Emily Dickinson did not abandon rhyme so much as she failed to get that far—her lines strike *as if* they intended to end in rhyme; and her assonances seem frequently incomplete substitutes, for rhyme and not assonances at all. She did not write in meter alone; her meters were most often exiguous or overrun proximations of common English meter—or again they met the pattern of meter in syllabification miter-perfect without meeting the enlivening movement of meter. And as for writing like a Greek it would be more nearly correct, metrically, to say that she wrote like an Italian with recurring pairs of stressed syllables. I do not refer here to the successful meters in Emily Dickinson, but only to the variously deficient meters.

But Mme. Bianchi is not half so dangerous in idealizing her aunt's technical inadequacy as absolute, as Ludwig Lewisohn is in magnifying her intellectual and mystical force —a composition of magnitudes not commonly come by outside Dante. "She can be," says Mr. Lewisohn, "of a compactness of expression and fullness of meaning not less than Goethean in Goethe's epigrammatic mood . . . She can soar like the intense mystical poets of the seventeenth century." This is the method of instilling prejudice by means of the unexpanded comparison. We are assumed to have the American poet in front of us and to know what she is; then our knowledge of her is heightened by a comparison with Goethe's epigrams, which are probably not in front of us except by reputation. As we think, we suddenly realize that the cognate qualities in Emily Dickinson are not with us either. They are precisely as far off as Goethe. Mr. Lewisohn has compared abstracted qualities for a concrete effect: the effect, I take it, of vivid moral insight; but he has not *made* the comparison. He has not shown us what it is in either

233

poet that he is talking about. If he expanded and did show us, he might prove right; I do not at the moment say he is wrong—although I suspect an intolerable identification: the target of insight for the two poets could hardly have been the same. What I want to emphasize is merely this: Mr. Lewisohn is actually only saying that Emily Dickinson's poetry possesses moral insight. What he pretends to do is to put her insight on the level of the supreme type of moral insight—by mentioning Goethe's name. He would have done better to distinguish the *difference* between the achieved qualities in the epigrams of the two poets—the difference between insight as wisdom, say, and insight as vision.

Mr. Lewisohn's other comparison, with the intense mystical poets of the seventeenth century, is equally unexpanded and equally misleading. He does not say which poets nor in what respects; and what we actually get out of his comparison is the idea that Emily Dickinson was intensely mystical in an exciting and inexpensive way. The spread of such a prejudice may multiply readers, but it fosters bad reading. Poetic mysticism, as the term is loosely used, is a kind of virus that gets about through the medium of the printed page, and its chief effect is to provide a matchless substitute for the discipline of attention in incapable minds. By making ultimate apprehension of God—or matter—free in words, it relieves the poet of the necessity to make his words first apprehend the *manifestation*—what is actually felt—in this world; and it relieves the reader of the obligation to apprehend anything at all when everything may always be apprehended at once. To exercise this sort of prejudice on a really interesting poet is to carry politeness too far—and far beyond, as it happens, Emily Dickinson's poems' own idea of their operative reach and willed intention. I quote, as facts worth counting in this connection, the following lines and phrases: they illuminate Mr. Lewisohn's prejudice by reducing it to the actual scope of the poems.

234

The missing All prevented me
From missing minor things . . .
Almost we wish the end
Were further off—too great it seems
So near the Whole to stand . . .

Was the Pine at my window a "Fellow"
Of the Royal Infinity?
Apprehensions are God's introductions
Extended inscrutably.

These lines are, I think, characteristic of the general "mystical" attitude in the poems. It is not mysticism itself. It is an attitude composed partly of the English Hymnal, partly of instinctive protestant transcendentalism, partly of instinctively apprehended Puritan theology, and partly of human sensibility bred with experience to the point of insight. There is besides an element of composition at work, which is the most important of all the distinguishable elements, and which makes the lines quoted, at least in their contexts, into poetry.

Admittedly this language is as loose as Mr. Lewisohn's and as open to reduction; but I, too, am dealing with initial prejudice. My prejudice is that Emily Dickinson is a mid-nineteenth century New England Christian poet. Christianity moved her, and experience moved through her poems upon the machinery of Christianity, which is a machinery for the worship of God in all His works, and, among other things, for the redemption, which is to say the completion, of the soul. Christianity in action, especially in poetry, often looks to the outsider like an exercise in mysticism; and that is perhaps the mistake Mr. Lewisohn makes—just as so many have made a similar mistake about Gerard Manley Hopkins, or, for that matter, about Herbert and Vaughan. All these poets approached the mystery of God which is unity, but they approached it in human terms; they did what every Christian must; but they never seized or lost themselves in the unity of God as St. Francis and St. Theresa seemed to do—or as the great cathedrals and the great Church music, to the lay imagination, indubitably did. Put another way, there is nothing in the poems of Hopkins or Emily Dickinson which passes the willing understanding; if their poems sometimes confront the supersensible—and they mostly do not—it is always on the plane of the rational imagination, never in the incomprehensible terms of the mystical act. The mystery is there, but like the mystery of physical death the relation of the poetry to it is heuristic—an affair of discovery of which the very excitement, promise, and terror are that it never takes place, yet may, indeed momently, must.

Those who persist in calling this relationship mystical underestimate the scope of rational imagination working in language and in the face of mystery. That scope is exhausted only in the instance; the mystery is never exhausted merely by being expressed; and the mystery, as a fact, is always the same. When Shakespeare, who never troubled directly about God, mastered the emotion of jealousy in *Othello*, he was precisely as rational or precisely as "mystical" in his approach to mystery—and the same mystery, the mystery of the actual —as Emily Dickinson was in her deliberate approach to God in terms of nature and death. What differs is the machinery, or sometimes the formula, of approach.

Here we come on a different type of prejudice, in its own way as general and as beyond the point if taken too solemnly as those we have been discussing, but with an air of specificity about it which is disarming. This is the prejudice about the poet in relation to his time, where the poet is taken as a fatal event in cultural history. The time produced the poet, we say, and the poet crowned the time—crowned it with its own meaning. If we go far enough on this line, the time, or the age, tends to disappear in the meaning—as for many of us early Greece disappears in Homer; which is only a way of bringing the time up to date, of telescoping all the coördinates rashly into the one image of meaning. Mr. Allen Tate has in an admirable essay (in his *Reactionary Essays*) performed this labor upon Emily Dickinson, with the further labor that when he has got his image all made he proceeds to sort out its component parts. It is hard to separate what Mr. Tate found in Emily Dickinson as traces or inklings from what he brought with him on his own account; which is all in his favor if you like what he says, as I do, and if the combination illuminates and enlivens Emily Dickinson, as I believe it does. Mr. Tate as a critic has the kind of rightness that goes with insight, and not at all the kind of wrongness that goes with sincerity—which is perhaps how we should characterize Mr. Lewisohn.

At any rate, Mr. Tate builds up a pretty good historical prejudice and makes it available in the guise of insight. Emily Dickinson came, he says, exactly at the dying crisis of Puritan New England culture—not at the moment of death, but at the moment—it was years long—when the matrix began to be felt as broken. Spiritual meaning and psychic stability were no longer the unconscious look and deep gesture worn and rehearsed lifelong; they required the agony of doubt and the trial of deliberate expression in specifically, wilfully objective form. Faith was sophisticated, freed, and terrified—but still lived; imagination had suddenly to do all the work of embodying faith formerly done by habit, and to embody it with the old machinery so far as it could be used. There was no other machinery available. Thus the burden of poetry was put upon the New England version of the Christian sensibility.

It is arguable that Greek tragedy came at the analogous moment in Athenian history, when the gods were seen as imaginative instead of magical myths. The advantage for the poet is in both instances double and pays in poetry for the burden. There is the advantage of the existing machinery of meaning in the specific culture, which is still able to carry any weight and which is universally understood; and there is the advantage of a new and personal plasticity in the meanings themselves. Faith, in the agonized hands of the individual, becomes an imaginative experiment of which all the elements are open to new and even blasphemous combinations, and which is subject to the addition of new insights. It is no longer enough to repeat prayers and to rehearse Mass or its protestant equivalent; indeed the institutional part of culture is the first to show itself as dead; faith becomes to the secularized imagination of Emily Dickinson "the Experiment of our Lord!"—which it could never have seemed, on the same foundation, half a century earlier. The great advantage for a poet to come at a time of disintegrating culture is, then, to sum up, just this: the actuality of what we are and what we believe is suddenly seen to be nearly meaningless as habit, and must, to be adequately known, be translated to the terms and modes of the imagination. Nothing can be taken for granted but the machinery, which is there, all available, and which indeed cannot help being taken for granted. These are the conditions of belief—though not the only conditions—which may produce great poetry: the conditions of spiritual necessity and mechanical freedom. It is worth adding, for proportion, that the opposite conditions—spiritual freedom (a unity of belief and discipline) and mechanical necessity—produced such a great poet as Dante; and, again, it is quite possible that Shakespeare may have been produced at the nexus of quite a different set of conditions which had more to do with the state of language than with the state of belief. Here we are concerned with the occurrence of Emily Dickinson at the precise time when it became plain that Puritan Christianity was no longer the vital force in New England culture and before any other force had recognizably relieved the slack. If we are inclined to see a causal connection it is only as a more vivid and dramatic way of seeing the association it may really and only have been.

Now I do not want to let it appear that Mr. Tate would assent to my treatment of his idea; he has his own treatment, which is certainly not so highfalutin as mine; and besides, I am not sure how far I can assent to my own remarks without

238

a feeling that I am merely succumbing to the temptation of a bright idea, which like the idea of chance explains less and less the more you look into it. Let us take the idea provisionally, and more provisionally for me than for Mr. Tate. So taken, it indicates a source, and with the source a tragic strength, for the fund and flow of Emily Dickinson's meaning. As the Massachusetts theocracy failed, became, say, more humane and individualized, its profoundly dramatic nature—all that it had left—became sharper and plainer, until in the imagination of Hawthorne and Melville and Emily Dickinson it took in, or implied, pretty near the whole of human experience. Then it died. It fed the imagination; then it died; and at the same time that particular form of the New England imagination reached its small surfeit and died too.

In the last sentence lies buried, but not in the least dead, the fundamental prejudice we have been looking for all the time: the prejudice contained in the idea of imagination being fed and dying, or for that matter living or doing anything whatever—that is to say, a prejudice about the nature of poetry itself as the chief mode of imagination. Poetry is composed of words and whenever we put anything into poetry —such as meaning or music; whenever poetry is affected by anything—such as the pattern of a culture or the structure of a stanza; whenever anything at all happens in poetry it happens in the medium of words. It is also near enough the truth to say that whenever we take anything out of poetry, either to use it or to see just what it is, we have to take it out in the words—and then put it right back before it gets lost or useless. The greatness of Emily Dickinson is not—to review our select list of prejudices—going to be found in anybody's idea of greatness, or of Goethe, or intensity, or mysticism, or historical fatality. It is going to be found in the words she used and in the way she put them together; which we will observe, if we bother to discriminate our observations, as a series of facts about words. What is behind the words or beyond them, we cannot know as facts, as any discussion amply demonstrates. Our knowledge of implication and inkling, quite as much as our knowledge of bald sound and singing sense, will be governed solely by what we can recognize, and perhaps by a good deal that we cannot recognize, of the poetic relations of the words—that is to say, by what they make of each other. This rule, or this prejudice, applies, which is why it is mentioned at all, exactly as strongly to our method of determining the influence of a culture or a church or a philosophy, alive, dead, or dying, upon the body of Emily Dickinson's poetry. We will see what the influence did to the words, and more important, what the words did to the influence.

So far as poetry goes, then, the influence of intellectual or other abstracted considerations can be measured only as it effects the choice and arrangement of words—as it richens or impoverishes the texture of the imaginative vehicle of the poetry. The puritan theory of renunciation, for example, will be not at all the same thing in a hortatory tract, no matter how eloquent and just, as in a poem of Emily Dickinson, which might well have drawn from the tract, however loose or fragmentary the poem may be. Imagination, if it works at all, works at the level of actualized experience. Here is the example, pat to the purpose, and to other purposes as well.

> Renunciation
> Is a piercing virtue,
> The letting go
> A presence for an expectation—
> Not now.

There is no forensic here, nor eloquence, nor justness; it is a bare statement amounting to vision—vision being a kind of observation of the ideal. It has nothing to do with wisdom, there is no thinking in it; and there is no ordinary observation in it—in the sense that there is no relation between an observer and a thing observed. The lines do not prove themselves, or anything else; they make a statement. Yet it is not a naïve statement—it is not directly itself—however much it

240

may seem to be. It rises rather out of a whole way of life—the protestant, puritan way, felt suddenly at what can be called nothing less than a supremely sophisticated level. The feeling is in the sophistication. As a religious or philosophical statement it is probably vain and tragic and an example of self-arrogation; certainly it is without humility. Perhaps I am not competent to judge, being in a worse predicament than the poet, but it is possible to say that this is the sort of thing that happens to a religious notion when one's awareness of it becomes personal and without authority, when one is driven to imagine—in words or otherwise—the situation actually felt.

We do not examine these lines with a view to calling them great poetry but in order to present a series of facts as to how they derive their being and to afford a clue to the facts about a whole species of Dickinson poems—those that deal with the renunciation of love, the death of the beloved, and the heavenly reward. The machinery of meaning remains roughly the same throughout the group; what differs is the degree or amount of experience actualized in the verse. The machinery and the experience are perhaps inseparable, or at any rate are in their varying proportions equally necessary to the production of the kind of poetry Emily Dickinson wrote. When the balance is lost, when the fusion is not made, or when resort is had to feeling alone or to machinery insufficiently felt, something less than good poetry appears. We have either a poem without mooring or a poem without buoyancy.

Let us provisionally inquire what it is in the words that makes poetry of the statement about renunciation. Let us treat the machinery, not as what we may or may not know it to be intellectually, but as an example of words in operation; and let us look at the image—what is imagined—as the emergent fact of the words in operation, indeed, as the operation itself. That is how our best reading takes poetry in its stride; here we arrest the stride or make slow motion of it. The words are all simple words, parts of our stock vocabulary.

Only one, *renunciation*, belongs to a special department of experience or contains in itself the focus of a particular attitude, a department and an attitude we condition ourselves to keep mostly in abeyance. We know what renunciation is; we know it turns up as heroism or hypocrisy or sentimentality; and we do as little as possible about it. Only one word, *piercing*, is directly physical; something that if it happens cannot be ignored but always shocks us into reaction. It is the shock of this word that transforms the phrase from a mere grammatical tautology into a metaphorical tautology which establishes as well as asserts identity. Some function of the word *pierce* precipitates a living intrinsic relation between renunciation and virtue; it is what makes the phrase incandesce. The two adjectives in the last line of the following quatrain exhibit a similar incandescent function.

> Rehearsal to ourselves
> Of a withdrawn delight
> Affords a bliss like murder,
> Omnipotent, acute.

It is the adjectives that transform the verbal and mutually irrelevant association of delight and murder into a self-completing metaphor. But, to return to our other quotation, the word *pierce* enlivens not only the first phrase but the whole statement about renunciation; it is the stress or shock of it that is carried forward into and makes specific the general notion—physical but vague—of letting go; and letting go, in its turn, perhaps by its participial form, works back upon the first phrase. The piercing quality of renunciation is precisely, but not altogether, that it is a continuing process, takes time, it may be infinite time, before the renounced presence transpires in expectation in the "Not now." It is—if we may provisionally risk saying so—the physical elements in the word *pierce* and the participial phrase *letting go* that, by acting upon them, make the other words available to feeling, and it is the word *renunciation* that, so enlightened, focuses the

242

feeling as actuality. That operation is almost enough to make the statement poetry; we have only pseudo-names for whatever else it is that it takes. There is no advantage here of meter or rhyme. There is instead the speech-tone of authority, a directness in the manner of the words which has nothing to do with their meaning, and the speech-quality of speed, an inner speed of the syllables like the inner velocity of an atom, which has nothing directly to do with the outward relations of the words. These qualities are characteristic of verse that is felt as actual; at least we say that these qualities exist in verse that exacts the sense of precise feeling in the reader. Perhaps it is simpler to say that there is an excitement in the language beyond the excitement of any meaning we can communicate through any medium different from that of the poem itself: the excitement of being. It is gained, that excitement, by the exercise of the fundamental technique of language as a mode of finding objective form for even the most abstract feelings. A further, and I hope not absurd, simplification is to say that the poet whose work showed these qualities had an aptitude for language; and if that is so, then all we have been saying merely illustrates how much that is complicated and beyond conscious control the word *aptitude* may sometimes simplify.

So be it. Emily Dickinson had an aptitude for language, and in the passage we have examined she needed nothing else to induce her verses to reach their appropriate objective level; for the aptitude included every necessary mechanical relation both to her age and to the general craft of verse. Although the same aptitude persists superficially through the rest of the poem, the persistence is only superficial and not substantial. The rest of the poem is not transformed, as the quoted stanza was, into something felt as actual in which the parts work upon themselves mutually. We can say either that the aptitude was not carried far enough *per se*—the poet did not pay enough attention to the words; or we can say that the conceiving imagination was not strong enough to carry the ma-

243

terial through; or we can say that the poet was not sufficiently master of the compositional devices of external form—form as the organizing agent—to give the work crisis and consistency. The first statement is true anyway; the second is probably true; and the third is true in relation to the other two. Perhaps the three statements are merely different emphases of the same idea: the idea we took up a little while ago of the imagination being insufficiently fed into the words of the poem. Either the machinery of the poem was inadequate to objectify its purpose, or the motive of the poem, as it emerged, was inadequate to activate the machinery. The alternatives are not mutually exclusive; a combined view is possible. It is at least plausible to consider that if there is a state of culture which produces or precipitates a body of poetry, then there may also be a state of language—a general level of poetic habit—which is necessary to give that body of poetry relative perfection, and that, further, if there is failure in one quarter, no matter which, it is a likely sign of failure in the other, if not at the same point then round the nearest corner. The trouble is that the condition of language at a given time is just as hard to determine as the condition of a culture. We guess at something wrong or swear that everything was right, and are not sure which case produced the better poetry.

We can say, amiably enough, that the verse-language of mid-nineteenth century America was relatively nerveless, unsupple, flat in pattern, had very little absorptive power and showed no self-luxuriating power whatever. The mounting vitality that shows itself as formal experiment and the matured vitality that shows itself as the masterly penetration of accepted form (say Kyd followed by the mature Shakespeare) were equally absent. The great estate of poetry as an available condition of language lay flat in a kind of desiccated hibernation, and the clue to resurrection was unknown. It is not for nothing that our poets never mastered form in language. Poe and Longfellow accepted the desiccation, contributing a personal music which perhaps redeemed but never transfigured their talents. Whitman and Emily Dickinson, with more genius, or as we have been saying with more favorable cultural situations, were unable to accept the desiccation and drove forward on the élan of their natural aptitudes for language, resorting regardless to whatever props, scaffolds, obsessive symbols, or intellectual mechanisms came to hand, but neither of them ever finding satisfactory form—and neither, apparently, ever consciously missing it. The great bulk of the verse of each appears to have been written on the sustaining pretense that everything was always possible. To see boundless good on the horizon, to see it without the limiting discipline of the conviction of evil, is in poetry as in politics the great stultifier of action.

Hence the great, repetitious wastes in both poets. With no criterion of achievement without there could be no criterion of completion within. Success was by accident, by the mere momentum of sensibility. Failure was by rule, although the rule was unknown, and often doubtless thought of in the shameless guise of simple self-expression. The practice of craft came to little more than so many exercises in self-expression. Thus something over two-thirds of Emily Dickinson's nine hundred odd printed poems are exercises, and no more, some in the direction of poetry, and some not. The object is usually in view, though some of the poems are but exercises in pursuit of an unknown object, but the means of attainment are variously absent, used in error, or ill-chosen. The only weapon constantly in use is, to repeat once more, the natural aptitude for language; and it is hardly surprising to find that that weapon, used alone and against great odds, should occasionally produce an air of frantic strain instead of strength, of conspicuous oddity instead of indubitable rightness.

Let us take for a first example a reasonably serious poem on one of the dominant Dickinson themes, the obituary theme of the great dead—a theme to which Hawthorne and

Henry James were equally addicted—and determine if we can where its failure lies.

> More life went out, when He went,
> Than ordinary breath,
> Lit with a finer phosphor
> Requiring in the quench
>
> A power of renownéd cold—
> The climate of the grave
> A temperature just adequate
> So anthracite to live.
>
> For some an ampler zero,
> A frost more needle keen
> Is necessary to reduce
> The Ethiop within.
>
> Others extinguish easier—
> A gnat's minutest fan
> Sufficient to obliterate
> A tract of citizen.

The first thing to notice—a thing characteristic of exercises— is that the order or plot of the elements of the poem is not that of a complete poem; the movement of the parts is downwards and towards a disintegration of the effect wanted. A good poem so constitutes its parts as at once to contain them and to deliver or release by the psychological force of their sequence the full effect only when the poem is done. Here the last quatrain is obviously wrongly placed; it comes like an after-thought, put in to explain why the third stanza was good. It should have preceded the third stanza, and perhaps with the third stanza—both of course in revised form—might have come at the very beginning, or perhaps in suspension between the first and second stanzas. Such suggestions throw the poem into disorder; actually the disorder is already there. It is not the mere arrangement of stanzas that is at fault; the

246

units in disorder are deeper in the material, perhaps in the compositional elements of the conception, perhaps in the executive elements of the image-words used to afford circulation to the poem, perhaps elsewhere in the devices not used but wanted. The point for emphasis is that it is hard to believe that a conscientious poet could have failed to see that no amount of correction and polish could raise this exercise to the condition of a mature poem. The material is all there—the inspiration and the language; what it requires is a thorough revision—a reseeing calculated to compose in objective form the immediacy and singleness of effect which the poet no doubt herself felt.

Perhaps we may say—though the poem is not near so bad an example as many—that the uncomposed disorder is accepted by the poet because the poem was itself written automatically. To the sensitive hand and expectant ear words will arrange themselves, however gotten hold of, and seem to breed by mere contact. The brood is the meaning we catch up to. Is not this really automatic writing *tout court?* Most of the Dickinson poems seems to have been initially as near automatic writing as may be. The bulk remained automatic, subject to correction and multiplication of detail. Others, which reach intrinsic being, have been patterned, inscaped, injected one way or another with the élan or elixir of the poet's dominant attitudes. The poem presently examined remains too much in the automatic choir; the élan is there, which is why we examine it at all, but without the additional advantage of craft it fails to carry everything before it.

The second stanza of the poem is either an example of automatic writing unrelieved, or is an example of bad editing, or both. Its only meaning is in the frantic strain towards meaning—a strain so frantic that all responsibility towards the shapes and primary significance of words was ignored. "A temperature just adequate/So anthracite to live" even if it were intelligible, which it is not, would be beyond bearing awkward to read. It is not bad grammar alone that works ill;

247

words sometimes make their own grammar good on the principle of ineluctable association—when the association forces the words into meaning. Here we have fiat meaning. The word *anthracite* is the crux of the trouble. Anthracite is coal, is hard, is black, gives heat, and has a rushing crisp sound; it has a connection with carbuncle and with a fly-borne disease of which one symptom resembles a carbuncle; it is stratified in the earth, is formed of organic matter as a consequence of enormous pressure through geologic time; etc., etc. One or several of these senses may contribute to the poem; but because the context does not denominate it, it does not appear which. My own guess is that Emily Dickinson wanted the effect of something hard and cold and perhaps black and took *anthracite* off the edge of her vocabulary largely because she liked the sound. This is another way of saying that *anthracite* is an irresponsible product of her aptitude for language.

The word *phosphor* in the third line of the first stanza is a responsible example of the same aptitude. It is moreover a habitual symbol word rather than a sudden flight; it is part of her regular machinery for concentrating meaning in a partly willful, partly natural symbol. Phosphor or phosphorus—in various forms of the word—is used by Emily Dickinson at least twelve times to represent, from the like characteristic of the metal, the self-illumining and perhaps self-consuming quality of the soul. The "renownéd cold," "ampler zero," and "frost more needle keen," are also habitual images used to represent the coming or transition of death as effected seasonally in nature and, by analogue, in man. Examples of these or associated words so used run to the hundreds. The "gnat" in the fourth stanza with his "minutest fan" (of cold air?) is another example of a portmanteau image always ready to use to turn on the microcosmic view. In the word *Ethiop* in the third stanza we have a mixture of a similar general term—this time drawn from the outside and unknown world—and a special significance released and warranted by the poem. Ethiops live in tropical Africa; and we have here a kind of synecdoche which makes the Ethiop himself so full of heat that it would take great cold to quench it. That the contrary would be the case does not affect the actuality of the image, but makes it more intriguing and gives it an odd, accidental character. The misconception does, however, bring out the flavor of a wrong image along with the shadow of the right one; and it is a question whether the flavor will not last longer in the memory than the shadow. Another nice question is involved in the effect of the *order* of the verbs used to represent the point of death: *quench, reduce, extinguish, obliterate.* The question is, are not these verbs pretty nearly interchangeable? Would not any other verb of destructive action do just as well? In short, is there any word in this poem which either fits or contributes to the association at all exactly? I think not—with the single exception of "phosphor."

The burden of these observations on words will I hope have made itself plain; it is exactly the burden of the observations on the form of the whole poem. The poem is an exercise whichever way you take it: an approach to the organization of its material but by no means a complete organization. It is almost a rehearsal—a doing over of something not done—and a variation of stock intellectual elements in an effort to accomplish an adventure in feeling. The reader can determine for himself—if he can swallow both the anthracite and the gnat—how concrete and actual the adventure was made.

Perhaps determination will be assisted by a few considerations on Emily Dickinson's vocabulary as a whole and how it splits up under inspection into different parts which are employed for different functions, and which operate *from*, as it were, different levels of sensibility. It is not a large vocabulary compared to Whitman's, nor rich like Melville's, nor perspicuous like Henry James', nor robust like Mark Twain's. Nor is it a homogeneous vocabulary; its unity is specious for the instance rather than organic for the whole of her work. Its constant elements are mostly found, like most of the poems, in arrangements, not in compositions. The pattern of association is kaleidoscopic and extraneous far more frequently than it is crystalline and inwardly compelled. What it is, is a small, rigidly compartmented vocabulary of general and conventional groups of terms, plus a moderately capacious vocabulary of homely, acute, directly felt words from which the whole actualizing strength of her verse is drawn. The extraordinary thing is how much of the general and conventional vocabulary got activated by the homely word. In the fragment about renunciation, "piercing" and "letting go" are examples. The depressing thing is how much of the conventional vocabulary was not activated by the homely word but distracted by the homely word strained odd.

Let us list a few of the conventional types that turn up most often and most conspicuously. The most conspicuous of all is the vocabulary of romance royalty, fairy-tale kings, queens and courts, and the general language of chivalry. Emily Dickinson was as fond as Shakespeare of words like *imperial, sovereign, dominion,* and the whole collection of terms for rank and degree. Probably she got them more from Scott and the Bible and the Hymnal than from Shakespeare. There is none of Shakespeare's specific and motivating sense of kings and princes as the focus of society, and none of his rhetoric of power; there is nothing tragic in Emily Dickinson's royal vocabulary. On the other hand, there is a great deal of vague and general assumption that royalty is a good thing and that escape into the goodness of it is available to everyone: like the colorful escape into romance and fairy tale. Besides this general assumption, and more important, there is continuous resort to the trope of heavenly coronation for the individual and a continuous ascription of imperial titles and a chivalric, almost heraldic, code to God and the angels, to flowers and bees. This vocabulary, taken as a

whole, provides a mixed formula which rehearsed like a
ritual or just a verbal exercise sometimes discovers a poem
and sometimes does not. I extract one stanza as example.

> He put a belt around my life,—
> I heard the buckle snap,
> And turned away, imperial,
> My lifetime folding up
> Deliberate as a duke would do
> A kingdom's title-deed,—
> Henceforth a dedicated sort,
> A member of the cloud.

Other vocabularies include words taken from sewing
and the kinds of cloth used in women's clothes—*stitch,
seam, needle, dimity, serge, silk, satin, brocade,* etc.; legal
words—*tenant, rent, litigant, title,* etc.; the names of jewels—
diamond, ruby, pearl, opal, amethyst, beryl, and *amber;*
words taken from the Civil War—*bayonet,* various images
of musket and cannon fire, and of the soldier's heroism;
words taken from sea-borne commerce—*port, harbor,* various kinds of ships and the parts of ships; the names of distant places—especially of mountains and volcanoes; and, not
to exhaust but merely to stop the list, words taken from the
transcendental theology of her time. It should be noted that
only the first, second, and possibly the last of these groups
named or activated anything she found in her daily life; but
they had, like the vocabulary of royalty, everything to do
with the stretching of her daily fancy, and they made a constant provision, a constant rough filling and occupation, for
what did actually concern her—her prevision of death and
her insight into the spiritual life. This is another way of
saying that in what is quantitatively the great part of her
work Emily Dickinson did not put the life of meaning into
her words; she leaned on the formulas of words in the hope
that the formulas would fully express what she felt privately
—sometimes the emotion of escape and sometimes the conviction of assent—in her own self-centered experience. This

is partly the mode of prayer, partly the mode of nonce-popular romance (which must always be repeated) and partly the mode of the pathetic fallacy applied to form—the fiat mode of expression which asserts that the need is equivalent to the object, that if you need words to mean something then they will necessarily mean it. But it is not except by accident the mode of the rational or actualizing imagination. The extraordinary thing in Emily Dickinson is, to repeat, that fragmentary accidents occur so often, and the terrible thing is that they need not have been accidents at all. The net result may be put as a loss of consistent or sustained magnitude equal to the impulse. We have a verse in great body that is part terror, part vision, part insight and observation, which must yet mostly be construed as a kind of *vers de société* of the soul—not in form or finish but in achievement.

This is to say that control was superficial—in the use, not the hearts, of words. We saw an example in the word *anthracite* a little above. Let us present two more examples and stop. We have the word *plush* in different poems as follows. "One would as soon assault a plush or violate a star . . . Time's consummate plush . . . A dog's belated feet like intermittent plush . . . We step like plush, we stand like snow . . . Sentences of plush." The word is on the verge of bursting with wrong meaning, and on account of the bursting, the stress with which the poet employed it, we are all prepared to accept it, and indeed do accept it, when suddenly we realize the wrongness, that "plush" was not what was meant at all, but was a substitute for it. The word has been distorted but not transformed on the page; which is to say it is not in substantial control. Yet it is impossible not to believe that to Emily Dickinson's ear it meant what it said and what could not otherwise be said.

The use of the word *purple* is another example of a word's getting out of control through the poet's failure to maintain an objective feeling of responsibility towards language. We have, in different poems, a "purple host" meaning "soldiers"; "purple territories," associated with salvation in terms of "Pizarro's shores"; "purple" meaning "dawn"; a "purple finger" probably meaning "shadow"; a purple raveling of cloud at sunset; ships of purple on seas of daffodil; the sun quenching in purple; a purple brook; purple traffic; a peacock's purple train; purple none can avoid—meaning death; no suitable purple to put on the hills; a purple tar wrecked in peace; the purple well of eternity; the purple or royal state of a corpse; the Purple of Ages; a sowing of purple seed which is inexplicable; the purple of the summer; the purple wheel of faith; day's petticoat of purple; etc., etc. Taken cumulatively, this is neither a distortion nor a transformation of sense; it is very near an obliteration of everything but a favorite sound, meaning something desirable, universal, distant, and immediate. I choose the word as an example not because it is particularly bad—it is not; it is relatively harmless—but because it is typical and happens to be easy to follow in unexpanded quotation. It is thoroughly representative of Emily Dickinson's habit of so employing certain favorite words that their discriminated meanings tend to melt into the single sentiment of self-expression. We can feel the sentiment but we have lost the meaning. The willing reader can see for himself the analogous process taking place—with slightly different final flavors—in word after word: for example in the words *dateless, pattern, compass, circumference, ecstasy, immortality, white, ruby, crescent, peninsula*, and *spice*. The meanings became the conventions of meanings, the asserted agreement that meaning is there. That is the end towards which Emily Dickinson worked, willy nilly, in her words. If you can accept the assertion for the sake of the knack—not the craft—with which it is made you will be able to read much more of her work than if you insist on actual work done.

But there were, to repeat and to conclude, three saving accidents at work in the body of Emily Dickinson's work sufficient to redeem in fact a good many poems to the state of their original intention. There was the accident of cultural crisis, the skeptical faith and desperately experimental mood, which both released and drove the poet's sensibility to express the crisis personally. There was the accident that the poet had so great an aptitude for language that it could seldom be completely lost in the conventional formulas towards which her meditating mind ran. And there was the third accident that the merest self-expression, or the merest statement of recognition or discrimination or vision, may sometimes also be, by the rule of unanimity and a common tongue, its best objective expression.

When two or more of the accidents occur simultaneously a poem or a fragment of a poem may be contrived. Sometimes the thing is done directly—with the compactness which Mr. Lewisohn compared to that of Goethe, but which had better be called the compactness of that which is unexpanded and depends for context entirely upon its free implications.

> Presentiment is that long shadow on the lawn
> Indicative that suns go down;
> The notice to the startled grass
> That darkness is about to pass.

If the reader compares this poem with Marvell's "To His Coy Mistress," he will see what can be gotten out of the same theme when fully expanded. The difference is of magnitude; the magnitude depends on craft; the Dickinson poem stops, Marvell's is completed. What happens when the poem does not stop may be shown in the following example of technical and moral confusion.

> I got so I could hear his name
> Without—
> Tremendous gain!
> That stop-sensation in my soul,
> And thunder in the room.

I got so I could walk across
That angle in the floor
Where he turned—so—and I turned how—
And all our sinew tore.

I got so I could stir the box
In which his letters grew—
Without that forcing in my breath
As staples driven through.

Could dimly recollect a Grace—
I think they called it "God,"
Renowned to ease extremity
When formula had failed—

And shape my hands petition's way—
Tho' ignorant of word
That Ordination utters—
My business with the cloud.

If any Power behind it be
Not subject to despair,
To care in some remoter way
For so minute affair
As misery—
Itself too vast for interrupting more,
Supremer than—
Superior to—

Nothing is more remarkable than the variety of inconsistency this effort displays. The first three stanzas are at one level of sensibility and of language and are as good verse as Emily Dickinson ever wrote. The next two stanzas are on a different and fatigued level of sensibility, are bad verse and flat language, and have only a serial connection with the first three. The last stanza, if it is a stanza, is on a still different level of sensibility and not on a recognizable level of language at all: the level of desperate inarticulateness to which no complete response can be articulated in return. One knows from the strength of the first three stanzas what might have been meant to come after and one feels like writing the poem oneself—the basest of all critical temptations. We feel that Emily Dickinson let herself go. The accidents that provided her ability here made a contrivance which was not a poem but a private mixture of first-rate verse, bad verse, and something that is not verse at all. Yet—and this is the point—this contrivance represents in epitome the whole of her work; and whatever judgment you bring upon the epitome you will, I think, be compelled to bring upon the whole.

No judgment is so persuasive as when it is disguised as a statement of facts. I think it is a fact that the failure and success of Emily Dickinson's poetry were uniformly accidental largely because of the private and eccentric nature of her relation to the business of poetry. She was neither a professional poet nor an amateur; she was a private poet who wrote indefatigably as some women cook or knit. Her gift for words and the cultural predicament of her time drove her to poetry instead of antimacassars. Neither her personal education nor the habit of her society as she knew it ever gave her the least inkling that poetry is a rational and objective art and most so when the theme is self-expression. She came, as Mr. Tate says, at the right time for one kind of poetry: the poetry of sophisticated, eccentric vision. That is what makes her good—in a few poems and many passages representatively great. But she never undertook the great profession of controlling the means of objective expression. That is why the bulk of her verse is not representative but mere fragmentary indicative notation. The pity of it is that the document her whole work makes shows nothing so much as that she had the themes, the insight, the observation, and the capacity for honesty, which had she only known how—or only known why—would have made the major instead of the minor fraction of her verse genuine poetry. But her dying society had no tradition by which to teach her the one lesson she did not know by instinct.

Edmund Wilson

THE AMBIGUITY OF HENRY JAMES

A DISCUSSION of Henry James's ambiguity may appropriately begin with "The Turn of the Screw." This story, which seems to have proved more fascinating to the general reading public than anything else of James's except "Daisy Miller," apparently conceals another horror behind the ostensible one. I do not know who first propounded the theory; but Miss Edna Kenton, whose insight into James is profound, has been one of its principal exponents, and the late Charles Demuth did a set of illustrations for the story based on this interpretation.

According to this theory, the young governess who tells the story is a neurotic case of sex repression, and the ghosts are not real ghosts at all but merely the hallucinations of the governess.

Let us go through the story from the beginning. It opens with an introduction. The man who is presenting the governess's manuscript tells us first who she is. She is the youngest daughter of a poor country parson, but "the most agreeable woman I've ever known in her position," who would have been "worthy of any whatever." She had come up to London and answered an advertisement and found a man who wanted a governess for his orphaned nephew and niece. "This prospective patron proved a gentleman, a bachelor in the prime of life, such a figure as had never risen, save in a dream or an old novel, before a fluttered, anxious girl out of a Hampshire vicarage." It is made clear that the young woman has become thoroughly infatuated with her employer. He is charming to her and lets her have the job on condition that she will never bother him about the children; and she goes down to the house in the country where they have been left with a housekeeper and some other servants.

The boy, she finds, has been sent home from school for reasons into which she does not inquire but which she colors, on no evidence at all, with a significance somehow sinister. She learns that the former governess left, and that she has since died, under circumstances which are not explained but which are made in the same way to seem ominous. She is alone with the illiterate housekeeper, a good and simple soul, and the children, who seem innocent and charming. As she wanders about the estate, she thinks often how delightful it would be to come suddenly round the corner and find that the master had arrived: there he would stand, smiling, approving and handsome.

She is never to meet her employer again, but what she does meet are the apparitions. One day when his face has been vividly in her mind, she comes out in sight of the house and sees the figure of a man on the tower, a figure which is not the master's. Not long afterwards, the figure appears again, toward the end of a rainy Sunday. She sees him at closer range and more clearly: he is wearing smart clothes but is not a gentleman. The housekeeper, meeting the governess immediately afterwards, behaves as if the governess herself were a ghost: "I wondered why she should be scared." The governess tells her about the apparition and learns that it answers the description of one of the master's valets who had stayed down there and used to wear his clothes. The valet had been a bad character, who used "to play with the boy . . . to spoil him"; he had been found dead, having slipped on the ice coming out of a public house: it is impossible to say that he wasn't murdered. The governess believes that he has come back to haunt the children.

Not long afterwards, she and the little girl are out on the shore of a lake, the little girl playing, the governess sewing. The latter becomes aware of a third person on the opposite side of the lake. But she looks first at the little girl, who is turning her back in that direction and who, she notes, has

258

"picked up a small flat piece of wood, which happened to have in it a little hole that had evidently suggested to her the idea of sticking in another fragment that might figure as a mast and make the thing a boat. This second morsel, as I watched her, she was very markedly and intently attempting to tighten in its place." This somehow "sustains" the governess so that she is able to raise her eyes: she sees a woman "in black, pale and dreadful." She concludes that it is the former governess. The housekeeper tells her that her predecessor, though a lady, had had an affair with the valet. The boy had used to go off with the valet and then lie about it afterwards. The governess concludes that the boy must have known about the valet and the woman—the boy and girl have been corrupted by them.

Observe that there is never any real reason for supposing that anybody but the governess sees the ghosts. She believes that the children see them, but there is never any proof that they do. The housekeeper insists that she does not see them; it is apparently the governess who frightens her. The children, too, become hysterical; but this is evidently the governess's doing, too. Observe, also, from the Freudian point of view, the significance of the governess's interest in the little girl's pieces of wood and of the fact that the male apparition first appears on a tower and the female apparition on a lake. There seems here to be only a single circumstance which does not fit into the hypothesis that the ghosts are hallucinations of the governess: the fact that the governess's description of the first ghost at a time when she has never heard of the valet should be identifiable as the valet by the housekeeper. And when we look back, we see that even this has been left open to a double interpretation. The governess has never heard of the valet, but it has been suggested to her in a conversation with the housekeeper that there has been some other male somewhere about who "liked everyone young and pretty," and the idea of this other person has been ambiguously confused with the master and with

259

the master's possible interest in her, the present governess. And has she not, in her subconscious imagination, taking her cue from this, identified herself with her predecessor and conjured up an image who wears the master's clothes but who (the Freudian "censor" coming into play) looks debased, "like an actor," she says (would he not have to stoop to love her!)? The apparition had "straight, good features" and his appearance is described in detail. When we look back, we find that the master's appearance has never been described at all: we have merely been told that he was "handsome." It is impossible for us to know how much the ghost resembles the master—certainly the governess would never tell us.

The apparitions now begin to appear at night, and the governess becomes convinced that the children get up to meet them, though they are able to give plausible explanations of their behavior. The housekeeper tells the governess that she ought to report these phenomena to the master, if she is so seriously worried about them. The governess, who has promised not to bother him, is afraid he would think her insane; and she imagines "his derision, his amusement, his contempt for the breakdown of my resignation at being left alone and for the fine machinery I had set in motion to attract his attention to my slighted charms." The housekeeper threatens to send for the master herself; the governess threatens to leave if she does. After this, for a considerable period, the visions no longer appear.

The children become uneasy: they begin to wonder when their uncle is coming down; they want to write to him—but the governess suppresses their letters. The boy finally asks her frankly when she is going to send him to school, intimates that if he had not been so fond of her he would have written to his uncle long ago about her failure to do so, threatens to write him at once.

This upsets her: she thinks for a moment of leaving, but decides that this would be deserting them. She is apparently now in love with the boy. The ghost of the other governess immediately appears again, looking "dishonored and tragic," full of "unutterable woe." The new governess feels now—the morbid half of her split personality is getting the upper hand of the other—that it is she who is intruding upon the spirit instead of the spirit who is intruding upon her: "You terrible miserable woman!" she cries. The apparition disappears. She tells the housekeeper, who looks at her oddly, that the soul of the former governess is damned and wants the little girl to share her damnation. She finally agrees to write to the master, but no sooner has she sat down to the paper than she gets up and goes to the boy's bedroom, where she finds him lying awake. When he demands to go back to school, she embraces him and begs him to tell her why he was sent away; appealing to him with what seems to her desperate tenderness but what must seem queer and disquieting to the child, she insists that all she wants is to save him. There is the sudden gust of wind—it is a windy night outside—the casement rattles, the boy shrieks. She has been kneeling beside the bed: when she gets up, she finds the candle extinguished. "It was I who blew it, dear!" says the boy. For her, it has been the evil spirit disputing her domination. It does not occur to her that the boy may really have blown the candle out in order not to have to tell her with the light on about his disgrace at school. (Here, however, occurs the only detail which is not readily susceptible of double explanation: the governess has *felt* a "gust of frozen air" and yet sees that the window is "tight." Are we to suppose she merely fancied that she felt it?)

The next day, the little girl disappears. They find her beside the lake. The young woman now for the first time speaks openly to one of the children about the ghosts. "Where, my pet, is Miss Jessel?" she demands—and immediately answers herself. "She's there, she's there!" she cries, pointing across the lake. The housekeeper looks with a "dazed blink" and asks where she sees anything; the little girl turns upon the governess "an expression of hard, still gravity, an expression absolutely new and unprecedented and that appeared to read and accuse and judge me." The governess feels her "situation horribly crumble." The little girl breaks down, becomes feverish, begs to be taken away from the governess; the housekeeper sides with the child and hints that the governess had better go. But the young woman forces her, instead, to take the little girl away; and she tries to make it impossible, before their departure, for the children to see each other.

She is now left alone with the boy. A strange and dreadful scene ensues. "We continued silent while the maid was with us—as silent, it whimsically occurred to me, as some young couple who, on their wedding-journey, at the inn, feel shy in the presence of the waiter." When the maid has gone, and she presses him to tell her why he was expelled from school, the boy seems suddenly afraid of her. He finally confesses that he "said things"—to "a few," to "those he liked." It all sounds very harmless: there comes to her out of her "very pity the appalling alarm of his being perhaps innocent. It was for the instant confounding and bottomless, for if he *were* innocent, what then on earth was *I*?" The valet appears at the window—it is "the white face of damnation." (But is the governess condemning the spirits to damnation or is she succumbing to damnation herself?) She is aware that the boy does not see it. "No more, no more, no more!" she shrieks to the apparition. "Is she *here*?" demands the boy in panic. (He has, in spite of the governess's efforts, succeeded in seeing his sister and has heard from her of the incident at the lake.) No, she says, it is not the woman; "But it's at the window—straight before us. It's *there*!" . . . "It's *he*?" then. Whom does he mean by "he"? " 'Peter Quint—you devil!' His face gave again, round the room, its convulsed supplication. 'Where?' " "What does he matter now, my own?" she cries. "What will he *ever* matter? *I* have you, but he has lost you forever!" Then she shows him that the figure

262

has vanished: "There, *there!*" she says, pointing toward the window. He looks and gives a cry; she feels that he is dead in her arms. From her point of view, the disappearance of the spirit has proved too terrible a shock for him and "his little heart, dispossessed, has stopped"; but if we study the dialogue from the other point of view, we see that he must have taken her "There, *there!*" as an answer to his own "Where?" Instead of persuading him that there is nothing to be frightened of, she has, on the contrary, finally convinced him either that he has actually seen or that he is on the point of seeing something. He gives "the cry of a creature hurled over an abyss." She has literally frightened him to death.

When one has once been given this clue to "The Turn of the Screw," one wonders how one could ever have missed it. There is a very good reason, however, in the fact that nowhere does James unequivocally give the thing away: almost everything from beginning to end can be read equally in either of two senses. In the preface to the collected edition, however, as Miss Kenton has pointed out, James does seem to want to put himself on record. He asserts here that "The Turn of the Screw" is "a fairy-tale pure and simple"— but adds that the apparitions are of the order of those involved in witchcraft cases rather than of those in cases of psychic research. And he goes on to tell of his reply to one of his readers, who had complained that he had not characterized the governess sufficiently. At this criticism, he says, "One's artistic, one's ironic heart shook for the instant almost to breaking"; and he answered: "It was *'déjà très-joli'* . . . please believe, the general proposition our young woman's keeping crystalline her record of so many intense anomalies and obscurities—*by which I don't mean of course her explanation of them, a different matter.* . . . She has 'authority,' which is a good deal to have given her" . . . The italics above are mine: these words seem impossible to explain except on the hypothesis of hallucination. And note, too, in the collected edition that James has not included "The Turn of the

263

Screw" in the volume with his other ghost stories but in a volume of stories of another kind, between "The Aspern Papers" and "The Liar"—this last the story of a pathological liar, whose wife protects his lies against the world, acting with very much the same sort of deceptive "authority" as the governess in "The Turn of the Screw."

When we look back in the light of these hints, we become convinced that the whole story has been primarily intended as a characterization of the governess: her visions and the way she behaves about them, as soon as we look at them from the obverse side, present a solid and unmistakable picture of the poor country parson's daughter, with her English middle-class class-consciousness, her inability to admit to herself her sexual impulses and the relentless English "authority" which enables her to put over on inferiors even purposes which are totally deluded and not at all to the other people's best interests. Add to this the peculiar psychology of governesses, who, by reason of their isolated position between the family and the servants, are likely to become ingrown and morbid. The writer knows of an actual case of a governess who used to frighten the servants by opening doors and smashing mirrors and who tortured the parents by mythical stories of kidnappers. The poltergeist, once a figure of demonology, is now a recognized neurotic type.

When we examine "The Turn of the Screw" in this light, we understand for the first time its significance in connection with Henry James's other fiction—(the story, on any other hypothesis, would be, so far as I remember, the only thing James ever wrote which did not have some more or less serious point). We see now that it is simply a variation on one of James's familiar themes: the frustrated Anglo-Saxon spinster; and we remember that he has presented other cases of women who deceive themselves and others about the sources and character of their emotions. The most obvious example is that remarkable and too little read novel, "The Bostonians." The subject of "The Bostonians" is the struggle for the attractive daughter of a poor evangelist between a young man from the South who wants to marry her and a well-to-do Boston lady with a Lesbian passion for her. The strong-minded and strong-willed spinster is herself apparently quite in the dark as to the real reason for her interest in the girl: she is convinced that her desire to dominate her, to make her live with her, to teach her to make speeches on women's rights, to prevent the eligible young Southerner from marrying her, is all ardor for the Feminist cause. But James does not leave the reader in doubt—and he presents Olive Chancellor in a setting of other self-deluded New England idealists.

There is a theme of the same kind in the short story called "The Marriages," which amused Robert Louis Stevenson so hugely. But here the treatment is comic. A young English girl, described by one of the characters as of the unmarriageable type, much attached to an attractive father and obsessed by the memory of a dead mother, breaks up her father's projected second marriage. She goes to his fiancée and tells her that her father is an impossible character who had made her late mother miserable. When her brother calls her a raving maniac, she remains serene in the conviction that, by ruining the happiness of her father, she has been loyal to her duty to her mother.

James's world is full of these women. They are not always emotionally perverted. Sometimes they are emotionally apathetic—like the amusing Francie Dosson of "The Reverberator," who, though men are always falling madly in love with her, seems never really to understand what courtship and marriage mean and is apparently quite content to go on all her life eating *marrons glacés* with her father and sister in their suite in a Paris hotel. Sometimes they are emotionally starved—like the pathetic Milly Theale of "The Wings of the Dove," who wastes away in Venice and whose doctor recommends a lover.

II

James's men are not precisely neurotic; but they are the masculine counterparts of his women. They have a way of missing out on emotional experience, either through timidity or caution or through heroic renunciation.

The extreme and fantastic example is the hero of "The Beast in the Jungle," who is finally crushed by the realization that his fate is to be the man in the whole world to whom nothing at all is to happen. Some of these characters are presented ironically: Mr. Wentworth of "The Europeans," so smug and secure in his neat little house, deciding not to marry the baroness who has proved such an upsetting element in the community, is a perfect comic portrait of a certain kind of careful Bostonian. Others are made sympathetic: the starved and weary Lambert Strether of "The Ambassadors," who comes to Paris too late in life.

Sometimes, however, the effect is ambiguous. Though the element of irony in Henry James is often underestimated by his readers, there are stories which leave us in doubt as to whether or not the author knew how his heroes would strike his readers. Is the fishy Bernard Longueville of the early novel "Confidence" really intended for a sensitive and interesting young man or is he a prig in the manner of Jane Austen? And some of James's later heroes are just as unsympathetic. The very late short story "Flickerbridge," in which a young American painter decides not to marry a young newspaper woman (the men are always deciding *not* to marry the women in Henry James) because he is afraid she will spoil by publicizing it a delightful old English house, the property of her own family, in which he has greatly enjoyed living without her, affects us in the same unpleasant way.

But "Flickerbridge" seems merely a miscue: evidently James intends it to be taken seriously. How is "The Sacred Fount" to be taken? This short novel, surely one of the curiosities of literature, which inspired the earliest parody—by Owen Seaman—I ever remember to have seen of James and which apparently marked his passing over some borderline into a region where he was to become for the public unassimilably exasperating and ridiculous, was written not long after "The Turn of the Screw" and is a sort of companionpiece to it. There is the same setting of an English country house, the same passages of a sad and strange beauty, the same furtive and disturbing goings-on in an atmosphere of clarity and brightness, the same dubious central figure, the same almost inscrutable ambiguity. As in the case of "The Turn of the Screw," the fundamental question presents itself and never seems to get definitely answered: What is the reader to think of the protagonist?—who is here a man instead of a woman.

It would be tedious to analyze "The Sacred Fount" as I have done with "The Turn of the Screw"—and it would be a somewhat more difficult undertaking. "The Sacred Fount" is mystifying, even maddening. But I believe that if anyone really got to the bottom of it, he would throw a good deal of light on Henry James. Rebecca West has given a burlesque account of this novel as the story of how "a week-end visitor spends more intellectual force than Kant can have used on 'The Critique of Pure Reason' in an unsuccessful attempt to discover whether there exists between certain of his fellow-guests a relationship not more interesting among these vacuous people than it is among sparrows." A gentleman, who tells the story, goes to a week-end party in the country; there he observes that certain of his friends appear to have taken a new lease on life whereas others seem to have been depleted. He evolves a theory about them: the theory is that the married couples have been forming new combinations and that the younger individuals have been feeding the older individuals from the sacred fount of their youth at the price of getting used up themselves.

This theory seems obviously academic: older people feed

younger people with their vitality quite as often as younger people feed older ones—and does James really mean us to accept it? Are not the speculations of the narrator intended to characterize the narrator as the apparitions characterize the governess? As this detached and rather eerie individual proceeds to spy on and cross-examine his friends in order to find out whether the facts fit his theory, we decide, as we do in "The Turn of the Screw," that there are two separate things to be kept straight: a false hypothesis which the narrator is putting forward and a reality which we are supposed to guess from what he tells us about what actually happens. We remember the narrator of "The Aspern Papers," another inquisitive and annoying fellow, who is finally foiled and put to rout by the old lady whose private papers he is trying to get hold of. In the case of "The Aspern Papers," there is no uncertainty about James's attitude toward the narrator: James lets us know that the papers were none of the journalist's business and that the rebuff served him right. And the amateur detective of "The Sacred Fount" is foiled and rebuffed in precisely the same manner by one of his recalcitrant victims. "My poor dear, you *are* crazy, and I bid you goodnight!" she says to him at the end of the story. "Such a last word," the narrator remarks, "the word that put me altogether nowhere—was too inacceptable not to prescribe afresh that prompt test of escape to other air for which I had earlier in the evening seen so much reason. I *should* certainly never again, on the spot, quite hang together, even though it wasn't really that I hadn't three times her method. What I too fatally lacked was her tone." But why *did* he lack her tone?—why *would* he never again hang together? What are we supposed to conclude about his whole exploit?

Mr. Wilson Follett, the only writer on James who has given "The Sacred Fount" special attention (in "Henry James's Portrait of Henry James," *New York Times Book Review*, August 23, 1936), believes that the book is a parable —even a conscious parody—of James's own role as an artist.

The narrator may or may not have been right as to the actual facts of the case. The point is that, in elaborating his theory, he has constructed a work of art, and that it is a mistake to make the validity of works of art depend on a correspondence with actuality. Art has only its own kind of validity, and a collision with actuality would destroy it and put an end to the activities of the artist.

Certainly James has put himself into "The Sacred Fount," and certainly he has intended some sort of fable about the imaginative mind and the material with which it works. But it seems to me that Mr. Follett's theory assumes on James's part a conception of artistic truth which would hardly be worthy of him. After all, the novelist must know what people are actually up to, however much he may rearrange actuality; and it is not clear in "The Sacred Fount" whether the narrator really knew what he was talking about. If "The Sacred Fount" is a parody, what is the point of the parody? Why should James have represented the artist as defeated by the breaking-in of life?

The truth is, I believe, that Henry James was not clear about the book in his own mind. Already, with "The Turn of the Screw," he has carried his ambiguous procedure to a point where it seems almost as if he did not want the reader to get through to the hidden meaning. See his curious replies in his letters to correspondents who write him about the story: to what seem to have been leading questions, he seems to have given evasive answers, dismissing the tale as a mere "potboiler," a mere "*jeu d'esprit*." Olive Chancellor in "The Bostonians," though tragic perhaps, is horrid, and she is vanquished by Basil Ranson. But he was willing to leave his readers in doubt as to whether the governess was horrid or nice. And now in "The Sacred Fount," we do not know whether the week-end guest, though he was unquestionably obnoxious to the other guests, is intended to be taken as one of the élite, a fastidious highly civilized sensibility, or merely as a little bit cracked and a bore. The man who wanted to get the Aspern papers was fanatically inquisitive and a nuisance; but many of James's inquisitive observers who never take part in the action are presented as most superior people. James confessed to being this sort of person himself. Ambiguity was certainly growing on James. It was to pass all bounds in those scenes in his later novels (of which the talks in "The Turn of the Screw" between the housekeeper and the governess are only comparatively mild examples) in which the characters are able to carry on long conversations with each consistently mistaking the other's meaning and neither ever yielding to the impulse to say any of the obvious things which would clear the situation up.

What if the hidden theme of "The Sacred Fount" is simply sex again? What if the real sacred fount, from which the people observed by the narrator have been drawing their new vitality, is love instead of youth? They have something which he has not had, know something which he does not know; and, lacking the clue of love, he can only pedantically misunderstand them. And they, since they have the forces of life on their side, are able to frighten him away.

This theory may be dubious, also; but there is certainly involved in "The Sacred Fount" the conception of a man shut out from love and doomed to barren speculation on human relations, who will be shocked by direct contact with reality.

Hitherto, it has usually been quite plain what James wanted us to think of his characters; but now there appears in his work a morbid element which is not always handled objectively but has invaded the storyteller himself. He seems to be dramatizing the frustrations of his own life without quite being willing to confess it, without always fully admitting it to himself.

But before we pursue this line of inquiry, let us look at him in a different connection.

Who *are* these characters of Henry James's about whom we come to be less and less certain as to precisely what he means us to think?

The type is the cultivated American bourgeois, like Henry James himself, who lives on an income derived from some form (usually left extremely vague) of American business activity but who has taken no part in the achievements which made the income possible. These men turn their backs on business; they attempt to enrich their experience through the society and art of Europe. But they bring to it the bourgeois qualities of timidity, prudence, primness, the habits of mind of a narrow morality which, even when they wish to be open-minded, cause them to be easily shocked. They wince alike at the brutalities of the aristocracy and at the vulgarities of the working-class; they shrink most of all from the "commonness" of the less cultivated bourgeoisie, who, having acquired their incomes more recently, are not so far advanced in self-improvement. The women have the corresponding qualities: they are innocent, conventional and rather cold—sometimes they suffer from Freudian complexes or a kind of arrested development, sometimes they are neglected or cruelly cheated by the men to whom they have given their hearts. And even when James's heroes and heroines are English, they assimilate themselves to these types.

It is illuminating in this connection to compare James's attitude to Flaubert's. The hero of "L'Education Sentimentale" is a perfect Henry James character: he is sensitive, cautious, afraid of life, he lives on a little income and considers himself superior to the common run. But Flaubert's attitude toward Frédéric Moreau is devastatingly ironic. Frédéric has his aspects of pathos, his occasional flashes of spirit: but Flaubert is quite emphatic in his final judgment of Frédéric. He considers Frédéric a worm.

Now James has his own kind of irony, but it is not Flaubert's kind. Frédéric Moreau is really the hero of most of James's novels, and you can see very plainly how James's estimate of him usually differs from Flaubert's if you compare certain kinds of scenes which tend to recur in Henry James with scenes in "L'Education Sentimentale" from which James has evidently imitated them: those situations of a sensitive young man immersed in some kind of gathering or having a succession of meetings with various characters without being able in his innocence precisely to figure out what they are up to. The reader is able to guess that they are more worldly and unscrupulous persons than the hero and that they are talking over his head, acting behind his back. You have this pattern, as I say, both in Flaubert and in James; but the difference is that, whereas in James the young man is made wondering and wistful and is likely to turn out a pitiful victim, in Flaubert he is made to look like a fool and is as ready to double-cross these other people who seem to him so inferior to himself as they are to double-cross him.

In this difference between Flaubert's attitude toward Frédéric and James's attitude toward, say Hyacinth Robinson of "The Princess Casamassima" is to be discovered, I believe, the real reason for James's peculiar resentment of Flaubert. Flaubert interested James deeply: they had in common that they were both trying to give dignity to the novel of modern life by bringing it to intense esthetic form. And James returned to Flaubert again and again, wrote three essays on him at different periods. But though he obviously cannot help admiring Flaubert, he usually manages in the long run to belittle him—and he is especially invidious on the subject of "L'Education Sentimentale." His great complaint is that Flaubert's characters are so ignoble that they do not deserve to have so much art expended on them and that there must have been something basically wrong with Flaubert ever to have supposed that they did. James never seems to understand that Flaubert intends all his characters to be "middling" and that the greatness of his work

272

arises from the fact that it constitutes a criticism of something bigger than they are. James praises the portrait of Mme. Arnoux: thank God at least, he exclaims, that here Flaubert was able to muster the good taste to deal delicately with a pure and fine-grained woman! He seems completely unaware that Mme. Arnoux is treated as ironically as any of the other characters—that the virtuous bourgeois wife with her inhibitions and superstitions is pathetic only as a part of the bigger thing of which Flaubert is showing the failure. Henry James mistakes Mme. Arnoux for a refined portrait of an American lady and he is worried because Frédéric isn't a quietly vibrating young American. Yet at the same time he must have his uneasy suspicion that young Americans of that kind are being made fun of. I believe that James's antagonism to Flaubert may be primarily due to the fact that Flaubert's criticism of the pusillanimity of the bourgeois has really touched James himself. James's later heroes are always regretting having lived and loved too meagerly; and James distills from these sensitive nonparticipants all the sad self-effacing nobility, all the fine and thin beauty, he can get out of them. Whereas Flaubert extracts something quite different and bitter: when Frédéric recalls in middle age his first clumsy and frightened visit to a brothel as the best that life has had to offer him, it is a damnation of a whole society.

But there was another kind of modern society which Flaubert did not know and which Henry James did know. Henry James was that new anomalous thing, an American. He is an American who has spent much of his childhood and youth in Europe, and he is imbued to a considerable extent with the European point of view. The monuments of feudal and ancient Europe, the duchesses and princesses and princes who seem to carry on the feudal tradition, are still capable of making modern life look to him dull, undistinguished and tame. But the past for him does not completely dwarf the present, as the vigil of Saint Anthony and the impacts of pagan armies dwarf Flaubert's Frédéric Moreau. The American in Henry James insistently asserts himself against Europe. After all, Frédéric Moreau and Madame Arnoux are the best people of Albany and Boston!—but they are not characters in Flaubert there. There their scruples and their renunciations possess a real value—for Frédéric Moreau at home possesses a real integrity; and when they visit Europe, they judge the whole thing in a new way. Henry James speaks somewhere of his indignation at an Englishwoman's saying to him in connection with something: "That is true of the aristocracy, but in one's own class it is quite different." As an American, it had never occurred to him that he could be described as a middle-class person. When Edith Wharton accused him in his later years of no longer appreciating Flaubert and demanded of him why Emma Bovary was not as good a subject for a novel as Anna Karenina, he replied: "Ah, but one paints the fierce passions of a luxurious aristocracy; the other deals with the petty miseries of a little bourgeoise in a provincial town!" But if Emma Bovary is small potatoes, what about Daisy Miller? Why, Daisy Miller is an American girl! Emma Bovary has her debts and adulteries, but she is otherwise a conventional person, she remains in her place in the social scheme, even when she dreams of rising out of it: when she goes to visit the château, the sugar seems to her whiter and finer than elsewhere. Whereas Daisy Miller represents something which has walked quite out of the frame of Europe. When it comes back to Europe again, it disregards the social system. Europe is too much for Daisy Miller: she catches cold in the Coliseum, where according to European conventions she oughtn't to have been at that hour. But the great popularity of her story was certainly due to her creator's having somehow conveyed the impression that her spirit went marching on.

In Henry James's mind, there disputed all his life the European and the American points of view; and their debate, I believe, is closely connected with his inability sometimes to be clear as to what he thinks of a certain sort of person. It is quite mistaken to talk as if James had uprooted himself from America in order to live in England. He had traveled so much from his earliest years that he had never had any real roots anywhere. His father had himself been a wandering intellectual, oscillating back and forth between the United States and Europe. And even in America, the Jameses oscillated back and forth between Boston and New York. They were not New Englanders but New Yorkers, and they had none of the tight local ties of New Enganders—they always came to Boston from a larger outside world and their attitude toward it was critical and objective.

To James's critical attitude toward Boston was probably partly due the failure in America of "The Bostonians"; and to this failure is possibly due his discouragement with his original ambition of becoming the American Balzac. At any rate, it marks the moment of his taking up his residence in England and of his turning from the Americans to the English.

He was in London, and he found he liked living in London better than living in Boston or New York. His parents in the States had just died, and his sister came over to join him.

IV

And this brings us to what seems to have been the principal crisis in Henry James's life and work. We know so little about his personal life that it is impossible to give any account of it save as it reflects itself in his writings.

Up to the period of his playwriting his fiction has been pretty plain sailing. He has aimed to be a social historian, and, in a rather limited field, he has succeeded. His three long novels of the later eighties—"The Bostonians," "The Princess Casamassima," and "The Tragic Muse"—are, indeed, as social history, his most ambitious undertakings and, up to a point, his most brilliant. The first hundred pages of "The Bostonians," with the arrival of the Mississippian in

Boston and the crowded picture of the meeting of reformers is, in its way, one of the most masterly things that Henry James ever did. "The Princess Casamassima," with its prison and its revolutionary exiles in London, deals with issues and social contrasts of a kind that James had never before attempted. The familiar criticism of Henry James—the criticism made by H. G. Wells—does not, in fact, hold true of these books. Here his people do have larger interests and functions aside from their personal relations: they have professions, missions, practical aims; and they also engage in more drastic action than in his novels of any other period. Basil Ransom pursues Verena Tarrant and rescues her from the terrible Olive Chancellor; Hyacinth Robinson pledges himself to carry out a political assassination, then kills himself instead; Miriam Rooth makes her career as a great actress. Here there is a genuine will to do rather than a mere disposition to observe. Up to a point these three books are quite triumphant.

But there *is* a point—usually about half way through—at which every one of these novels begins strangely to run into the sands; the excitement seems to lapse at the same time that the color fades from the picture; and the ends are never up to the beginnings. This is most obvious, and even startling, in "The Tragic Muse," the first volume of which, when we read it, makes us think that it must be James's best novel, so solid and alive does it seem. There are in it a number of things which he has never given us before: a wonderful portrait of a retired parliamentarian with an implied criticism of British Liberal politics, a real scene—what one might have thought he could never do—between a man and a woman (Nick Dormer and Julia Dallow) instead of the polite conversations to which he has accustomed us; and Miriam Rooth, the Muse herself, comes nearer to carrying Henry James out of the enclosure of puritan scruples and prim prejudices on to the larger stage of human creative effort than any other character he has drawn. Here at last we seem to find our-

276

selves with real people, who have the same appetites and ambitions as other people—in comparison, the characters of his earlier works are real only in a certain convention. Then suddenly the story stops short: after the arrival of Miriam in London, "The Tragic Muse" is an almost total blank. Of the two young men who have been preoccupied with Miriam, one renounces her because she will not leave the stage and the other apparently doesn't fall in love with her. Miriam, to be sure, makes a great success as an actress, but we are never taken into her life, we know nothing at first hand about her emotions. And with nothing but these negative decisions in sight, the author himself seems to lose interest.

The first half of "The Tragic Muse" is the high point of the first part of James's career, after which something snaps. He announces that he will write no more long novels, but only fiction of shorter length. He may have been aware that a long novel demands a mounting-up to a point of intensity and revelation of a kind which he was unable to give it, whereas a short story need not go so deep. At any rate, he set himself to write plays, and for five years he produced little else.

Why did he do this? He complained at this time that he had difficulty in selling his fiction, and he confessed that his plays were written in the hope of a popular success, that they were intended merely to entertain and were not to be taken too seriously. Yet this is surely an inadequate explanation of the phenomenon of a novelist of the first order giving up the art in which he has perfected himself to write plays which do not even aim to be serious.

That there was something incomplete and unexplained about James's emotional life seems to appear unmistakably from his novels. I believe it may be said that up to this point there are no consummated love affairs in his fiction—that is, none among the principal actors and during the action of the story; and this fact must certainly have contributed to his increasing loss of hold on his readers. It is not merely that he gave in "The Bostonians" an unpleasant picture of Boston, and in "The Tragic Muse" an equally unpleasant picture of the English; it is not merely that "The Princess Casamassima" treated a social-revolutionary subject from a point of view which gave neither side best. It was not merely that he was thus at this period rather lost between America and England. It was also that you cannot long hold an audience with stories about men wooing women in which the parties either never get together or are never seen as really functioning as lovers. And you will particularly discourage your readers with a story about two men and a girl in which neither man ever gets her and in which she marries a third person, totally uninteresting. There is, as I have said, in "The Tragic Muse," a much more convincing man-and-woman relationship. Julia Dallow is really female and she really behaves like a woman with Nick Dormer; but here her political ambitions get between Nick and her, so that this, too, never comes to anything: here the man, again, must renounce. (In James's later novels, these healthily female women are always invested with a value frankly sinister and usually animated by evil designs: Kate Croy and Charlotte Stant.) Years later, Henry James explained in his preface to "The Tragic Muse" that he had been prevented from allowing Miriam Rooth to have a genuine love affair with anybody by the prudery of the American magazines; and certainly the skittishness of a reading public which was scandalized by "Jude the Obscure" is not to be underestimated. But, after all, Hardy and Meredith did write about Jude and Lord Ormont and his Aminta and let the public howl; and it would certainly have enhanced rather than diminished Henry James's reputation— as to which his ambitions seem by no means to have been modest—if he had done the same thing himself. Problems of passion in conflict with convention and law were coming to be subjects of burning interest; but James could not deal with that kind of passion and was much too honest to try to fake it.

One feels about the episode of his playwriting that it was an effort to put himself over, an effort to make himself felt, as he had never succeeded in doing before. His brother William James wrote home in the summer of 1889, at the beginning of Henry's playwriting period, that Henry, beneath the "rich sea-weeds and rigid barnacles and things" of "strange heavy alien manners and customs" with which he had covered himself like a "marine crustacean," remained the "same dear old, good, innocent and at bottom very powerless-feeling Harry." He had injured his back in an accident in his boyhood, and it was still necessary for him to lie down for regular rests. And now it is as if he were putting his back into playwriting as he had never been able to put it into a passion. His heroine Miriam Rooth in the novel has turned away from the Philistine English world, which rejects her, and taken into the theater the will of the artist, which will enable her to conquer that world; and her creator is now to imitate her.

But his plays were not produced or did not go. At the first night of "Guy Domville," he ran foul of a hissing and booing British audience (the play contained another of his confounded renunciations); and these five years put him under a severe strain. When he recovers from his disappointment, he is seen to have passed through a kind of crisis.

Now he enters upon a new phase, of which the most obvious feature is a subsidence back into himself. And now sex *does* appear in his work—and even becomes something like an obsession—in a queer and left-handed way. We have "The Turn of the Screw" and "The Sacred Fount"—and "What Maisie Knew" and "In the Cage." There are plenty of love affairs now and plenty of irregular relations, but there are always barriers between them and us; they are the chief object of interest, but they are seen from a distance.

For the Jamesian central observer, through whose intelligence the story is usually relayed to us, has undergone a strange diminution. This observer is no longer a complete and interesting person more or less actively involved in the events, but a small child, a telegraph operator who lives vicariously through the senders of telegrams, a week-end guest who seems not to exist in any other capacity except that of a week-end guest and who lives vicariously through his fellow visitors. The people who surround this observer tend to take on the diabolic value of the specters of "The Turn of the Screw," and this diabolic value is almost invariably connected with their concealed and only guessed-at sexual relations. The innocent Nanda Brookenham of "The Awkward Age," a work of the same period and group, has a whole host of creepy creatures around her. James is ceasing to sustain the objectivity which has kept the outlines of his stories pretty definite up through his middle novels: he has relapsed into a dreamy inner world, where values are often uncertain and where it is not even possible for him any longer to judge the effect of his stories on his audience—that audience which, as a matter of fact, has almost ceased to exist. One is dismayed in reading his comments on "The Awkward Age," which he seems to have considered highly successful, to realize that he is unaware of the elements in the book which, in spite of the technical virtuosity displayed in it, make it unpleasant and irritating. The central figure of "The Sacred Fount" may perhaps have been presented ironically; but James could never have known how we should feel about the gibbering disemboweled crew who hover about one another with sordid shadowy designs in "The Awkward Age."

This is accompanied by a kind of expansion of the gas of the psychological atmosphere—an atmosphere which has now a special odor. With "What Maisie Knew," as F. M. Ford says, the style first becomes a little gamey; and then, dropping off its old formality and what sometimes amounted

280

to a mechanical hardness, it becomes progressively, in the conventional sense, more poetic.

With all this, his experience of playwriting has done him no good in his fiction. He had set himself to emulate the most stultifying models of the mechanically well-made play. He turned certain of these pieces into novels—"Covering End" and "The Other House"—and dreadful novels they made; and in "The Awkward Age" and other works of this period, an artificial dramatic technique persists. It is one of the elements that make some of them so exasperating. They combine a lifeless trickery of logic with the ambiguous subjectivity of a nightmare.

In this period certainly originates that tendency on James's part to exploit the mysteries of technique for the purpose of diverting attention from his shortcomings which has imposed on some of his critics and which must of course have imposed on himself. One can see from his comments of various periods how a method like that of Tolstoy in "War and Peace" became more and more distasteful to him. Tolstoy, he insisted, was all over the shop, entering the minds of far too many of his characters and failing to exercise the principle of selection. He speaks in the preface to "The Tragic Muse" of his own difficulty in handling a complex subject— though here it is a question of going into the minds of only two of the characters. But, obviously, the question of whether the novelist enters into a variety of points of view has nothing to do with his technical proficiency or even with his effect of concentration. One trouble with "The Tragic Muse" is that James does not show us the inside of Miriam Rooth; and if he fails to do so, it is because, here as elsewhere, he does not know, as Tolstoy did, what the insides of such people are like. So, in "The Wings of the Dove," the "me-sengering," as the drama courses say, of Kate Croy's final scene with Merton Densher is evidently due to James's increasing incapacity for dealing directly with scenes of emotion rather than to the esoteric motives he alleges. And so his curious constant complaint that he is unable to do certain things because there is no longer space within the prescribed limits of the story is certainly only another hollow excuse: he never seems to be aware of the amount of space he is wasting through the roundabout locutions or quite gratuitous verbiage with which he habitually pads out his sentences—and which is itself a form of staving off his main problems. His censure of Tolstoy for his failure to select is a defensive reflex action on Henry James's part for his own failure to fill in his picture.

V

What happens after this, however, is interesting. In "The Ambassadors," "The Wings of the Dove" and "The Golden Bowl," the psychological atmosphere thickens, fills up the stories with the Jamesian gas instead of with detail and background. The characters (though usually apprehended as convincing personal entities) are seen dimly through a phantasmagoria of dream-like metaphors and similes, which seem sometimes, as Rebecca West has said, more vivid and solid than the settings.

But a positive element reappears. The novels of "The Awkward Age" period were written not merely from James's international limbo between the United States and Europe but under the oppression of defeat and self-doubt. But in these queer and neurotic stories—(some of them, of course—"The Turn of the Screw" and "What Maisie Knew" —among James's masterpieces)—moral values begin to assert themselves again. They sprout first in the infantile form of Maisie and Nanda Brookenham, whose innocence is the test of the other characters. Then in the longer novels that follow, in figures of a more mature innocence, they completely take the field; and these figures are now invariably Americans. We are back to the pattern of his earlier novels, where the typical conflict was between glamorous people who were also worldly and likely to be wicked, and people of superior scruples who were likely to be more or less homely, and where the former usually represented Europe and the latter the United States. In these novels, it was sometimes the Americans—as in "The Portrait of a Lady"—who were left with the moral advantage; sometimes—as in "The Europeans"—the Europeans. But in these late novels it is always the Americans who have the better of it from the moral point of view—scoring heavily off a fascinating Italian prince, an equally fascinating French lady and a formidable group of middle-class English people. Yes: there *was* a beauty and there was also a power in the goodness of these naïve and open people, which had not existed for Flaubert and his group. It *is* something different and new which does not fit into the formulas of Europe. What if Lambert Strether *had* missed in Woollett, Mass., many things that he would have enjoyed in Paris: he had brought to Paris something it did not have. And the burden of the book on "William Wetmore Story and His Friends," which was also written during this time—rather different from that of his early book on Hawthorne—is that American artists might much better stay at home.

And now—in 1904—Henry James revisits America, writes "The American Scene," returns to it in a novel, "The Ivory Tower," left unfinished at his death.

In his other unfinished novel, the fantasia called "The Sense of the Past," he makes a young contemporary American go back into eighteenth-century England. Here the Jamesian ambiguity serves an admirable artistic purpose. Is it the English of the past who are the ghosts or is it the American himself who is a dream?—will the moment come when *they* will vanish or will he himself cease to exist? And, as before, there is a question of James's own asking at the bottom of the ambiguity: Which is real—America or Europe? It was, however, in the novel, the American who was to remain real. (It is curious to compare "The Sense of the Past" with "A Connecticut Yankee in King Arthur's Court," with which it really has a good deal in common.)

Yes: in spite of the popular assumption founded on his expatriation, it is America which gets the better of it in Henry James. His warmest tributes to American genius come out of these later years. Though he could not, in "Notes of a Son and Brother," resist the impulse to remove references to Lincoln as "old Abe" from William James's early letters of the war-time, it contains pages on Lincoln's death of a touching appreciation and pride. "It was vain to say," he writes of Andrew Johnson, of whom he says that the American people felt him unworthy to represent them, "that we had deliberately invoked the 'common' in authority and must drink the wine we had drawn. No countenance, no salience of aspect nor composed symbol, could superficially have referred itself less than Lincoln's mold-smashing mask to any mere matter-of-course type of propriety; but his admirable unrelated head had itself revealed a type—as if by the very fact that what made in it for roughness of kind looked out only less than what made in it for splendid final stamp; in other words for commanding Style." And of the day when the news reached Boston: "I was fairly to go in shame of its being my birthday. These would have been the hours of the streets if none others had been—when the huge general gasp filled them like a great earth-shudder and people's eyes met people's eyes without the vulgarity of speech. Even this was, all so strangely, part of the lift and the swell, as tragedy has but to be of a pure enough strain and a high enough connection to sow with its dark hand the seed of greater life. The collective sense of what had occurred was of a sadness too noble not somehow to inspire, and it was truly in the air that, whatever we had as a nation produced or failed to produce, we could at least gather round this perfection of classic woe." In "The American Scene," he writes of Concord: "We may smile a little as we 'drag in' Weimar, but I confess myself, for my part, much more satisfied than not by our happy equivalent, 'in American money,' for Goethe and Schiller. The money is a potful in the second case as in the first, and if Goethe, in the one, represents the gold and Schiller the silver, I find (and quite putting aside any bimetallic prejudice) the same good relation in the other between Emerson and Thoreau. I open Emerson for the same benefit for which I open Goethe, the sense of moving in large intellectual space, and that of the gush, here and there, out of the rock, of the crystalline cupful, in wisdom and poetry, in *Wahrheit* and *Dichtung;* and whatever I open Thoreau for (I needn't take space here for the good reasons) I open him oftener than I open Schiller." Edith Wharton says that he used to read Walt Whitman aloud "in a mood of subdued ecstasy" and with tremendous effect on his hearers.

Henry James's career had been affected by the shift in the national point of view which occurred after the Civil War. It is being shown by Mr. Van Wyck Brooks in his cultural history of New England how the Bostonian of the first part of the century was inspired—as, in our time, the Russians have been—to present the world with a new humanity, set free from the caste-barriers and poverties of Europe, which should return to the mother-country only to plunder her for elements of culture which might contribute to the movement at home; and how, with the triumph of the industrial system, the persons who were occupied with art and thought became gradually ashamed of the United States and tended to take refuge in Europe. Henry James belonged to this second phase, but he had a good deal of the idealism of the first one. It appears in the name of the hero of "The American": Newman, and in his phrase about Lincoln's "mold-smashing mask"; and, after a period of partial abeyance, when he had been writing largely about Europeans, it cropped up again, as I have shown, and took the field.

But Henry James is a reporter, not a prophet. With less

political philosophy even than Flaubert, he can only chron-
icle the world as it passes, and in his picture the elements
are mixed. In the Americans of Henry James's later novels—
the Milly Theales, the Lambert Strethers, the Maggie Ver-
vers—he shows us all that was magnanimous, reviving and
human in the Americans at the beginning of the new century along with all that was frustrated, sterile, excessively
refined, depressing—all that they had in common with the
Frédéric Moreaus and with the daughters of poor English
parsons. There they are with their ideals and their blights.
Milly Theale, for example—quite real at the core of the
cloudy integument with which James has swathed her about
—is one of the best portraits of a rich New Yorker in fiction.
It is the great period of the heyday of Sargent; but compare
these figures of Henry James's with Sargent's and see with
what profounder insight as well as with what superior deli-
cacy James has caught the rich Americans of this race.

VI

And between the first and the second blooming something
tragic has happened to these Americans. What has become
of Christopher Newman? He is Lambert Strether now: he
has been worn down by the factories of Woollett. And these
Americans of the later novels, who still bring Europe the
American sincerity—what has happened to them to make
them so wan? Well, for one thing, they have become very
rich, and being rich is a terrible burden: in the process of
getting rich, they have starved themselves spiritually at
home; and now that they are trying to get something for their
money, they find that they have put themselves at the mercy
of all the schemers and adventurers of Europe. It seems to
me foolish to reproach Henry James for having neglected
the industrial background. Like sex, we never get very close
to it, but its effects are a part of his picture. James's tone is
more often old-maidish than his sense of reality is feeble;

and the whole development of American society during his absence is implied in these later books.

Now when he returns—late in the day though it is for him—he reacts strongly and reports vividly what he finds.

The returning New Yorker of "The Jolly Corner" encounters the apparition of himself as he would have been if he had stayed in America: "Rigid and conscious, spectral yet human, a man of his own substance and stature waited there to measure himself with his power to dismay." At first the apparition covers its face with its hands; then it advances upon the returned native "as for aggression, and he knew himself give ground. Then harder pressed still, sick with the force of his shock, and falling back as under the hot breath and the sensed passion of a life larger than his own, a rage of personality before which his own collapsed, he felt the whole vision turn to darkness," and he fainted.

But at contact with the harsh new America, the old Balzac in James revives. I do not know why more has not been made by James's critics—especially by the critics of the Left, who are so certain that there is nothing in him—of his unfinished novel, "The Ivory Tower." The work of his all but final period has been "poetic" rather than "realistic"; but now he passes into still a further phase, in which the poetic treatment is applied to what is for James a new kind of realism. The fiction of his latest period is preoccupied in a curious way with the ugly, the poor and the old, even with—what is unprecedented for James—the grotesque. It is perhaps the reflection of his own old age, his own lack of worldly success, the strange creature that he himself has become. This new vein begins, I think, with "The Papers," with its fantastically amusing picture of the sordid lives of journalists in London. "Fordham Castle," in which he said he had attempted to do some justice to the parents of the Daisy Millers, whose children had left them behind, is an excursion into the America of Sinclair Lewis. "The Bench of Desolation"—one of the most beautifully written and wonderfully developed pieces in the whole range of Henry James's work, and, I believe, the last piece of fiction he published—is a sort of poem of loneliness and poverty among the nondescript small shopkeepers and former governesses of an English sea-side resort.

And now the revelation of Newport, as it presented itself in the nineteen hundreds—so different from the Newport which he had described years ago in "An International Episode"—stimulates him to something quite new: a kind of nightmare of the American new rich. Here his gusto for the varied forms of life, his interest in social phenomena for their own sake, seems suddenly to wake up from its reveries. The actual appearances of things become suddenly vivid again. In the novels which preceded "The Ivory Tower," the carefully selected and charming old-world settings had been steadily fading out; but now, to our amazement, there starts into relief the America of the millionaires, at its crudest, corruptest and phoniest: the immense summer mansions full of equipment which no one ever seems to have selected or used, the old men of the Rockefeller-Frick generation, landed, with no tastes and no interests, amidst an unlimited magnificence which dwarfs them, the silly or clumsy young people of the second generation with their off-color relationships, their enormous meaningless parties, their touching longings and resolute strivings for an elegance and cultivation they cannot manage. The apparition in "The Jolly Corner" came upon the Europeanized American "quite as one of those expanding fantastic images projected by the magic lantern of childhood"; and in the same way, for the reader of James, with the opening of "The Ivory Tower," there emerges the picture of old Abner Gaw sitting and rocking his foot and looking out on the sparkling Atlantic while he waits for his partner to die.

"The Ivory Tower" is immensely comic, deeply human and brilliantly observed—and it is poetic in the highest sense, like all these later novels: in the sense that its characters and

288

images, individualized though they are, shine out with the incandescence which shows them as symbols of phases through which the human soul has passed.

The moral of the book—which seems quite plain from the scenario left by James—is also of particular interest. The ivory tower itself, a fine piece of Chinese carving, figures the spiritual isolation, the cultivation of sensations and the literary activity which are to be made possible for the young American, returned from Europe, who has inherited his uncle's fortune; but it contains, also, the fatal letter in which the vindictive Mr. Gaw has revealed all the swindles and perfidies by which the fortune has been created. So that the young man (he has always had a *little* money) is to come finally to be glad enough to give up the ivory tower with the fortune.

James dropped "The Ivory Tower" when the War broke out in 1914, because it seemed to him too remote from the present. The War seems to have presented itself to him as simply a struggle between, on the one hand, French and English civilization and, on the other, German barbarism. He had believed in, and had been writing rather vaguely about, the possible salutary effect on human affairs of a sort of international élite such as he tended to depict in his novels; and now he spoke of the past as "the age of the mistake," the time when people had thought that things would be all right. He now became violently nationalistic, or at least violently pro-Ally, and took out citizen's papers in England, because America had not yet gone into the War. It never seems to have occurred to him that in "The Ivory Tower" he had been much closer to contemporary realities than in becoming an English citizen, that the partnership of Betterman and Gaw was a European phenomenon, too—any more than it ever occurred to him that the class antagonisms of "The Princess Casamassima"—his response to the depression of the eighties—must inevitably appear again. But as Hycinth Robinson died of the class struggle, so Henry James died of the War.

Before he died, the English gave him the Order of Merit. But I do not think that anybody has yet done justice to the genius that, overriding personal deficiencies of a peculiarly disabling kind, finding its bearings in a social situation almost as bewildering as the astronomical one with which the mathematics of relativity deals, surviving the ridicule and indifference of the two peoples whose critic he had made himself, was able to re-create itself to the end and actually to break fresh ground at seventy.

For Henry James *is* a great artist, in spite of everything. His deficiencies are obvious enough. He was certainly rather short on invention; and he tended to hold life at arm's-length. Yet when a novelist with a real inventive gift—say Compton Mackenzie—can invent till the cows come home without his inventions' making any lasting impression on us, the things that James *does* invent have so perfect an appropriateness and beauty, even floating though they sometimes are in rather a gray sea of abstract exposition, that they remain in our minds as luminous symbols; and the objects and beings at the end of James's arm, or rather, at the end of his antennae, are grasped with an astonishing firmness, gauged with a marvelous intelligence. His work is incomplete as his experience was; but it is in no respect second-rate, and he can be judged only in the company of the greatest. My argument has not given me an occasion to call attention to the classical equanimity, the classical combination of realism with harmony—I have tried to describe them in writing about Pushkin—which have been so rare in American and in English literature alike and of which James is one of the only examples.

T. S. Eliot

TRADITION AND
THE INDIVIDUAL TALENT

IN ENGLISH writing we seldom speak of tradition, though
we occasionally apply its name in deploring its absence. We
cannot refer to "the tradition" or to "a tradition"; at most,
we employ the adjective in saying that the poetry of So-and-
so is "traditional" or even "too traditional." Seldom, perhaps,
does the word appear except in a phrase of censure. If otherwise, it is vaguely approbative, with the implication, as to
the work approved, of some pleasing archæological reconstruction. You can hardly make the word agreeable to English ears without this comfortable reference to the reassur-
ing science of archæology.

Certainly the word is not likely to appear in our appreci-
ations of living or dead writers. Every nation, every race, has
not only its own creative, but its own critical turn of mind;
and is even more oblivious of the shortcomings and limitations of its critical habits than of those of its creative genius.
We know, or think we know, from the enormous mass of
critical writing that has appeared in the French language
the critical method or habit of the French; we only conclude
(we are such unconscious people) that the French are "more
critical" than we, and sometimes even plume ourselves a
little with the fact, as if the French were the less spontaneous.
Perhaps they are; but we might remind ourselves that criticism is as inevitable as breathing, and that we should be none
the worse for articulating what passes in our minds when
we read a book and feel an emotion about it, for criticizing
our own minds in their work of criticism. One of the facts

that might come to light in this process is our tendency to insist, when we praise a poet, upon those aspects of his work in which he least resembles anyone else. In these aspects or parts of his work we pretend to find what is individual, what is the peculiar essence of the man. We dwell with satisfaction upon the poet's difference from his predecessors, especially his immediate predecessors; we endeavour to find something that can be isolated in order to be enjoyed. Whereas if we approach a poet without his prejudice we shall often find that not only the best, but the most individual parts of his work may be those in which the dead poets, his ancestors, assert their immortality most vigorously. And I do not mean the impressionable period of adolescence, but the period of full maturity.

Yet if the only form of tradition, of handing down, consisted in following the ways of the immediate generation before us in a blind or timid adherence to its successes, "tradition" should positively be discouraged. We have seen many such simple currents soon lost in the sand; and novelty is better than repetition. Tradition is a matter of much wider significance. It cannot be inherited, and if you want it you must obtain it by great labour. It involves, in the first place, the historical sense, which we may call nearly indispensable to anyone who would continue to be a poet beyond his twenty-fifth year; and the historical sense involves a perception, not only of the pastness of the past, but of its presence; the historical sense compels a man to write not merely with his own generation in his bones, but with a feeling that the whole of the literature of Europe from Homer and within it the whole of the literature of his own country has a simultaneous existence and composes a simultaneous order. This historical sense, which is a sense of the timeless as well as of the temporal and of the timeless and of the temporal together, is what makes a writer traditional. And it is at the same time what makes a writer most acutely conscious of his place in time, of his contemporaneity.

No poet, no artist of any art, has his complete meaning alone. His significance, his appreciation is the appreciation of his relation to the dead poets and artists. You cannot value him alone; you must set him, for contrast and comparison, among the dead. I mean this as a principle of æsthetic, not merely historical, criticism. The necessity that he shall conform, that he shall cohere, is not one-sided; what happens when a new work of art is created is something that happens simultaneously to all the works of art which preceded it. The existing monuments form an ideal order among themselves, which is modified by the introduction of the new (the really new) work of art among them. The existing order is complete before the new work arrives; for order to persist after the supervention of novelty, the *whole* existing order must be, if ever so slightly, altered; and so the relations, proportions, values of each work of art toward the whole are readjusted; and this is conformity between the old and the new. Whoever has approved this idea of order, of the form of European, of English literature, will not find it preposterous that the past should be altered by the present as much as the present is directed by the past. And the poet who is aware of this will be aware of great difficulties and responsibilities.

In a peculiar sense he will be aware also that he must inevitably be judged by the standards of the past. I say judged, not amputated, by them; not judged to be as good as, or worse or better than, the dead; and certainly not judged by the canons of dead critics. It is a judgment, a comparison, in which two things are measured by each other. To conform merely would be for the new work not really to conform at all; it would not be new, and would therefore not be a work of art. And we do not quite say that the new is more valuable because it fits in; but its fitting in is a test of its value —a test, it is true, which can only be slowly and cautiously applied, for we are none of us infallible judges of conformity. We say: it appears to conform, and is perhaps individual,

293

or it appears individual, and may conform; but we are hardly likely to find that it is one and not the other.

To proceed to a more intelligible exposition of the relation of the poet to the past: he can neither take the past as a lump, an indiscriminate bolus, nor can he form himself wholly on one or two private admirations, nor can he form himself wholly upon one preferred period. The first course is inadmissible, the second is an important experience of youth, and the third is a pleasant and highly desirable supplement. The poet must be very conscious of the main current, which does not at all flow invariably through the most distinguished reputations. He must be quite aware of the obvious fact that art never improves, but that the material of art is never quite the same. He must be aware that the mind of Europe—the mind of his own country—a mind which he learns in time to be much more important than his own private mind—is a mind which changes, and that this change is a development which abandons nothing *en route*, which does not superannuate either Shakespeare, or Homer, or the rock drawing of the Magdalenian draughtsmen. That this development, refinement perhaps, complication certainly, is not, from the point of view of the artist, any improvement. Perhaps not even an improvement from the point of view of the psychologist or not to the extent which we imagine; perhaps only in the end based upon a complication in economics and machinery. But the difference between the present and the past is that the conscious present is an awareness of the past in a way and to an extent which the past's awareness of itself cannot show.

Some one said: "The dead writers are remote from us because we *know* so much more than they did." Precisely, and they are that which we know.

I am alive to a usual objection to what is clearly part of my programme for the *métier* of poetry. The objection is that the doctrine requires a ridiculous amount of erudition (pedantry), a claim which can be rejected by appeal to the

294

lives of poets in any pantheon. It will even be affirmed that much learning deadens or perverts poetic sensibility. While, however, we persist in believing that a poet ought to know as much as will not encroach upon his necessary receptivity and necessary laziness, it is not desirable to confine knowledge to whatever can be put into a useful shape for examinations, drawing-rooms, or the still more pretentious modes of publicity. Some can absorb knowledge, the more tardy must sweat for it. Shakespeare acquired more essential history from Plutarch than most men could from the whole British Museum. What is to be insisted upon is that the poet must develop or procure the consciousness of the past and that he should continue to develop this consciousness throughout his career.

What happens is a continual surrender of himself as he is at the moment to something which is more valuable. The progress of an artist is a continual self-sacrifice, a continual extinction of personality.

There remains to define this process of depersonalization and its relation to the sense of tradition. It is in this depersonalization that art may be said to approach the condition of science. I shall, therefore, invite you to consider, as a suggestive analogy, the action which takes place when a bit of finely filiated platinum is introduced into a chamber containing oxygen and sulphur dioxide.

II

Honest criticism and sensitive appreciation is directed not upon the poet but upon the poetry. If we attend to the confused cries of the newspaper critics and the susurrus of popular repetition that follows, we shall hear the names of poets in great numbers; if we seek not Blue-book knowledge but the enjoyment of poetry, and ask for a poem, we shall seldom find it. In the last article I tried to point out the importance of the relation of the poem to other poems by other authors, and suggested the conception of poetry as a living whole of all the poetry that has ever been written. The other aspect of this Impersonal theory of poetry is the relation of the poem to its author. And I hinted, by an analogy, that the mind of the mature poet differs from that of the immature one not precisely in any valuation of "personality," not being necessarily more interesting, or having "more to say," but rather by being a more finely perfected medium in which special, or very varied, feelings are at liberty to enter into new combinations.

The analogy was that of the catalyst. When the two gases previously mentioned are mixed in the presence of a filament of platinum, they form sulphurous acid. This combination takes place only if the platinum is present; nevertheless the newly formed acid contains no trace of platinum, and the platinum itself is apparently unaffected; has remained inert, neutral, and unchanged. The mind of the poet is the shred of platinum. It may partly or exclusively operate upon the experience of the man himself; but, the more perfect the artist, the more completely separate in him will be the man who suffers and the mind which creates; the more perfectly will the mind digest and transmute the passions which are its material.

The experience, you will notice, the elements which enter the presence of the transforming catalyst, are of two kinds: emotions and feelings. The effect of a work of art upon the person who enjoys it is an experience different in kind from any experience not of art. It may be formed out of one emotion, or may be a combination of several; and various feelings, inhering for the writer in particular words or phrases or images, may be added to compose the final result. Or great poetry may be made without the direct use of any emotion whatever: composed out of feelings solely. Canto XV of the *Inferno* (Brunetto Latini) is a working up of the emotion evident in the situation; but the effect, though single as that of any work of art, is obtained by considerable complexity of detail. The last quatrain gives an image, a feeling attaching to an image, which "came," which did not develop simply out of what precedes, but which was probably in suspension in the poet's mind until the proper combination arrived for it to add itself to. The poet's mind is in fact a receptacle for seizing and storing up numberless feelings, phrases, images, which remain there until all the particles which can unite to form a new compound are present together.

If you compare several representative passages of the greatest poetry you see how great is the variety of types of combination, and also how completely any semi-ethical criterion of "sublimity" misses the mark. For it is not the "greatness," the intensity, of the emotions, the components, but the intensity of the artistic process, the pressure, so to speak, under which the fusion takes place, that counts. The episode of Paolo and Francesca employs a definite emotion, but the intensity of the poetry is something quite different from whatever intensity in the supposed experience it may give the impression of. It is no more intense, furthermore, than Canto XXVI, the voyage of Ulysses, which has not the direct dependence upon an emotion. Great variety is possible in the process of transmutation of emotion: the murder of Agamemnon, or the agony of Othello, gives an artistic effect apparently closer to a possible original than the scenes from Dante. In the *Agamemnon*, the artistic emotion approximates to the emotion of an actual spectator; in *Othello* to the emotion of the protagonist himself. But the difference between art and the event is always absolute; the combination which is the murder of Agamemnon is probably as complex as that which is the voyage of Ulysses. In either case there has been a fusion of elements. The ode of Keats contains a number of feelings which have nothing particular to do with the nightingale, but which the nightingale, partly, perhaps, because of its attractive name, and partly because of its reputation, served to bring together.

The point of view which I am struggling to attack is perhaps related to the metaphysical theory of the substantial unity of the soul: for my meaning is, that the poet has, not a "personality" to express, but a particular medium, which is only a medium and not a personality, in which impressions and experiences combine in peculiar and unexpected ways. Impressions and experiences which are important for the man may take no place in the poetry, and those which become important in the poetry may play quite a negligible part in the man, the personality.

I will quote a passage which is unfamiliar enough to be regarded with fresh attention in the light—or darkness—of these observations:

> And now methinks I could e'en chide myself
> For doating on her beauty, though her death
> Shall be revenged after no common action.
> Does the silkworm expend her yellow labours
> For thee? For thee does she undo herself?
> Are lordships sold to maintain ladyships
> For the poor benefit of a bewildering minute?
> Why does yon fellow falsify highways,
> And put his life between the judge's lips,
> To refine such a thing—keeps horse and men
> To beat their valours for her? . . .

In this passage (as is evident if it is taken in its context) there is a combination of positive and negative emotions: an intensely strong attraction toward beauty and an equally intense fascination by the ugliness which is contrasted with it and which destroys it. This balance of contrasted emotion is in the dramatic situation to which the speech is pertinent, but that situation alone is inadequate to it. This is, so to speak, the structural emotion, provided by the drama. But the whole effect, the dominant tone, is due to the fact that a number of floating feelings, having an affinity to this emotion by no means superficially evident, have combined with it to give us a new art emotion.

It is not in his personal emotions, the emotions provoked by particular events in his life, that the poet is in any way

298

remarkable or interesting. His particular emotions may be simple, or crude, or flat. The emotion in his poetry will be a very complex thing, but not with the complexity of the emotions of people who have very complex or unusual emotions in life. One error, in fact, of eccentricity in poetry is to seek for new human emotions to express; and in this search for novelty in the wrong place it discovers the perverse. The business of the poet is not to find new emotions, but to use the ordinary ones and, in working them up into poetry, to express feelings which are not in actual emotions at all. And emotions which he has never experienced will serve his turn as well as those familiar to him. Consequently, we must believe that "emotion recollected in tranquillity" is an inexact formula. For it is neither emotion, nor recollection, nor, without distortion of meaning, tranquillity. It is a concentration, and a new thing resulting from the concentration, of a very great number of experiences which to the practical and active person would not seem to be experiences at all; it is a concentration which does not happen consciously or of deliberation. These experiences are not "recollected," and they finally unite in an atmosphere which is "tranquil" only in that it is a passive attending upon the event. Of course this is not quite the whole story. There is a great deal, in the writing of poetry, which must be conscious and deliberate. In fact, the bad poet is usually unconscious where he ought to be conscious, and conscious where he ought to be unconscious. Both errors tend to make him "personal." Poetry is not a turning loose of emotion, but an escape from emotion; it is not the expression of personality, but an escape from personality. But, of course, only those who have personality and emotions know what it means to want to escape from these things.

III

ὁ δὲ νοῦς ἴσως θειότερόν τι καὶ ἀπαθές ἐστιν

This essay proposes to halt at the frontier of metaphysics or mysticism, and confine itself to such practical conclusions as can be applied by the responsible person interested in poetry. To divert interest from the poet to the poetry is a laudable aim: for it would conduce to a juster estimation of actual poetry, good and bad. There are many people who appreciate the expression of sincere emotion in verse, and there is a smaller number of people who can appreciate technical excellence. But very few know when there is expression of *significant* emotion, emotion which has its life in the poem and not in the history of the poet. The emotion of art is impersonal. And the poet cannot reach this impersonality without surrendering himself wholly to the work to be done. And he is not likely to know what is to be done unless he lives in what is not merely the present, but the present moment of the past, unless he is conscious, not of what is dead, but of what is already living.

IV

ACKNOWLEDGMENTS

E. E. Cummings, JEAN LE NÈGRE from "The Enormous Room," copyright 1929 by E. E. Cummings (Horace Liveright, Inc.); Glenway Wescott, THE SAILOR from "Good-bye Wisconsin," copyright 1928 by Harper & Bros.; Kay Boyle, DEFEAT, by permission of Kay Boyle; Stark Young, SUNDAY RACES from "A Southern Treasury of Life and Literature," copyright 1937 by Charles Scribner's Sons; William Faulkner, A ROSE FOR EMILY from "These Thirteen," by permission of William Faulkner; Julian Green, CHRISTINE, by permission of Harper & Bros.; Eudora Welty, PETRIFIED MAN from "A Curtain of Green," copyright 1941 by Eudora Welty (Doubleday, Doran & Co.); William Saroyan, THE SUMMER OF THE BEAUTIFUL WHITE HORSE from "My Name Is Aram," copyright 1940 by Harcourt, Brace & Co.

E. E. Cummings

JEAN LE NÈGRE

On a certain day, the ringing of the bell and accompanying rush of men to the window facing the entrance gate was supplemented by an unparalleled volley of enthusiastic exclamations in all the languages of La Ferté Macé—provoking in me a certainty that the queen of fair women had arrived. This certainly thrillingly withered when I heard the cry: '*Il y a un noir!*' Fritz was at the best peep-hole, resisting successfully the onslaughts of a dozen fellow-prisoners, and of him I demanded in English, 'Who's come?'—'Oh, a lot of girls,' he yelled, 'and there's a NIGGER too'—hereupon writhing with laughter.

I attempted to get a look, but in vain; for by this at least two dozen men were at the peep-hole, fighting and gesticulating and slapping each other's backs with joy. However, my curiosity was not long in being answered. I heard on the stairs the sound of mounting feet, and knew that a couple of *plantons* would before many minutes arrive at the door with their new prey. So did everyone else—and from the farthest beds uncouth figures sprang and rushed to the door, eager for the first glimpse of the *nouveau:* which was very significant, as the ordinary procedure on arrival of prisoners was for everybody to rush to his own bed and stand guard over it.

Even as the *plantons* fumbled with the locks I heard the inimitable, unmistakable divine laugh of a negro. The door opened at last. Entered a beautiful pillar of black strutting muscle topped with a tremendous display of the whitest teeth on earth. The muscle bowed politely in our direction, the grin remarked musically; *'Bo'jour, tou'l'monde';* then came a cascade of laughter. Its effect on the spectators was instantaneous: they roared and danced with joy. *'Comment vous appelez-vous?'* was fired from the hubbub.—*'J'm'appelle Jean, moi,'* the muscle rapidly answered with sudden solemnity, proudly gazing to left and right as if expecting a challenge to this statement: but when none appeared, it relapsed as suddenly into laughter—as if hugely amused at itself and everyone else including a little and tough boy, whom I had not previously noted, although his entrance had coincided with the muscle's.

Thus into the *misère* of La Ferté Macé stepped lightly and proudly Jean Le Nègre.

Of all the fine people in La Ferté, Monsieur Jean (*'le noir'* as he was entitled by his enemies) swaggers in my memory as the finest.

Jean's first act was to complete the distribution (begun, he announced, among the *plantons* who had escorted him upstairs) of two pockets full of Cubebs. Right and left he gave them up to the last, remarking carelessly, *'J'ne veux, moi.'*

Après la soupe (which occurred a few minutes after *le noir's* entry) B. and I and the greater number of prisoners descended to the *cour* for our afternoon promenade. The cook spotted us immediately, and desired us to 'catch water'; which we did, three cartfulls of it, earning our usual *café sucré*. On quitting the *cuisine* after this delicious repast (which as usual mitigated somewhat the effects of the swill that was our official nutriment) we entered the *cour*. And we noticed at once a well-made figure standing conspicuously by itself, and poring with extraordinary intentness over the pages of a London *Daily Mail* which it was holding upside-down. The reader was culling choice bits of news of a highly sensational nature, and exclaiming from time to time—*'Este-ce vrai! V'la, le roi d'Angleterre est malade. Quelque chose!—Comment? La reine aussi? Bon Dieu!*

Qu'est-ce que c'est?—Mon père est mort! Merde!—Eh, b'en! La guerre est fini. Bon.'—it was Jean Le Nègre, playing a little game with himself to beguile the time.

When we had mounted *à la chambre,* two or three tried to talk with this extraordinary personage in French; at which he became very superior and announced: *'J'suis anglais, moi. Parlez anglais. Comprends pas français, moi.'* At this a crowd escorted him over to B. and me—anticipating great deeds in the English language. Jean looked at us critically and said, *'Vous parlez anglais? Moi parlez anglais.'*—'We are Americans, and speak English,' I answered.—*'Moi anglais,'* Jean said. *'Mon père, capitaine de gendarmerie, Londres. Comprends pas français, moi. SPEE-Kingliss'*—he laughed all over himself.

At this display of English on Jean's part the English-speaking Hollanders began laughing. 'The son of a bitch is crazy,' one said.

And from that moment B. and I got on famously with Jean.

His mind was a child's. His use of language was sometimes exalted fibbing, sometimes the purely picturesque. He courted above all the sound of words, more or less disdaining their meaning. He told us immediately (in pidgin-French) that he was born without a mother because his mother died when he was born, that his father was (first) sixteen (then) sixty years old, that his father *gagnait cinq cent francs par jour* (later, *par année*), that he was born in London and not in England, that he was in the French army and had never been in any army.

He did not, however, contradict himself in one statement: *'Les français sont des cochons'*—to which we heartily agreed, and which won him the approval of the Hollanders.

The next day I had my hands full acting as interpreter for *'le noir qui comprend pas français.'* I was summoned from the *cour* to elucidate a great grief which Jean had been unable to explain to the *Gestionnaire.* I mounted with a

305

planton to find Jean in hysterics; speechless; his eyes starting out of his head. As nearly as I could make out, Jean had
had sixty francs when he arrived, which money he had given
to a *planton* upon his arrival, the *planton* having told Jean
that he would deposit the money with the *Gestionnaire* in
Jean's name (Jean could not write). The *planton* in question,
who looked particularly innocent, denied this charge upon
my explaining Jean's version; while the *Gestionnaire* puffed
and grumbled, disclaiming any connection with the alleged
theft and protesting sonorously that he was hearing about
Jean's sixty francs for the first time. The *Gestionnaire* shook
his thick piggish finger at the book wherein all financial trans-
actions were to be found—from the year one to the present
year, month, day, hour and minute (or words to that effect).
'*Mais c'est pas là,*' he kept repeating stupidly. The *Surveillant* was uh-ahing at a great rate and attempting to pacify
Jean in French. I myself was somewhat fearful for Jean's
sanity and highly indignant at the *planton*. The matter ended
with the *planton's* being sent about his business; simultaneously with Jean's dismissal to the *cour*, whither I accompanied him. My best efforts to comfort Jean in this
matter were quite futile. Like a child who has been unjustly
punished he was inconsolable. Great tears welled in his eyes.
He kept repeating 'Sees-tee franc—*planton voleur,*' and—
absolutely like a child who in anguish calls itself by the name
which has been given itself by grown-ups—'steel Jean
munee.' To no avail I called the *planton* a *menteur,* a *voleur,*
a *fils de chienne* and various other names. Jean felt the wrong
itself too keenly to be interested in my denunciation of the
mere agent through whom injustice had (as it happened)
been consummated.

But—again like an inconsolable child who weeps his heart
out when no human comfort avails and wakes the next day
without an apparent trace of the recent grief—Jean Le Nègre,
in the course of the next twenty-four hours, had completely
recovered his normal buoyancy of spirit. The sees-tee franc

were gone. A wrong had been done. But that was yesterday. To-day—

And he wandered up and down, joking, laughing, singing: '*après la guerre fini.*' . . .

In the *cour* Jean was the mecca of all female eyes. Handkerchiefs were waved to him; phrases of the most amorous nature greeted his every appearance. To all these demonstrations he by no means turned a deaf ear; on the contrary, Jean was irrevocably vain. He boasted of having been enormously popular with the girls wherever he went and of having never disdained their admiration. In Paris one day—(and thus it happened that we discovered why *le gouvernement français* had arrested Jean)—

One afternoon, having *rien à faire*, and being flush (owing to his success as a thief, of which vocation he made a great deal, adding as many ciphers to the amounts as fancy dictated) Jean happened to cast his eyes in a store window where were displayed all possible appurtenances for the *militaire*. Vanity was rooted deeply in Jean's soul. The uniform of an English captain met his eyes. Without a moment's hesitation he entered the store, bought the entire uniform, including leather puttees and belt (of the latter purchase he was especially proud), and departed. The next store contained a display of medals of all descriptions. It struck Jean at once that a uniform would be incomplete without medals. He entered this store, bought one of every decoration—not forgetting the Colonial, nor yet the Belgian Cross (which on account of its size and colour particularly appealed to him)—and went to his room. There he adjusted the decorations on the chest of his blouse, donned the uniform, and sallied importantly forth to capture Paris.

Everywhere he met with success. He was frantically pursued by women of all stations from *les putains* to *les princesses*. The police salaamed to him. His arm was wearied with the returning of innumerable salutes. So far did his medals carry him that, although on one occasion a gendarme dared to arrest him for beating in the head of a fellow English officer (who being a mere lieutenant, should not have objected to Captain Jean's stealing the affections of his lady), the *sergent de gendarmerie* before whom Jean was arraigned on a charge of attempting to kill refused to even hear the evidence, and dismissed the case with profuse apologies to the heroic Captain. ' "*Le gouvernement français, Monsieur,* extends to you through me its profound apology for the insult which your honour has received." *Ils sont des cochons, les français,*' said Jean, and laughed throughout his entire body.

Having had the most blue-blooded ladies of the capital cooing upon his heroic chest, having completely beaten up with the full support of the law whosoever of lesser rank attempted to cross his path or refused him the salute—having had 'great fun' saluting generals on *les grands boulevards* and being in turn saluted ('*tous les généraux, tous,* salute me, Jean have more medal'), and this state of affairs having lasted for about three months—Jean began to be very bored ('me *très ennuyé*'). A fit of temper ('me *très fâché*') arising from this ennui led to a *rixe* with the police, in consequence of which (Jean, though outnumbered three to one, having almost killed one of his assailants) our hero was a second time arrested. This time the authorities went so far as to ask the heroic captain to what branch of the English army he was at present attached; to which Jean first replied, '*Parle pas français, moi,*' and immediately after announced that he was a Lord of the Admiralty, that he had committed robberies in Paris to the tune of sees-meel-i-own franc, that he was a son of the Lord Mayor of London by the Queen, that he had lost a leg in Algeria, and that the French were *cochons*. All of which assertions being duly disproved, Jean was remanded to La Ferté for psychopathic observation and safe keeping on the technical charge of wearing an English officer's uniform.

Jean's particular girl at La Ferté was 'LOO-Loo.' With

Lulu it was the same as with *les princesses* in Paris—'me no *travaille, ja MAIS. Les femmes travaillent*, geev Jean mun-ee, sees, sees-tee, see-*cent francs. Jamais travaille, moi.*' Lulu smuggled Jean money; and not for some time did the woman who slept next Lulu miss it. Lulu also sent Jean a lace embroidered handkerchief, which Jean would squeeze and press to his lips with a beatific smile of perfect contentment. The affair with Lulu kept Mexique and Pete the Hollander busy writing letters; which Jean dictated, rolling his eyes and scratching his head for words.

At this time Jean was immensely happy. He was continually playing practical jokes on one of the Hollanders, or Mexique, or the Wanderer, or in fact anyone of whom he was particularly fond. At intervals between these demonstrations of irrepressibility (which kept everyone in a state of laughter) he would stride up and down the filth-sprinkled floor with his hands in the pockets of his stylish jacket, singing at the top of his lungs his own version of the famous song of songs:

> *après la guerre fini,*
> *soldat anglais parti*
> *mademoiselle que je laissai en France*
> *avec des pickaninee. PLENTY!*

and laughing till he shook and had to lean against a wall.

B. and Mexique made some dominoes. Jean had not the least idea of how to play, but when we three had gathered for a game he was always to be found leaning over our shoulders, completely absorbed, once in a while offering us sage advice, laughing utterly when some one made a cinque or a multiple thereof.

One afternoon, in the interval between *la soupe* and promenade, Jean was in especially high spirits. I was lying down on my collapsible bed when he came up to my end of the room and began showing off exactly like a child. This time it was the game of *l'armée française* which Jean was

309

playing.—'*Jamais soldat, moi. Connais toute l'armée fran-*
çaise.' John the Bathman, stretched comfortably in his bunk
near me, grunted. '*Tous*,' Jean repeated.—And he stood in
front of us; stiff as a stick in imitation of a French lieutenant
with an imaginary company in front of him. First he would
be the lieutenant giving commands, then he would be the
Army executing them. He began with the manual of arms.
'*Com-pag-nie . . .*' then, as he went through the manual
holding his imaginary gun—'htt, htt, htt.'—Then as the
officer commending his troops: '*Bon. Très bon. Très bien
fait*'—laughing with head thrown back and teeth aglitter
at his own success. John Le Baigneur was so tremendously
amused that he gave up sleeping to watch. *L'armée* drew a
crowd of admirers from every side. For at least three-quarters of an hour this game went on. . . .

Another day Jean, being angry at the weather and having
eaten a huge amount of *soupe*, began yelling at the top of
his voice '*MERDE à la France*,' and laughing heartily. No
one paying especial attention to him, he continued (happy
in this new game with himself) for about fifteen minutes.
Then The Sheeney With The Trick Raincoat (that under-
sized specimen, clad in feminine-fitting raiment with flashy
shoes), who was by trade a pimp, being about half Jean's
height and a tenth of his physique, strolled up to Jean—who
had by this time got as far as my bed—and, sticking his sallow face as near Jean's as the neck could reach, said in a
solemn voice: '*Il ne faut pas dire ça.*' Jean, astounded, gazed
at the intruder for a moment; then demanded, '*Qui dit ça?
Moi? Jean? Jamais, ja-MAIS. MERDE à la France?*' nor
would he yield a point, backed up as he was by the moral
support of every one present except the Sheeney—who
found discretion the better part of valour and retired with
a few dark threats; leaving Jean master of the situation
and yelling for the Sheeney's particular delectation:
'*MAY-RRR-DE à la France!*' more loudly than ever.

A little after the epic battle with stovepipes between The

310

Young Pole and Bill the Hollander, the wrecked *poêle* (which was patiently waiting to be repaired) furnished Jean with perhaps his most brilliant inspiration. The final section of pipe (which conducted the smoke through a hole in the wall to the outer air) remained in place all by itself, projecting about six feet into the room at a height of seven or eight feet from the floor. Jean noticed this; got a chair; mounted on it, and by applying alternately his ear and his mouth to the end of the pipe created for himself a telephone, with the aid of which he carried on a conversation with The Wanderer (at that moment visiting his family on the floor below) to this effect:

—Jean, grasping the pipe and speaking angrily into it, being evidently nettled at the poor connection—'Heh-loh, hello, hello, hello'—surveying the pipe in consternation—'*Merde. Ça marche pas*'—trying again with a deep frown—'heh-LOH!'—tremendously agitated—'HEH-LOH!'—a beatific smile supplanting the frown—'hello *Barbu. Est-ce que tu es là? Qui? Bon!*'—evincing tremendous pleasure at having succeeded in establishing the connection satisfactorily—'*Barbu? Est-ce que tu m'écoutes? Qui? Qu'est-ce que c'est Barbu? Comment? Moi? Qui, MOI? JEAN? jaMAIS! jamais, jaMAIS, Barbu. J'ai jamais dit que vous avez des puces. C'était pas moi, tu sais. JaMAIS, c'était un autre. Peut-être c'était Mexique*'—turning his head in Mexique's direction and roaring with laughter—'Hello, HEH-LOH. *Barbu? Tu sais, Barbu, j'ai jamais dit ça. Au contraire, Barbu. J'ai dit que vous avez des totos*'—another roar of laughter—'*Comment? C'est pas vrai? Bon. Alors. Qu'est-ce que vous avez, Barbu? Des poux*—OHHHHHH-HHH. *Je comprends. C'est mieux*'—shaking with laughter, then suddenly tremendously serious—'Hellohellohellohello HEHLOH!'—addressing the stovepipe—'*C'est une mauvaise machine, ça*—speaking into it with the greatest distinctness—'HEL-L-LOH. *Barbu? Liberté, Barbu. Oui. Comment? C'est ça. Liberté pour tou'l'monde. Quand? Après la*

311

soupe. Oui. Liberté pour tou'l'monde après la soupe!'—to which jest astonishingly reacted a certain old man known as the West Indian Negro (a stocky, credulous creature with whom Jean would have nothing to do, and whose tales of Brooklyn were indeed outclassed by Jean's *histoires d'amour*) who leaped rheumatically from his *paillasse* at the word *'Liberté'* and rushed limpingly hither and thither inquiring Was it true?—to the enormous and excruciating amusement of The Enormous Room in general.

After which Jean, exhausted with laughter, descended from the chair and lay down on his bed to read a letter from Lulu (not knowing a syllable of it). A little later he came rushing up to my bed in the most terrific state of excitement, the whites of his eyes gleaming, his teeth bared, his kinky hair fairly standing on end, and cried:

'You f— me, me f— you? Pas bon. You f— you, me f— me: —bon. Me f— me, you f— you!' and went away capering and shouting with laughter, dancing with great grace and as great agility and with an imaginary partner the entire length of the room.

There was another game—a pure child's game—which Jean played. It was the name game. He amused himself for hours together by lying on his *paillasse*, tilting his head back, rolling up his eyes, and crying in a high quavering voice— 'JAW-neeeeeee.' After a repetition or two of his own name in English, he would demand sharply *'Qui m'appelle? Mexique? Est-ce que tu m'appelle,* Mexique?' and if Mexique happened to be asleep, Jean would rush over and cry in his ear shaking him thoroughly—*'Est-ce tu m'appelles, toi?'* Or it might be *Barbu,* or Pete the Hollander, or B. or myself, of whom he sternly asked the question—which was always followed by quantities of laughter on Jean's part. He was never perfectly happy unless exercising his inexhaustible imagination. . . .

Of all Jean's extraordinary selves, the moral one was at once the most rare and most unreasonable. In the matter of

les femmes he could hardly have been accused by his bitterest enemy of being a Puritan. Yet the Puritan streak came
out one day, in a discussion which lasted for several hours.
Jean, as in the case of France, spoke in dogma. His conten-
tion was very simple: '*La femme qui fume n'est pas une
femme.*' He defended it hotly against the attacks of all the
nations represented; in vain did Belgian and Hollander, Rus-
sian and Pole, Spaniard and Alsatian, charge and counter-
charge—Jean remained unshaken. A woman could do anything but smoke—if she smoked she ceased automatically to
be a woman and became something unspeakable. As Jean
was at this time sitting alternately on B.'s bed and mine, and
as the alternations became increasingly frequent as the discussion waxed hotter, we were not sorry when the *planton's*
shout, '*A la promenade les hommes!*' scattered the opposing
warriors. Then up leaped Jean (who had almost come to
blows innumerable times) and rushed laughing to the door,
having already forgotten the whole thing.

Now we come to the story of Jean's undoing, and may
the gods which made Jean Le Nègre give me grace to tell it
as it was.

The trouble started with Lulu. One afternoon, shortly
after the telephoning, Jean was sick at heart and couldn't be
induced either to leave his couch or to utter a word. Every
one guessed the reason—Lulu had left for another camp that
morning. The *planton* told Jean to come down with the rest
and get *soupe*. No answer. Was Jean sick? '*Oui, me seek.*'
And steadfastly he refused to eat, till the disgusted *planton*
gave it up and locked Jean in alone. When we ascended after
le soupe we found Jean as we had left him, stretched on his
couch, big tears on his cheeks. I asked him if I could do anything for him; he shook his head. We offered him cigarettes
—no, he did not wish to smoke. As B. and I went away we
heard him moaning to himself, 'Jawnee no see Loo-Loo no
more.' With the exception of ourselves, the inhabitants of
La Ferté Macé took Jean's desolation as a great joke. Shouts

313

of Lulu! rent the welkin on all sides. Jean stood it for an hour; then he leaped up, furious; and demanded (confronting the man from whose lips the cry had last issued)— 'Feeneesh Loo-Loo?' The latter coolly referred him to the man next to him; he in turn to some one else; and round and round the room Jean stalked, seeking the offender, followed by louder and louder shouts of Lulu! and Jawnee! the authors of which (so soon as he challenged them) denied with innocent faces their guilt and recommended that Jean look closer next time. At last Jean took to his couch in utter misery and disgust.—The rest of *les hommes* descended as usual for the promenade—not so Jean. He ate nothing for supper. That evening not a sound issued from his bed.

Next morning he awoke with a broad grin, and to the salutations of Lulu! replied, laughing heartily at himself, 'FEENEESH LooLoo.' Upon which the tormentors (finding in him no longer a victim) desisted; and things resumed their normal course. If an occasional Lulu! upraised itself, Jean merely laughed, and repeated (with a wave of his arm) 'FEENEESH.' Finished Lulu seemed to be.

But *un jour* I had remained upstairs during the promenade, both because I wanted to write and because the weather was worse than usual. Ordinarily, no matter how deep the mud in the *cour*, Jean and I would trot back and forth, resting from time to time under the little shelter out of the drizzle, talking of all things under the sun. I remember on one occasion we were the only ones to brave the rain and slough— Jean in paper-thin soled slippers (which he had recently succeeded in drawing from the *Gestionnaire*) and I in my huge sabots—hurrying back and forth with the rain pouring on us, and he very proud. On this day, however, I refused the challenge of the *boue*.

The promenaders had been singularly noisy, I thought. Now they were mounting to the room making a truly tremendous racket. No sooner were the doors opened than in rushed half a dozen frenzied friends, who began telling me

314

all at once about a terrific thing which my friend the *noir* had just done. It seems that The Sheeney With The Trick Raincoat had pulled at Jean's handkerchief (Lulu's gift in other days) which Jean wore always conspicuously in his outside breast pocket; that Jean had taken the Sheeney's head in his two hands, held it steady, abased his own head, and rammed the helpless Sheeney as a bull would do—the impact of Jean's head upon the Sheeney's nose causing that well-known feature to occupy a new position in the neighbourhood of the right ear. B. corroborated this description, adding the Sheeney's nose was broken and that everyone was down on Jean for fighting in an unsportsmanlike way. I found Jean still very angry, and moreover very hurt because every one was now shunning him. I told him that I personally was glad of what he'd done; but nothing would cheer him up. The Sheeney now entered, very terrible to see, having been patched up by Monsieur Richard with copious plasters. His nose was not broken, he said thickly, but only bent. He hinted darkly of trouble in store for *le noir;* and received the commiserations of everyone present except Mexique, The Zula, B. and me. The Zulu, I remember, pointed to his own nose (which was not unimportant), then to Jean, then made a *moue* of excruciating anguish, and winked audibly.

Jean's spirit was broken. The wellnigh unanimous verdict against him had convinced his minutely sensitive soul that it had done wrong. He lay quietly, and would say nothing to anyone.

Some time after the soup, about eight o'clock, The Fighting Sheeney and The Trick Raincoat suddenly set upon Jean Le Nègre à propos nothing; and began pommelling him cruelly. The conscience-stricken pillar of beautiful muscle —who could have easily killed both his assailants at one blow—not only offered no reciprocatory violence but refused even to defend himself. Unresistingly, wincing with pain, his arms mechanically raised and his head bent, he was battered frightfully to the window by his bed, thence into the corner (upsetting the stool in the *pissoir*), thence along the wall to the door. As the punishment increased he cried out like a child: '*Laissez-moi tranquille!*'—again and again; and in his voice the insane element gained rapidly. Finally, shrieking in agony, he rushed to the nearest window; and while the Sheeneys together pommelled him yelled for help to the *planton* beneath.—

The unparalleled consternation and applause produced by this one-sided battle had long since alarmed the authorities. I was still trying to break through the five-deep ring of spectators—among whom was The Messenger Boy, who advised me to desist and got a piece of advice in return—when with a tremendous crash open burst the door, and in stepped four *plantons* with drawn revolvers, looking frightened to death, followed by the *Surveillant* who carried a sort of baton and was crying faintly: '*Qu'est-ce que c'est!*'

At the first sound of the door the two Sheeneys had fled, and were now playing the part of innocent spectators. Jean alone occupied the stage. His lips were parted. His eyes were enormous. He was panting as if his heart would break. He still kept his arms raised as if seeing everywhere before him fresh enemies. Blood spotted here and there the wonderful chocolate carpet of his skin, and his whole body glistened with sweat. His shirt was in ribbons over his beautiful muscles.

Seven or eight persons at once began explaining the fight to the *Surveillant*, who could make nothing out of their accounts and therefore called aside a trusted older man in order to get his version. The two retired from the room. The *plantons*, finding the expected wolf a lamb, flourished their revolvers about Jean and threatened him in the insignificant and vile language which *plantons* use to anyone whom they can bully. Jean kept repeating dully, '*Laissez-moi tranquille. Ils voulaient me tuer.*' His chest shook terribly with vast sobs.

Now the *Surveillant* returned and made a speech, to the

316

effect that he had received independently of each other the stories of four men, that by all counts *le nègre* was absolutely to blame, that *le nègre* had caused an inexcusable trouble to the authorities and to his fellow-prisoners by this wholly unjustified conflict, and that as a punishment the *nègre* would now suffer the consequences of his guilt in the *cabinot.*—Jean had dropped his arms to his sides. His face was twisted with anguish. He made a child's gesture, a pitiful hopeless movement with his slender hands. Sobbing, he protested: *'C'est pas ma faute, monsieur le surveillant! Ils m'attaquaient! J'ai rien fait! Ils voulaient me tuer! Demandez à lui'*—he pointed to me desperately. Before I could utter a syllable the *Surveillant* raised his hand for silence; *le nègre* had done wrong. He should be placed in the *cabinot.*

—Like a flash, with a horrible tearing sob, Jean leaped from the surrounding *plantons* and rushed for the coat which lay on his bed screaming—'AHHHHH—*mon couteau!*'— 'Look out or he'll get his knife and kill himself!' some one yelled; and the four *plantons* seized Jean by both arms just as he made a grab for his jacket. Thwarted in this hope and burning with the ignominy of his situation, Jean cast his enormous eyes up at the nearest pillar, crying hysterically: *'Tout le monde me fout au cabinot parce que je suis noir.'* —In a second, by a single movement of his arms, he sent the four *plantons* reeling to a distance of ten feet; leaped at the pillar: seized it in both hands like a Samson, and (gazing for another second with a smile of absolute beatitude at its length) dashed his head against it. Once, twice, thrice he smote himself, before the *plantons* seized him—and suddenly his whole strength wilted; he allowed himself to be overpowered by them and stood with bowed head, tears streaming from his eyes—while the smallest pointed a revolver at his heart.

This was a little more than the *Surveillant* had counted on. Now that Jean's might was no more, the bearer of the *croix de guerre* stepped forward and in a mild placating voice endeavoured to soothe the victim of his injustice. It was also slightly more than I could stand, and slamming aside the spectators I shoved myself under his honour's nose. 'Do you know,' I asked, 'whom you are dealing with in this man? A child. There are a lot of Jeans where I come from. You heard what he said? He is black, is he not, and gets no justice from you. You heard that. I saw the whole affair. He was attacked, he put up no resistance whatever, he was beaten by two cowards. He is no more to blame that I am.'— The *Surveillant* was waving his wand and cooing, *'Je comprends, je comprends, c'est malheureux.'*—'You're god damn right it's *malheureux*,' I said, forgetting my French. *'Quand même*, he has resisted authority.' The *Surveillant* gently continued: 'Now, Jean, be quiet, you will be taken to the *cabinot*. You may as well go quietly and behave yourself like a good boy.'

At this I am sure my eyes started out of my head. All I could think of to say was: *'Attends, un petit moment.'* To reach my own bed took but a second. In another second I was back, bearing my great and sacred pelisse. I marched up to Jean. 'Jean,' I remarked with a smile, *'tu vas au cabinot, mais tu vas revenir tout de suite. Je sais bien que tu as parfaitement raison. Mets cela'*—and I pushed him gently into my coat. *'Voici mes cigarettes, Jean; tu peux fumer comme tu veux'*—I pulled out all I had, one full *paquet jaune* of Marylands and half a dozen loose ones, and deposited them carefully in the right-hand pocket of the pelisse. Then I patted him on the shoulder and gave him the immortal salutation—*'Bonne chance, mon ami!'*

He straightened proudly. He stalked like a king through the doorway. The astounded *plantons* and the embarrassed *Surveillant* followed, the latter closing the doors behind him. I was left with a cloud of angry witnesses.

An hour later the doors opened, Jean entered quietly, and the doors shut. As I lay on my bed I could see him perfectly. He was almost naked. He laid my pelisse on his mattress,

318

then walked calmly up to a neighbouring bed and skilfully and unerringly extracted a brush from under it. Back to his own bed he tiptoed, sat down on it, and began brushing my coat. He brushed it for a half-hour, speaking to no one, spoken to by no one. Finally he put the brush back, disposed the pelisse carefully on his arm, came to my bed, and as carefully laid it down. Then he took from the right-hand outside pocket a full *paquet jaune* and six loose cigarettes, showed them for my approval, and returned them to their place. '*Merci*,' was his sole remark. B. got Jean to sit down beside him on his bed and we talked for a few minutes, avoiding the subject of the recent struggle. Then Jean went back to his own bed and lay down.

It was not till later that we learned the climax—not till *le petit belge avec le bras cassé, le petit balayeur*, came hurrying to our end of the room and sat down with us. He was bursting with excitement, his well arm jerked and his sick one stumped about and he seemed incapable of speech. At length words came.

'*Monsieur Jean*' (now that I think of it, I believe some one had told him that all male children in America are named Jean at their birth) '*j'ai vu QUELQUE CHOSE! le nègre, vous savez?—il est FORT! Monsieur Jean, c'est un GÉANT, croyez moi! C'est pas un homme, tu sais? Je l'ai vu, moi*'— and he indicated his eyes.

We pricked our ears.

The *balayeur*, stuffing a pipe nervously with his tiny thumb, said: 'You saw the fight up here? So did I. The whole of it. *Le noir avait raison*. Well, when they took him downstairs, I slipped out too—*Je suis le balayeur, savez-vous?* and the *balayeur* can go where other people can't.'

—I gave him a match, and he thanked me. He struck it on his trousers with a quick pompous gesture, drew heavily on his squeaky pipe, and at last shot a minute puff of smoke into the air; then another, and another. Satisfied, he went on; his good hand grasping the pipe between its index and second fingers and resting on one little knee, his legs crossed, his small body hunched forward, wee unshaven face close to mine—went on in the confidential tone of one who relates an unbelievable miracle to a couple of intimate friends:

'Monsieur Jean, I followed. They got him to the *cabinot*. The door stood open. At this moment *les femmes descend-aient*, it was their *corvée d'eau, vous savez*. He saw them, *le noir*. One of them cried from the stairs, Is a Frenchman stronger than you, Jean? The *platons* were standing around him, the *Surveillant* was behind. He took the nearest *planton*, and tossed him down the corridor so that he struck against the door at the end of it. He picked up two more, one in each arm, and threw them away. They fell on top of the first. The last tried to take hold of Jean, and so Jean took him by the neck'—(the *balayeur* strangled himself for our benefit)—'and that *planton* knocked down the other three, who had got on their feet by this time. You should have seen the *Surveillant*. He had run away and was saying, "Capture him, capture him." The *plantons* rushed Jean; all four of them. He caught them as they came and threw them about. One knocked down the *Surveillant*. The *femmes* cried "*Vive, Jean,*" and clapped their hands. The *Surveillant* called to the *plantons* to take Jean, but they wouldn't go near Jean; they said he was a black devil. The women kidded them. They were so sore. And they could do nothing. Jean was laughing. His shirt was almost off him. He asked the *plantons* to come and take him, please. He asked the *Surveillant*, too. The women had set down their pails and were dancing up and down and yelling. The *Directeur* came down and sent them flying. The *Surveillant* and his *plantons* were as help-less as if they had been children. Monsieur Jean—*quelque chose.*'

I gave him another match. '*Merci*, Monsieur Jean.' He struck it, drew on his pipe, lowered it, and went on:

'They were helpless, and men. I am little. I have only one arm, *tu sais*. I walked up to Jean and said, "Jean, you

320

know me, I am your friend." He said, "Yes." I said to the *plantons*, "Give me that rope." They gave me the rope that they would have bound him with. He put out his wrists for me. I tied his hands behind his back. He was like a lamb. The *plantons* rushed up and tied his feet together. Then they tied his hands and feet together. They took the lacings out of his shoes for fear he would use them to strangle himself. They stood him up in an angle between two walls in the *cabinot*. They left him there for an hour. He was supposed to have been in there all night; but the *Surveillant* knew that he would have died, for he was almost naked, and *vous savez*, Monsieur Jean, it was cold in there. And damp. A fully-clothed man would have been dead in the morning. And he was naked . . . Monsieur Jean—*un géant!*'

—This same *petit belge* had frequently protested to me that *Il est fou, le noir*. He is always playing when sensible men try to sleep. The last few hours (which had made of the *fou a géant*) made of the scoffer a worshipper. Nor did 'le bras cassé' ever from that time forth desert his divinity. If as *balayeur* he could lay hands on a *morceau de pain* or *de viande*, he bore it as before to our beds; but Jean was always called over to partake of the forbidden pleasure.

As for Jean, one would hardly have recognized him. It was as if the child had fled into the deeps of his soul, never to reappear. Day after day went by, and Jean (instead of courting excitement as before) cloistered himself in solitude; or at most sought the company of B. and me and *Le Petit Belge* for a quiet chat or a cigarette. The morning after the three fights he did not appear in the *cour* for early promenade along with the rest of us (including The Sheeneys). In vain did *les femmes* strain their necks and eyes to find the *noir qui était plus fort que six français*. And B. and I noticed our bed-clothing airing upon the windowsills. When we mounted, Jean was patting and straightening our blankets, and looking for the first time in his life guilty of some enormous crime. Nothing however had disappeared. Jean said,

'Me feeks, *lits tous les jours.*' And every morning he aired and made our beds for us, and we mounted to find him smoothing affectionately some final ruffle, obliterating with enormous solemnity some microscopic crease. We gave him cigarettes when he asked for them (which was almost never) and offered them when we knew he had none or when we saw him borrowing from some one else whom his spirit held in less esteem. Of us he asked no favours. He liked us too well.

When B. went away, Jean was almost as desolate as I.

About a fortnight later, when the grey dirty snow-slush hid the black filthy world which we saw from our windows, and when people lived in their ill-smelling beds, it came to pass that my particular *amis*—The Zulu, Jean, Mexique—and I and all the remaining miserables of La Ferté descended at the decree of Cæsar Augustus to endure our bi-weekly *bain*. I remember gazing stupidly at Jean's chocolate-coloured nakedness as it strode to the tub, a rippling texture of muscular miracle. *Tout le monde* had *baigné* (including the Zulu, who tried to escape at the last minute and was nabbed by the *planton* whose business it was to count heads and see that none escaped the ordeal) and now *tout le monde* was shivering all together in the ante-room, begging to be allowed to go upstairs and get into bed—when *Le Baigneur*, Monsieur Richard's strenuous successor that is, set up a hue and cry that one *serviette* was lacking. The Fencer was sent for. He entered; heard the case; and made a speech. If the guilty party would immediately return the stolen towel, he, The Fencer, would guarantee that party pardon; if not, everyone present should be searched, and the man on whose person the *serviette* was found *va attraper quinze jours de cabinot*. This eloquence yielding no results. The Fencer exhorted the culprit to act like a man and render to Cæsar what is Cæsar's. Nothing happened. Everyone was told to get in single file and make ready to pass out the door. One after one we were searched; but so general was the curiosity that as fast as they were inspected the erstwhile bed-en-thusiasts, myself included, gathered on the side-lines to watch their fellows instead of availing themselves of the opportunity to go upstairs. One after one we came opposite The Fencer, held up our arms, had our pockets run through and our clothing felt over from head to heel, and were exonerated. When Cæsar came to Jean, Cæsar's eyes lighted, and Cæsar's hitherto perfunctory proddings and pokings became inspired and methodical. Twice he went over Jean's entire body, while Jean, his arms raised in a bored gesture, his face completely expressionless, suffered loftily the examination of his person. A third time the desperate Fencer tried; his hands, starting at Jean's neck, reached the calf of his leg— and stopped. The hands rolled up Jean's right trouser leg to the knee. They rolled up the underwear on his leg—and there, placed perfectly flat to the skin, appeared the missing *serviette*. As The Fencer seized it, Jean laughed—the utter laughter of old days—and the onlookers cackled uproariously, while with a broad smile The Fencer proclaimed: 'I thought I knew where I should find it.' And he added, more pleased with himself than anyone had ever seen him—'*Maintenant, vous pouvez tous monter à la chambre.*' We mounted, happy to get back to bed; but none so happy as Jean le Nègre. It was not that the *cabinot* threat had failed to materialize—at any minute a *planton* might call Jean to his punishment: indeed this was what everyone expected. It was that the incident had absolutely removed that inhibition which (from the day when Jean *le noir* became Jean *le gént*) had held the child, which was Jean's soul and destiny, prisoner. From that instant till the day I left him he was the old Jean—joking, fibbing, laughing, and always playing—Jean L'Enfant.

And I think of Jean Le Nègre . . . you are something to dream over, Jean; summer and winter (birds and darkness) you go walking into my head; you are a sudden and choco-late-coloured thing, in your hands you have a habit of hold-

323

ing six or eight *plantons* (which you are about to throw away) and the flesh of your body is like the flesh of a very deep cigar. Which I am still and always quietly smoking: always and still I am inhaling its very fragrant and remarkable muscles. But I doubt if ever I am quite through with you, if ever I will toss you out of my heart into the sawdust of forgetfulness. Kid, Boy, I'd like to tell you: *la guerre est finie*.

O yes, Jean: I do not forget, I remember Plenty; the snow's coming, the snow will throw again a very big and gentle shadow into The Enormous Room and into the eyes of you and me walking always and wonderfully up and down. . . .

—Boy, Kid, Nigger with the strutting muscles– take me up into your mind once or twice before I die (you know why: just because the eyes of me and you will be full of dirt some day). Quickly take me up into the bright child of your mind, before we both go suddenly all loose and silly (you know how it will feel). Take me up (carefully; as if I were a toy) and play carefully with me, once or twice, before I and you go suddenly all limp and foolish. Once or twice before you go into great Jack roses and ivory—(once or twice Boy before we together go wonderfully down into the Big Dirt laughing, bumped with the last darkness).

Glenway Wescott

THE SAILOR

TERENCE or Terrie Riley, back from sea, leaned on the edge
of the water-trough in the barnyard. His brother beside
him, with a hog-crate for a table, was mending harness.
Terrie could have helped him, but as if to suggest that having come home he would not stay, did nothing. A cigarette
was always fuming in one of his heavy hands, the other was
tucked under his belt. His almond finger nails were out-
lined with tar. On the back of the fingers at the ring-joint
had been tattooed in blue ink, a letter to a finger: H O L D
F A S T.

His brother's country eyes rested now and then on these
two animated words which could not be washed away, but
he would not make any inquiry concerning them. Neither
did he comment on the less definite alterations in the sailor's
appearance. He wore, for example, a belt instead of suspenders, and wore it about his hips rather than his waist.
His body thus elongated, if he stood on one leg, curved
out loosely in the opposite direction. If he stood erect he
held the initialled hands close to his sides like someone
always about to begin a dance. His eyes looked even bluer
now that the eyelids were coarsened and ruddy. His mouth
had hardened into an expression; once it had been like a
sturdy girl's, in spite of the drink. He still had curly hair
the color of bee's-wax and pointed teeth which seemed to
bite his tongue when he smiled. It seemed sinister to his
brother that he laughed less and smiled more.

The elder Riley had fancied that the sea was a hard place
and that sailors were rude, bow-legged creatures, perhaps
dark as a result of storms and salt, perhaps tongue-tied from
perpetual solitude. So he was astonished by this merely

325

flushed and tired homecomer, in whose face instead of age there was a look of strange precocity—knots of worn muscle, soft shadows of grimaces left by foreign emotions—indifferent to all that he had left behind several years before, voluble as an aged man.

In spite of his talkativeness, he was somehow inexpressive. He was not thinking in the words he used or, for that matter, in any words. He repeated himself, uttered sentences in which there was nothing remarkable very emphatically, and combined the weakest phrases with the coarsest ejaculations, as if to give his past actions a virility which his ideas did not have, about which he might even have had certain doubts. Meanwhile his eyes lost their precision, and he seemed to be gazing at the very fruits of experience, with the bloom still upon them, his greed unsatisfied.

The sky was burning all about the big Wisconsin sun. Hogs sighed in the mud-hole behind the straw-stack. There were no human beings to be seen in any field.

"It was just luck to get sent on the other side," Terrie said. "They work 'em hard in the Pacific, they tell me. We got around a lot. Brest and Cardiff and Kiel and Marseilles and all those places. Where I liked it best was Villefranche."

He was never going back there again, it had made him miserable, he loathed it yet liked it best; and he thought of the little boys on the water-front with wet-looking eyes, cigarette butts, dirty habits, some of them blond, supposed to be American, sailors having got ignorant or merely scheming girls into trouble. He wished he had done so, to have left a baby there like him, but he guessed his girl Zizi and her friend Minette would not want to be bothered with one —neither would he, in their place.

A young steer came down the lane to drink from the trough. Its hide kept rippling under a swarm of flies. It sighed with its plump, emasculate muzzle under water. The water was dark and there were vivid lumps of slime in it.

326

"Yeah, I liked Villefranche all right. A good town, but awful dirty."

A little half-moon of stone-and-plaster town in a narrow-necked harbor, all the buildings facing the sea, flesh-pink and yellow like a faded canary-bird and different shades of white with blue shutters; all one cliff of tenements, a street which was a staircase crossing at right angles another which was a filthy tunnel; around little squares the walls painted with false windows and false half-open or closed shutters and ornaments in false relief, like opera settings of canvas seeming to hang diagonally overhead, seeming to sway because of the brightness of the air; with a constant festivity of washing on strings from window to window, worn-out banners and ragged flags of underwear, with glimpses of dishevelled beds, and shapeless females leaning out of the upper stories with their dresses slipping off their shoulders; and all the ground floors breathing forth an odor of the saliva of a vast beast. Above the tenements a church which looked like a tombstone and higher up, in walled gardens, the villas, bright and ugly and muffled in spectral vegetation—instead of moist lawns and trees a stiff plumage of palms and other palms shaped like pineapples and cactus with its big blades of paralyzed grass and the nervous, translucent olive-orchards; and still higher up, insignificant mountains of stones and stone-pines, without peaks, without snow, without color, looking dried-up in the diamond light. A landscape wisely spoiled for the sake of the people; down below in the port the young women harmed whenever the men enjoyed it (when Terrie first came there he could not bear to see women crying and gave them anything to stop it) and nothing done to the men, little or nothing required of them—a peaceful, immoral liberty left to do its work for good or ill. The air was always scented; added to the different odors of the sea there were roses and lilies, orange blossoms and carnations, in a mixture; one morning one of these would fade out of the potpourri and another take its

327

place; you never knew which was which, you never spoke of it, most of the time you did not smell it at all, tirelessly breathing instead the odor given off along the quay by the row of bars—an acrid compound of sweat, stale liquor, cheaply perfumed girls, sour mops, bad breath—the odor exhaled in furnished rooms by love and sleep.

"It's a small town, but you could raise hell," Terrie Riley told his brother, back in Wisconsin. "They don't have any winter. There's quite a good-sized city near, too."

The wages of a common sailor in francs were the equivalent of a rich young Frenchman's allowance; if his record and his health were good he was entitled to every other night on shore, and the work on board was easy, like sleep a chance to sober up and a regular refreshment of desire; all of which wealth of time and money and vitality was spent in the neighboring great city on complicated amusements that they simplified to suit their tastes, or right there in the sight of the battleship, in the Villefranche bars, their back walls jewelled with bottles, a coughing music from the tin morning-glories of old-fashioned phonographs in most of them; only the "Home Hotel" bar (the headquarters of the flock of women who followed the navy from port to port) had an orchestra: a tuberculous girl violinist, a very muscular pianist, a drummer like a rat with a diagonal mouth and no hair.

In Wisconsin an old horse came down to the trough in its turn, the hide of its shoulders worn out, its bones making their way out and up through the flesh. It stood between the two brothers, and for a moment one of its sagging, gelatinous eyes rested on Terrie's face. Certainly he was no farmer any more; animals made him vaguely uncomfortable, though he had learned that it was not when human beings were like animals that they were most terrible or dangerous.

He remembered the great orgy at Mother Seraphine's the night before the ship left for home, the last night he spent with his girl Zizi whom he thought he loved and was glad to

328

get rid of. The sailors bought hard-boiled eggs by the dozen to throw at each other; one danced with a full bottle balanced in his mouth, the brandy streaming down his neck and all over his uniform; some, as close together as they could get in a corner, tried to sing, but were choked by who could tell what vague emotion; some danced and fell down, but would not fall alone; through the air, smoky like an olive-tree, you could see a mix-up of the ecstasy of faces, of limp knees, of the admirable gestures of drunken hands, vaguely keeping time with several hoarse banjos; suddenly with a shattering of glass a grinning man made his entrance through a high window, having climbed up on the grape-arbor, and Mother Seraphine's fat husband, beside himself, ran around in circles, but smiled, able to afford to smile. The women were sad, especially the youngest, and preferred to sit in corners, though the one they called Tata held on to two sailors and her old hair which was like hay came down —it was she who sold dope. Terrie's girl Zizi had some bills in her stocking and counted them impassively; she had made a fool of him, but he could afford to be tender because he was never going to see her again and besides he was too drunk to know the difference between enemy and friend— no one was his enemy, no one was his friend. The sea, like a bird or a jewel in the daytime, had turned black that night; there was nothing left of the battleship but some sparkling balconies up in the dark and a sparkling staircase leading from nowhere to nowhere, or in fact from Villefranche to Wisconsin; and Terrie was going to take away with him the lesson of the former without quite knowing what it was.

"The only trouble with Villefranche was: there were too many women," he told his brother. "There was one they called the Folle. That means, the Nut."

She had married an American sergeant who was killed in the war and drew a pension from the government, so she was well-to-do; she was still young and healthy; she followed the ships but did not care for the men, followed the women;

she wore her hat wrong side before or two skirts, one over and higher than the other, and imagined that she started all the fashions; the girls often got her to dance with Zizi, who whirled her around until she had a fit of hysterics, at which everyone laughed, but it was not cruel because she enjoyed it; and late at night she walked up and down the quay singing operas that she made up as she went along, a symbol of abnormal ways of passing the time, agitating a ghostly shawl.

Pressed down in one corner of the Wisconsin landscape between the sunshine and the monotonous fields there was a mass of clouds full of spasmodic thunder—anger about to break, a humiliating story untold. Probably it was going to rain.

Terrie could have gone on all afternoon telling anecdotes about women, but his brother did not seem particularly interested. There was a girl who came down from Paris in the height of fashion, a white turtle-necked sweater with a string of pearl beads over it and a little dog on a leash; she played cards with the men, lost all her money one night, and had no room; she had cheated at poker, so they did nothing but laugh at her, and she paced up and down the quay, sobbing as loudly as she could, "Where'm I going to sleep? Where'm I going to sleep?" Then a big sailor from Kansas swung down the staircase street, and not knowing what was the matter, walked up to her, said, "Aw shut up! You make too much noise," slapped her face, and got into the launch going to the ship; the girl staggered back against the wall, too astonished to fight back, then whimpered with a disturbing, soft simplicity, and finally went off somewhere.

As far as one could see in Wisconsin that afternoon, trees were rolling in their deep valley beds, and there was an atmosphere of sorrow which nothing had happened to cause.

Fleshy, serene women, heartsick girls making a violent effort to amuse, others hungry and fantastic, some rosy with fever as well as rouge, adolescent beggars making exciting equivocal appeals for pity, old spent saleswomen, all with

330

the happy look of intoxicating sterility. . . . There was one, almost a child, with the protruding mouth and fine glazed eyes of an alley cat, Terrie forgot her name; there was one who wore glasses and looked like a school-teacher; there was Minette, Zizi's friend, a pallid beast who never slept.

Along the Wisconsin road passed two hired girls in gingham aprons. Their cool faces with a mingled expression of fear and independence meant nothing to the returned sailor. In spite of their youth, their long bodies already looked hollow, like those of mothers after childbirth . . .

Whereas the women abroad were short-legged and rounded out, even the thin ones; their glances were both brazen and dependent; around their eyes the eyelids were ashen; the moistly painted mouths were hard in the middle and broken in the corners; they did not walk like men; and even their dishonesty, their anger, were flattery of a sort.

There were two Turks, one vigorous and handsome, the other enormously fat but more popular, especially with the older sailors, who spoke a little English and no French, having taken off the veil to follow the ships, and late at night the vigorous one, tying about her a shawl with fringes, often gave an exhibition of their dances, turning all the middle of her body as if it were a wheel, jerking her neck almost out of joint rhythmically, drumming softly with one index finger against the other over her head, Pauline, her friend, grovelling at her feet with the glittering nickel tray on which drinks were served; and a certain sailor in his excitement covered his eyes, whimpered, and cried aloud, "Ooh, take her away . . ."

"I took turns with most of 'em," Terrie boasted without enthusiasm to his brother. "Then after a while I got to playing around steady with a girl from there. That was Zizi. One was enough for me, I figured. And she was healthy and kind'a steady. She didn't cost much. She was a good kid in a lot'a ways."

Once an adolescent girl of a miserable Algerian family who wanted to have sweethearts and better clothes and whose mother beat her, was driven down the street by one of her young brothers, and took refuge in a bar, among the women; an unlovely little animal, she sobbed and beat her forehead with her dark fists; the sailors bought her sandwiches, the women petted her; she wanted to return home but was afraid, and it was Zizi who had the courage to go with her to the one-room home in the underground street, hoping to conciliate the Mohammedans; but they gave her a black eye before they began to punish the girl.

When she came back, shedding tears but trying to laugh, she and Terrie went to a quieter place, a green-painted café under an arbor of wistaria, empty but for two Filipinos, cooks on board, playing checkers; over the zinc bar there was a framed poster of a woman with blushing breasts and violets in her hair, a sort of patron saint; and there Zizi sat, wistful at the right moment, smoking, the smoke curling up over her tempting tired mouth, holding his hand; and later, in her poor room, she was like a little fern, moist and colorless, motionless but opening.

"I got real crazy about her," Terrie told his brother. "Crazy, I tell you."

The mimosa was in bloom, clinging branches dipped in a sweet yellow snuff, its odor tickling the throat with a mysterious thirst; and in the morning on the quay of slabs of stone, where some of the fishing-nets dried like splashes of sepia applied with a brush while old women mended the others, the girls of the bar were lazy and restless, preening themselves. In the evening the sea slept, and when the moon rose the villas and roads and precipices lay in complete reflections on the surface of the harbor; and in her little room where Zizi lay in a torn pink blanket, by moonlight, by street-lamp light, by the sparkle of the lighthouse, her body was now snowy, now gray as a pearl, and all was perfect. She caressed him from head to foot, mechanically, carefully, like

332

a cat with its kitten. He could not make her laugh, and as the night passed and he grew quite sober a sort of meek and pure delirium took command; yet this woman was no novelty to him, there was no novelty in women. . . He wanted her in the very moment of possession, wanted her not there but in Wisconsin, felt homesick for the farm and the snow. When he went back to the ship early in the morning it was misty and soundless, and there in the harbor with Cap Ferrat's arm around it, floated the battleship like an insane silver-gray palace; he was grateful to it for having brought him there, thought how he had made fun of other sailors who had married or wanted to marry their girls in port, and thought that he had not known what he was talking about.

Terrie would have liked to explain to his brother how and why he had considered marrying this French girl. But it had come to nothing in the end. So he kept it to himself.

He told Zizi that if she behaved well he would marry her at the end of the year and take her to America, whereupon she clenched her fists excitedly as if the promise were a sumptuous gift, but only for a moment; then gazed out to sea with a sort of patient grimace, not deigning to believe good news; but after that loved him with a new vitality—systematic, oppressive, interested—which hurt and excited him still more; an extreme jealousy was added to his pleasure, he saying "You're my woman, see," the girl weeping sincerely; so in the tumult of drinks and rendezvous, appetites and punishments, friends in trouble, money lost or stolen, fights and dancing, weeks of their quiet, heedless, bitter idyll passed. Then, of course, the battleship went on to other ports; Zizi stayed there and he sent her money every month; meanwhile his relative continence was just another kind of sensuality, and he exasperated his friends by his sentimental bad temper.

"When we got back there my girl had a girl-friend they called Minette, the bastard. She was all right at first."

He could remember the day he met her, a plump, white,

333

older woman with gleaming eyes and a drooping pink mouth who stood beside Zizi in the square behind the hotel in front of a butcher shop with bead portières to keep out the flies, a pile of livers on a table upheld by an iron Cupid painted red. What could have been said with so little of two languages in common? So he put his arm around Zizi and mechanically caressed her, while the other stared at him shamelessly and licked her lips, and he felt a delicious uneasiness because Zizi did not seem jealous.

"She was a bad one, that Minette," he insisted to his brother, who went on working without a sign of being impressed. His eyes swept the scene in Wisconsin with irregular glances. There was a difference between his eyes and his brother's, which had the appearance of astigmatism that serenity and fatigue and long vistas make common among farmers. Terrie's were charged with nervous apathy, the apathy of appetites that have outlived desire, of satiety that is still sensitive. Essentially it was this difference which he needed to explain and could not.

In the afternoon, somewhat drunk, he went up to Zizi's room, found the two girls on the couch in each other's arms apparently reading a newspaper, and felt something which resembled a high fever before he had had time to shut the door behind him—the new girl rich and pale, as if bloodless, with shadows of dimples here and there, and dark willowy familiar Zizi; clumsily he forced his way between them, for a moment preferred the blonde, and there was a barbaric luxury in the poor room which he understood then only as one more indulgence to the male among women, the sailor on shore, feeling shame for the first time and liking it. Presently he kept quiet, having had just enough drink neither to sleep soundly nor to stay wide awake; it was hard to focus his attention on certain sounds which he heard, certain movements which he felt, but they made him think himself somehow neglected in his drowsiness, and when he opened his eyes he had to look at the two girls a

334

had stood for a moment outside, on a slab of stone at the water's edge, looking back through the open door where her friend Minette was laughing and stumbling to the music with one arm around a sailor and the other around a young man of the town; and she had a strange expression both of hate and sympathy, an expression which seemed to affirm that she was the one who was neglected and betrayed, but her face had not looked living at all: like that of a stone statue amid the excess, the malice, the happiness, like the sculpture of a dried-up fountain he had seen in a crowded street somewhere over there—dried-up for him at least.

The next day all the women wept, which flattered and cheered up the men; even Minette cried; Terrie's own eyes were moist, and many others'. The ship put out to sea at dark; solemnly its three or four searchlights played over the mother-of-pearl tenements, the villas in the hills, the feathery orchards; the shore and the breakwater were covered with silhouettes of people, waving their clothing, more and more silent, more and more sober; he could not distinguish Zizi from the rest and did not try to; never again would he see the launches come in by day or night with one sailor standing still in front, straighter than a figurehead, a flag-pole in human form, nor be that sailor; never again would he lose himself in that night full of bottles, musical instruments, kisses; he had had enough; the ship's band played "Auld Lang Syne," a few men sang.

"Well, it's a great life," his brother admitted with a mingling of two accents: one of envy of the experiences he had missed, one of profound indifference to the results of those experiences, whatever they were. "And I guess once you've been a sailor you aren't fit for much of any other life. You wouldn't have the patience."

"Well, I've got to have some fun," Terrie replied, disturbed by his brother's tone. "I got used to it. But I know one thing, I'm not going to join the navy again. I guess I'll go east and get a job."

He gazed out of the high barn-door over Wisconsin: green, sumptuous, tedious, both rich and poor at once, with little sad houses and no night-life. What was odious in it was identical with what was dear. He wanted either the violence which causes sorrow or else—no sorrow. Wisconsin mourned without having any disappointment to mourn for. Very vaguely Terrie was lonesome for temptation and regret, for sharp contrasts, for distinct good and evil—in other words, for Europe—but at the same time he hated these things from the bottom of his heart because they had made a fool of him.

Down below in the barnyard more steers, the cows, and another old horse, one before another in a procession, drew near the trough to drink. The young ones brutally pushed the others out of the way. There was a great sunbeam in the water from the setting sun. Probably it was not going to rain.

"Well," his brother went on, "I guess you might as well clear out again when we've had our visit. This ain't no place for you. You can't even get all the drink you want any more—and it's a good thing. You'd get into trouble with girls."

Terrie thought that was not what he meant; he did not want any more sweethearts, or any more drink. Nevertheless, there was a kind of thirst which, like the animals down below, he would have to quench. Wisconsin was no place for one whom its rain, its thousand of luminous creeks, its ponds, its heavy and fertile dew, failed to satisfy. Terrie had no desire to stay there on the farm with a brother who did not know enough about life to understand what he was talking about.

Kay Boyle

DEFEAT

Toward the end of June that year and through July, there was a sort of uncertain pause, an undetermined suspension that might properly be called neither an armistice nor a .peace, and it lasted until the men began coming back from where they were. They came at intervals, trickling down from the north in twos or threes, or even one by one, some of them prisoners who had escaped and others merely a part of that individual retreat in which the sole destination was home. They had exchanged their uniforms for something else as they came along—corduroys, or workmen's blue, or whatever people might have given them in secret to get away in—bearded, singularly and shabbily outfitted men getting down from a bus or off a train without so much as a knapsack in their hands and all with the same bewildered, scarcely discrepant story to tell. Once they had reached the precincts of familiarity, they stood there a moment where the vehicle had left them, maybe trying to button the jacket that didn't fit them or set the neck or shoulders right, like men who have been waiting in a courtroom and have finally heard their names called and stand up to take the oath and mount the witness stand. You could see them getting the words ready—revising the very quality of truth—and the look in their eyes, and then someone coming out of the post office or crossing the station square in the heat would recognize them and go toward them with a hand out, and the testimony would begin.

They had found their way back from different places, by different means, some on bicycle, some by bus, some over the mountains on foot, coming home to the Alpes-Maritimes from Rennes, or from Clermont-Ferrand, or from Lyons, or from any part of France, and looking as incongruous to modern defeat as survivors of the Confederate Army might have looked, transplanted to this year and place (with their spurs still on and their soft-brimmed, dust-whitened hats), limping wanly back, half dazed and not yet having managed to get the story of what happened straight. Only, this time, they were the men of that tragically unarmed and undirected force which had been the French Army once but was no longer, returning to what orators might call reconstruction but which they knew could never be the same.

Wherever they came from, they had identical evidence to give: that the German ranks had advanced bareheaded, in short-sleeved summer shirts—young, blond-haired men with their arms linked, row on row, and their trousers immaculately creased, having slept all night in hotel beds and their stomachs full, advancing singing and falling singing before the puny coughing of the French machine guns. That is, the first line of them might fall, and part of the second, possibly, but never more, for just then the French ammunition would suddenly expire and the bright-haired, blond demi-gods would march on singing across their dead. Then would follow all the glittering display: the rust-proof tanks and guns, the chromium electric kitchens, the crematoriums. Legends or truth, the stories became indistinguishable in the mouths of the Frenchmen who returned—that the Germans were dressed as if for tennis that summer, with nothing but a tune to carry in their heads, while the French crawled out from under lorries where they'd slept maybe every night for a week, going to meet them like crippled, encumbered miners emerging from the pit of a warfare fifty years interred, with thirty-five kilos of kit and a change of shoes and a tin helmet left over from 1914 breaking them in two as they met the brilliantly nickelled Nazi dawn. They said their superiors were the first to run; they said their ammunition had been sabotaged; they said the ambulances had been transformed into accommodations for the officers' lady friends; they said "Nous avons été vendus" or "On nous a vendu" over and over, until you could have made a popular song of it—the words and the music of defeat. After their testimony was given, some of them added (not the young but those who had fought before) in grave, part-embittered, part vainglorious voices, "I'm ashamed to be a Frenchman" or "I'm ashamed of being French today," and then gravely took their places with the others.

There was one man, though, who didn't say any of these things, probably because he had something else on his mind. He was a dark, short, rather gracefully made man, not thirty yet, with hot, handsome eyes and a cleft chin. Even when he came back without his uniform and without the victory, a certain air of responsibility, of authority, remained because he had been the chauffeur of the mail bus before the war. He didn't sit talking in the bistro about what he had seen and where he had been, but he got the black beard off his face as quickly as he could, and bought a pair of new shoes, and went back to work in stubborn-lipped, youthful, almost violent pride. Except one night he did tell the story; he told it only once, about two months after he got back, and not to his own people or the people of the village but, as if by chance, to two commercial travellers for rival fruit-juice firms who were just beginning to circulate again from town to town in the Unoccupied Zone. They sat at the Café Central together, the three of them, drinking wine, talking about the anachronism of horse-and-mule-drawn cannon in Flanders and the beasts running amok under the enemy planes, and saying how they had all believed that the French line was going to hold somewhere, that it wasn't going to break.

"At first we thought it would hold at the Oise," one of the travelling men said. "We kept on retreating, saying the new front must be at the Oise, and believing it too, and then, when we dropped below the Oise, we kept saying it would hold at the Marne, and believing it, and then we thought it would be the Seine, and even when we were south of Paris we kept on believing about some kind of a line holding on the Loire . . ."

"I still don't know why we stopped retreating," said the other commercial traveller. He sat looking soberly at his glass. "We can't talk about the Italians any more. I still don't see why we didn't retreat right down to Senegal. I don't see what stopped us," he said. Then the quiet-mouthed little bus-driver began telling them about what had happened to him on the fourteenth of July.

He had been told, he said, that in some of the cities the enemy hadn't taken or had withdrawn from, processions formed on the fourteenth and passed through the streets in silence, the flagstaffs they carried draped with black and their heads bowed. In some of the villages, the mayor, dressed in mourning laid a wreath on the monument to the last war's dead while the peasants kneeled about him in the square.

"I was in Pontcharra on the fourteenth," said one of the travelling salesmen, "and when the mayor put the wreath down and the bugle called out like that for the dead, all the peasants uncovered themselves, but the military didn't even stand at attention."

"By that time none of the privates were saluting their officers in the street anywhere you went," said the other sales-man, but the bus-driver didn't pay any attention to what they said. He went on telling them that he'd been taken pri-soner near Rennes on the seventeenth of June, and that there he saw the tracts the Boche planes had showered down the week before. The tracts said, "Frenchmen, prepare your coffins! Frenchwomen, get out your ball dresses! We're go-ing to dance the soles off your shoes on the fourteenth of July!" He told the commercial travellers exactly what use they made of the tracts in the public places there. He was more than three weeks in the prison camp, he said, and on the night of the twelfth of July he and a copain made their escape. They went in uniform, on borrowed bicycles. They kept to the main road all night, wheeling along as free and unmolested in the dark as two young men cycling home from a dance, with their hearts light, and the stars out over them, and the night air mild. At dawn they took to the side roads, and toward eight o'clock of the new day they saw a house standing alone, a little in advance of the village that lay ahead.

"We'll ask there," the bus-driver had said, and they pushed their cycles in off the road and laid them down behind a tree. The house, they could see then, was the schoolhouse, with a sign for "Filles" over one door and for "Garçons" over the other. The copain said there would be nobody there, but the bus-driver had seen a woman come to the window and look at them, and he walked up to the door.

The desks were empty because of what had happened and the time of year but the bus-driver said he knew it must have been the schoolmistress who was standing in the middle of the room between the benches, a young woman with fair, wavy hair, eying them fearlessly and even sharply as they came. The bus-driver and his copain said good morning, and they saw at once the lengths of three-colored stuff in her hands and the work she had been doing. They looked around them and saw four French flags clustered in each corner of the classroom and great loops of bunting that were draped along three sides of the room. The first thing the bus-driver thought was that she ought to be warned, she ought to be told, and then, when he looked at her face again, he knew she knew as much as or more than they.

"You ought to keep the door locked," he had said, and the schoolmistress looked at him almost in contempt.

"I don't care who comes in," she said, and she went on folding the bunting into the lengths she wanted to cut it to drape across the farthest wall.

"So the village is occupied?" the bus-driver said.

"Yes," she said, but she began cutting the tricolor bunting.

"There's one thing," said the copain, looking a little

343

bleakly at the two others. "If you give yourself up, at least you don't get shot."

The schoolmistress had put her scissors down and said to the bus-driver, "You'll have to get rid of your uniforms before there's any chance of you getting through." She glanced around the classroom as though the demands of action had suddenly made it strange to her. "Take them off and put them in the cupboard there," she had said, "and cover yourselves with this stuff while you wait," and she heaped the blue and white and red lengths upon the desks. "In case they might come in," she said. She took her hat and filet off the hook as she said, "I'll come back with other clothes for you."

"If there would be any way of getting something to eat," the bus-driver had said, and because he asked this, the tide of courage seemed to rise even higher in her.

"Yes," she said. "I'll bring back food for you."

"And a bottle of pinard," said the copain, but he didn't say it very loud.

When she was gone, they took their uniforms off and wrapped the bunting around themselves, doing it for her and modesty's sake, and then they sat down at the first form's desks, swathed to their beards in red, white, and blue. Even if the Boches had walked into the schoolhouse then, there probably wasn't any military regulation made to deal with what they would have found, the bus-driver had said to his copain—just two Frenchmen in their underwear sitting quietly inside the colors of their country's flag. But whether he said the other thing to the teacher as soon as she brought the bread and sausage and wine and the scraps of other men's clothing back, he didn't know. Sometimes, when he thought of it afterward, he wasn't quite sure he had ever got the actual words out, but then he remembered the look on her face as she stood by the tree where the bicycles had lain and watched them pedalling toward the village just ahead, and he knew he must have said it. He knew he must have wiped the sausage grease and the wine off his mouth

344

with the back of his hand and said "A country isn't defeated as long as its women aren't" or "until its women are" or "As long as the women of a country aren't defeated, it doesn't matter if its army is"—something like that, perhaps saying it just before they shook hands with her and cycled away.

That was the morning of the thirteenth, and the bus-driver told how they rode all day in the heat, two what-might-have-been-peasants cycling slowly hour after hour across the hushed, summery, sunny land. The war was over for them, for this country the war was over; there was no sound or look of it in the meadows or the trees or grain. The war was finished, but the farmhouse they stopped at that evening would not take them in.

"Have you got your bread tickets with you?" the peasant said, and even the white-haired sows behind his legs eyed them narrowly with greed.

"We're prisoners escaped. We've got a bit of money," the bus-driver said. "We'll pay for our soup, and maybe you'll let us sleep in the loft."

"And when the Boches come in for the milk they'll shoot me and the family for having taken you in!" the peasant said, and the bus-driver stood looking at him bitterly a moment before he began to swear. When he had called the man the names he wanted to, he said, "Look here, we were soldiers—perhaps you haven't got that yet? We haven't been de-mobilized; we were taken prisoner, we escaped. We were fighting a little war up there."

"If you'd fought it better, the Boches wouldn't have got this far," the peasant said. He said it in cunning and tri-umph, and then he closed the door.

They slept the night at the next farm (the bus-driver told the commercial travellers), eating soup and bread and drink-ing red wine in the kitchen, and when they had paid for it they were shown up to the loft. But they were not offered the side on which the hay lay; the farmer was thinking of next winter and he told them they could lie down just as well on the boards. They slept heavily and well, and it was very light when the woke in the morning, and so that day, the day of the fourteenth, they did not get far. By six that night they were only another hundred kilometres on, and then the copain's tire went flat. But a little town stood just ahead and they pushed their bicycles toward it through the summer evening, and down its wide, treeless street. They hadn't seen the uniform yet, but they knew the Germans must be there. Even on the square in the heart of town they saw no sign, but still there was that unnatural quiet, that familiar uneasiness on the air, so they pushed their wheels through the open doors of a big garage, past the dry and padlocked gas pumps, and stood them up against the inside wall. There, in the garage's half-security and semi-dark, they looked around them; twenty or more cars stood one beside the other, halted as if forever because of the lack of fluid to flow through their veins. Overhead the glass panes of the roof were still painted blue; the military and staff cars parked in the shadowy silence still bore their green-and-khaki camouflage. The war was over, everything had stopped, and out beyond the wide-open automobile doorway they saw the dance platform that had been erected in the square, and the dark, leafy branches twined on its upright beams and balustrade, and the idle people standing looking. There were no flags up, only this rather dismal atmosphere of preparation, and it was then the bus-driver and his copain had remembered it was the fourteenth.

"It's a national holiday and we haven't had a drink yet," the copain said. He stood there in the garage with his hands in the pockets of the trousers that didn't belong to him, staring bleakly out across the square. Even when two German soldiers who were putting electric wiring up in the dance pavilion came into view, his face did not alter. He simply went on saying, "We haven't had the apéritif all day."

The bus-driver took a packet of cigarettes out of his

346

jacket pocket and put one savagely on his lip. As he lit it, he looked in hot, bitter virulence out to where the Germans were hanging strings of bulbs among the fresh, dark leaves.

" 'Frenchmen, prepare your coffins!' " he had said, and then he gave a laugh. "They've made only one mistake so far, just one," he said, and as he talked the cigarette jerked up and down in fury on his lip. "They've got the dance floor and the decorations all right, and they've probably got the music, and maybe the refreshments too. So far so good," he said. "But they haven't got the partners. That's what's going to be funny. That's what's going to be really funny."

The bus-driver sat there in the Café Central telling it to the two commercial travellers, perhaps because he had had more to drink than usual, telling them the story, or perhaps because it had been weighing long enough heavy on his heart. He told them about the dinner the garage owner gave him and his copain: civet and fried potatoes and salad and four kinds of cheese and armagnac with the coffee. He said they could scarcely get it all down and that then their host opened a bottle of champagne for them. That's the kind of man the garage owner was. And during the dinner or afterward, with the wine inside of him, it seems the bus-driver had said it again. He had said something about as long as the women of a nation weren't defeated the rest of it didn't matter, and just as he said it the music struck up in the dance pavilion outside.

The place the garage owner offered them for the night was just above the garage itself, a sort of storeroom, with three windows overlooking the square. First he repaired the copain's tire for him, and behind him on the wall as he worked they read the newspaper cutting he had pinned up, perhaps in some spirit of derision. It exhorted all Frenchmen to accept quietly and without protest the new regulations concerning the circulation of private and public vehicles.

"Without protest!" the garage owner had said, taking the

347

dripping red tube out of the basin of water and pinching the leak between his finger and thumb. "I'll have to close the place up, and they ask me to do it without protest." He stood rubbing sandpaper gently around where the imperceptible hole in the rubber was. "We weren't ready for war and yet we declared it just the same," he said, "and now we've asked for peace and we aren't ready for that, either." When he had finished with the tire he showed them up the stairs.

"I'll keep the light off," he said, "in case it might give them the idea of coming up and having a look," but there was no need for any light, for the illumination of the dance pavilion in the square shone in through the windows and lit the rows of storage batteries and the cases of spare parts and spark plugs. From outside, they heard the music playing—the exact waltz time and the quick, entirely martial version of swing.

"Somebody ought to tell them they're wasting their time," the bus-driver had said, jerking one shoulder toward the windows. He could have burst out laughing at the sight of them, he explained, some with white gloves on even, waiting out there to the strains of music for what wasn't going to come.

The garage owner shook out the potato sacks of waste on the floor and gave them the sacks to lie down on, and then he took one look out the window at the square and grinned and said good night and went downstairs. The copain was tired and he lay down at once on the soft rags on the floor and drew a blanket up over him, but the bus-driver had stood a while at one side of the window, watching the thing below. A little group of townspeople was standing around the platform where the variously colored lights hung, and the band was playing in one corner of the pavilion underneath the leaves. No one was dancing, but the German soldiers were hanging around in expectation, some standing on the steps of the platform and some leaning on the garnished rails.

"For a little while there wasn't a woman anywhere," the bus-driver told the commercial travellers. "There was this crowd of people from the town, perhaps thirty or forty of them looking on, and maybe some others further back in the dark where you couldn't see them, but that was all," and then he stopped talking.

"And then what happened?" said one of the travelling men after a moment, and the bus-driver sat looking in silence at his glass.

"They had a big, long table spread out with things to eat on it," he said in a minute, and he didn't look up. "They had fruit tarts, it looked like, and sweet chocolate, and bottles of lemonade and beer. They had as much as you wanted of everything," he said. "And perhaps once you got near enough to start eating and drinking, then the other thing just followed naturally afterward—or that's the way I worked it out," he said. "Or maybe, if you've had a dress a long time that you wanted to wear and you hadn't had the chance of putting it on and showing it off because all the men were away—I mean if you were a woman. I worked it out that maybe the time comes when you want to put it on so badly that you put it on just the same whatever's happened, or maybe, if you're one kind of a woman, any kind of a uniform looks all right to you after a certain time. The music was good, it was first class," he said, but he didn't look up. "And here was all this food spread out, and the corks popping off the bottles, and the lads in uniform, great, big fellows, handing out chocolates to all the girls. . . ."

The three of them sat at the table without talking for a while after the bus-driver's voice had ceased, and then one of the travelling men said, "Well, that was just one town."

"Yes, that was just one town," said the bus-driver, and when he picked up his glass to drink, something as crazy as tears was standing in his eyes.

Stark Young

SUNDAY RACES

IN THE midst of the flowers and graces of Heaven Trees, its
scented garden walks and affable ways, there stood an element of character, nevertheless: certain obligations, certain
codes, certain points of conscience and honor. In the same
way exactly among the figures of us stood Parson Bates, our
county preacher and my Uncle George's friend. In the
midst of the Sunday pleasures, the reunion of friends and
families and the merriment of cousins and neighbors, with
bright mornings and smiles and news of the week—in the
midst of such a Sunday he stood firm and hot. He had character, thunder, conscience, and every form of fiery strength.

Parson Bates was a sight you could look at a long time
without guessing who he was or what he did. He had a red
face, big red hands, towsled hair, and a more towsled stock
about his neck. He dressed in black, with a greenish gloss
about the knees and elbows. He looked violent, looked to be
made up of very human flesh that had been battered into
sanctity; the air of him was strong and aggressive, full of
tamed lions and flapping wings. In sum, he might have been
a sort of apostolic prize-fighter or a champion wrestler of
the church militant, boxing about like a divine Castor and
Pollux in a new religion. On week-days he preached in Sena-
tobia or Longtown, on Saturdays nearly always in Sardis. At
Cistern Hill, the church my uncle had built for the colored
people three miles way, Parson Bates preached twice a year;
at which times he gave them hell-fire, heavenly harmony and
brimstone enough to last them the rest of the season. They
could rise to heaven and wash their feet in milk before the
Saviour and eat honey if they behaved themselves, or could
roast in torment everlasting; they could take their choice.

On Sundays he preached at our own Fredonia church. He had preached all over north Mississippi and was known in every town, but of late years had settled more and more into Panola; and to Fredonia every Sunday we went, the ladies and little girls in their brightest gowns, the gentlemen at their best, the little boys very stiff and cautioned to be careful. And there we sat and heard him like a flowering meadow at the foot of an oak. . . .

The church at Fredonia, where Parson Bates preached on Sundays, was of brick with plaster columns across the porch and two huge doors leading inside. Here the light fell through high leaded windows over the plaster of the walls, the black beams and wainscoting, and the black pews, so high that you could see only the heads and bonnets of the congregation. In the gallery at the back a number of darkies sat, and from that place joined sometimes in the singing, not too loud, and moaned a little in the prayers, the older ones among them sometimes saying "Amen" and "Praise' be the Lord." There was a cool quietness and pride dwelling everywhere; it did not seem the house of a very jealous God.

A wide gate led into the grounds of the church, set between heavy arbor-vitæ trees, dark and pointed. The walk ran between box hedges, which left a lane of sunshine down the midst of it. The pleasant vagueness of the scent from the box was in the air and mingled indistinguishably with the fragrance of the crepe myrtles and syringas that were planted here and there.

How different it must have seemed to my Cousin Ellen that first Sunday she went, how different from the church at home in Pittsford, Vermont! . . .

Into this warm bright light my Cousin Ellen came again when the service was over. And I smile now to think of how that little face must have looked and what trouble or dismay or vague remoteness must have been in those gentle eyes, for she could not have been used to such power and volume in religion. If she had feared lest she fall into the sin of strayed thoughts, thinking of Pittsford and home when she should have heard the sermon at hand, she was mistaken; she had reckoned without her host if she had counted on any absent wandering among these reveries. Little she knew Parson Bates. She did not know that, though he always smiled when he approached the dinner-table, where she had already seen him, he always frowned when he went into the pulpit, where now he was to confront her among the other sinners. He gave out the hymn in a voice like thunder, so that the congregation when they began to sing, however loud they hit it off, always sounded like mere cowed mortals lifting up their wail to an angry God. Then Parson Bates took his text and preached. Hell-fire and eternal damnation were his central themes. He was one of those old-timers who lived a heavenly example and threatened hell.

Parson Bates had his moments of poetry too and what, I suppose, for his spirit, was a very serene and tranquil loveliness. He spoke of the golden censer in heaven and the golden altar before the throne with golden horns upon it. And once, he said, when the seventh seat was opened, "there was silence in heaven about the space of half an hour," which seemed to us quite a time in the midst of such violent offices as Parson Bates's.

He had some locusts, too, that he got from the Book of Revelation somewhere, who came out in smoke from the bottomless pit and were commanded not to hurt the grasses of the earth nor any green thing, nor any tree; but only those men which have not the seal of God in their foreheads. The shape of these locusts were like unto horses prepared unto battle; and on their heads were as it were crowns like gold and their faces were as the faces of men. And they had hair as the hair of women, and teeth as the teeth of lions, and they had breastplates as it were breastplates of iron; and the sound of their wings was as the sound of the chariots of many horses running to battle. And they had tails like unto

352

scorpions, and there were stings in their tails, and their power was to hurt men five months.

These locusts with the men's faces and women's hair and lions' teeth and stings that hurt you for five months, had a king over them with a pretty Greek name, I used to think, of Apollyon, meaning, Parson Bates said, destroyer; the Hebrew of it was Abaddon, he said.

There were also four angels loosed out of the River Euphrates and prepared for an hour and a day and a month and a year to assail the third part of man, and horses in a vision with breastplates of fire, jacinth, and brimstone, with lion heads, and fire and smoke and brimstone coming out of their mouths and power in their mouths and in their tails. They should make our bellies bitter, Parson Bates said.

My Cousin Ellen had heard him that first day pound and roar and exalt. "What is Behemoth," she thought, "what is Leviathan, to this man?" She felt thumped and thwacked all over. What vitality! What a voice among the beams and rafters! One almost expected heaven to open.

The children's eyes used to be big as saucers during these tremendous accounts of Parson Bates. I am excited when I think of these monstrous marvels even now. But I never was quite overcome, because I kept my eye on Uncle George and how he was taking it. When I was very small I used to slip my hand in his at the most terrifying climaxes, but later on I merely glanced at Uncle George to see how matters stood. He sat back in his pew with a pleased and hearty look on his face, with his gaze on Bates, as if he were peering down into a divine arena where a plucky little boy was raising the dust. He was not afraid of either Bates or God, but I thought he liked both of them better than any of us did.

When church had ended, every one had risen and begun pouring into the aisles, carrying my Cousin Ellen with them. What had been heads over the tops of the pews were now bodies. Ranks of hoopskirts bubbled out over the carpets, and little boys who had been hidden away up to now came

353

along with their elders or went wriggling through the worshippers' legs.

The congregation did not seem to Cousin Ellen so very much damped by the threats of hell and prophecies of fire, though some of the ladies had tears in their eyes as they greeted each other and withdrew into various groups for refreshments. My Aunt Martha was opening a hamper basket, out of which she took cakes and bottles of wine. And now that church was over, and there was still a ride home, every one was taking some of the refreshments and talking at the same time. There were compliments to the sermon and, in the midst of the banter, the old regular joke had come, some one passing the cherry bounce to Miss Mary Cherry and saying that it belonged to her family, and the regular burst of laughter. . . .

They told Cousin Ellen of Ellington Pegues, when she observed a tall shaft with the palm leaves wreathed upon it and asked whose monument that was. Ellington Pegues had been a young preacher in Sardis, a very handsome and romantic young man, of the Carolina Pegueses, killed in a duel for some rivalry over a lady's hand, Rosa Hunt was her name. But the duel, of course, had been fought on some other pretext to spare a lady's honor.

Palm wreaths, marble shafts, duels of pastors, cake and wine, so much pleasantry and conversation, angels and ministers of grace, how far the devout of Heaven Trees and Panola County must have seemed to my Cousin Ellen from her own people in Vermont, how far indeed! Like two races almost they were, different kinds of human beings.

What must she have thought of that other sort of race, a few moments later? For every Sunday, when roads were good and the weather permitted, it was the custom of my cousins, any of them who lived in the same neighborhood, to race one another home when the time came for them to go. And on this Sunday as she sat in my Uncle George's rockaway and every one got settled into his place, my Cousin

354

Ellen had suddenly seen Oscar, the coachman, with Solomon grinning beside him, give the horses a sharp flip with his whip and had felt the carriage leap forward. Uncle George called out: "The wing'd steeds are pawing the courts. Eros and Mars, let us go!" She felt Miss Mary Cherry, who sat beside her fanning herself, suddenly sit bolt upright, snapping her fan to with disapproval. Behind them came Mr. Bobo, his face beaming, in a kind of trap or yellow chaise, as some called it, driving his sorrels and pressing close, in the hope of passing the rockaway and so to win the race.

"But what is this?" Cousin Ellen had asked, and they explained that they were racing to see who could draw up first at the gate; and she had settled herself back with what thoughts may have been her own to await the end of the contest; her eyes were shining.

Horse-racing on the Sabbath!

Miss Mary Cherry looked down at her: "I don't wonder you inquire! It's sinful, I regard it."

Solomon had given the horses another crack and they went faster yet. The wine-bottles in the hamper rattled together. Behind them in a cloud of yellow dust the smooth rhythm of Mr. Bobo's perfect trotters came louder and louder. He was driving himself. It was not for nothing that his heart dwelt with his horses. Cousin Ellen could hear him talking to them: "Come on, boys! Steady, steady!" "What'll you bet," he called, "what'll you bet, ladies, that we win?"

Miss Mary Cherry, sitting back with her dignified contemplation and godly remoteness, suddenly leaned forward and boxed our driver over the ear with her fan.

"Get up, you fool," she cried; "don't you see he's going to pass us?"

William Faulkner

A ROSE FOR EMILY

WHEN Miss Emily Grierson died, our whole town went to her funeral: the men through a sort of respectful affection for a fallen monument, the women mostly out of curiosity to see the inside of her house, which no one save an old man-servant—a combined gardener and cook—had seen in at least ten years.

It was a big, squarish frame house that had once been white, decorated with cupolas and spires and scrolled balconies in the heavily lightsome style of the seventies, set on what had once been our most select street. But garages and cotton gins had encroached and obliterated even the august names of that neighborhood; only Miss Emily's house was left, lifting its stubborn and coquettish decay above the cotton wagons and the gasoline pumps—an eyesore among eyesores. And now Miss Emily had gone to join the representatives of those august names where they lay in the cedar-bemused cemetery among the ranked and anonymous graves of Union and Confederate soldiers who fell at the battle of Jefferson.

Alive, Miss Emily had been a tradition, a duty, and a care; a sort of hereditary obligation upon the town, dating from that day in 1894 when Colonel Sartoris, the mayor—he who fathered the edict that no Negro women should appear on the streets without an apron—remitted her taxes, the dispensation dating from the death of her father on into perpetuity. Not that Miss Emily would have accepted charity. Colonel Sartoris invented an involved tale to the effect that Miss Emily's father had loaned money to the town, which the town, as a matter of business, preferred this way of repaying. Only a man of Colonel Sartoris' generation and thought could have invented it, and only a woman could have believed it.

When the next generation, with its more modern ideas, became mayors and aldermen, this arrangement created some little dissatisfaction. On the first of the year they mailed her a tax notice. February came, and there was no reply. They wrote her a formal letter, asking her to call at the sheriff's office at her convenience. A week later the mayor wrote her himself, offering to call or to send his car for her, and received in reply a note on paper of an archaic shape, in a thin, flowing calligraphy in faded ink, to the effect that she no longer went out at all. The tax notice was also enclosed, without comment.

They called a special meeting of the Board of Aldermen. A deputation waited upon her, knocked at the door through which no visitor had passed since she ceased giving china-painting lessons eight or ten years earlier. They were admitted by the old Negro into a dim hall from which a stairway mounted into still more shadow. It smelled of dust and disuse—a close, dank smell. The Negro led them into the parlor. It was furnished in heavy, leather-covered furniture. When the Negro opened the blinds of one window, they could see that the leather was cracked; and when they sat down, a faint dust rose sluggishly about their thighs, spinning with slow motes in the single sun-ray. On a tarnished gilt easel before the fireplace stood a crayon portrait of Miss Emily's father.

They rose when she entered—a small, fat woman in black, with a thin gold chain descending to her waist and vanishing into her belt, leaning on an ebony cane with a tarnished gold head. Her skeleton was small and spare; perhaps that was why what would have been merely plumpness in another was obesity in her. She looked bloated, like a body long submerged in motionless water, and of that pallid hue. Her eyes, lost in the fatty ridges of her face, looked like two small pieces of coal pressed into a lump of dough as they moved from one face to another while the visitors stated their errand.

She did not ask them to sit. She just stood in the door and listened quietly until the spokesman came to a stumbling halt. Then they could hear the invisible watch ticking at the end of the gold chain.

Her voice was dry and cold. "I have no taxes in Jefferson. Colonel Sartoris explained it to me. Perhaps one of you can gain access to the city records and satisfy yourselves."

"But we have. We are the city authorities, Miss Emily. Didn't you get a notice from the sheriff, signed by him?"

"I received a paper, yes," Miss Emily said. "Perhaps he considers himself the sheriff . . . I have no taxes in Jefferson."

"But there is nothing on the books to show that, you see. We must go by the—"

"See Colonel Sartoris. I have no taxes in Jefferson."

"But, Miss Emily—"

"See Colonel Sartoris." (Colonel Sartoris had been dead almost ten years.) "I have no taxes in Jefferson. Tobe!" The Negro appeared. "Show these gentlemen out."

II

So she vanquished them, horse and foot, just as she had vanquished their fathers thirty years before about the smell. That was two years after her father's death and a short time after her sweetheart—the one we believed would marry her— had deserted her. After her father's death she went out very little; after her sweetheart went away, people hardly saw her at all. A few of the ladies had the temerity to call, but were not received, and the only sign of life about the place was the Negro man—a young man then—going in and out with a market basket.

"Just as if a man—any man—could keep a kitchen properly," the ladies said; so they were not surprised when the

358

smell developed. It was another link between the gross, teeming world and the high and mighty Griersons.

A neighbor, a woman, complained to the mayor, Judge Stevens, eighty years old.

"But what will you have me do about it, madam?" he said.

"Why, send her word to stop it," the woman said. "Isn't there a law?"

"I'm sure that won't be necessary," Judge Stevens said. "It's probably just a snake or a rat that nigger of hers killed in the yard. I'll speak to him about it."

The next day he received two more complaints, one from a man who came in diffident deprecation. "We really must do something about it, Judge. I'd be the last one in the world to bother Miss Emily, but we've got to do something." That night the Board of Aldermen met—three graybeards and one younger man, a member of the rising generation.

"It's simple enough," he said. "Send her word to have her place cleaned up. Give her a certain time to do it in, and if she don't . . ."

"Dammit, sir," Judge Stevens said, "will you accuse a lady to her face of smelling bad?"

So the next night, after midnight, four men crossed Miss Emily's lawn and slunk about the house like burglars, sniffing along the base of the brickwork and at the cellar openings while one of them performed a regular sowing motion with his hand out of a sack slung from his shoulder. They broke open the cellar door and sprinkled lime there, and in all the outbuildings. As they recrossed the lawn, a window that had been dark was lighted and Miss Emily sat in it, the light behind her, and her upright torso motionless as that of an idol. They crept quietly across the lawn and into the shadow of the locusts that lined the street. After a week or two the smell went away.

That was when people had begun to feel really sorry for her. People in our town, remembering how old lady Wyatt, her great-aunt, had gone completely crazy at last, believed that the Griersons held themselves a little too high for what they really were. None of the young men were quite good enough to Miss Emily and such. We had long thought of them as a tableau; Miss Emily a slender figure in white in the background, her father a spraddled silhouette in the foreground, his back to her and clutching a horsewhip, the two of them framed by the back-flung front door. So when she got to be thirty and was still single, we were not pleased exactly, but vindicated; even with insanity in the family she wouldn't have turned down all of her chances if they had really materialized.

When her father died, it got about that the house was all that was left to her; and in a way, people were glad. At last they could pity Miss Emily. Being left alone, and a pauper, she had become humanized. Now she too would know the old thrill and the old despair of a penny more or less.

The day after his death all the ladies prepared to call at the house and offer condolence and aid, as is our custom. Miss Emily met them at the door, dressed as usual and with no trace of grief on her face. She told them that her father was not dead. She did that for three days, with the ministers calling on her, and the doctors, trying to persuade her to let them dispose of the body. Just as they were about to resort to law and force, she broke down, and they buried her father quickly.

We did not say she was crazy then. We believed she had to do that. We remembered all the young men her father had driven away, and we knew that with nothing left, she would have to cling to that which had robbed her, as people will.

III

She was sick for a long time. When we saw her again, her hair was cut short, making her look like a girl, with a vague resemblance to those angels in colored church windows—sort of tragic and serene.

The town had just let the contracts for paving the side-walks, and in the summer after her father's death they began the work. The construction company came with niggers and mules and machinery, and a foreman named Homer Barron, a Yankee—a big, dark, ready man, with a big voice and eyes lighter than his face. The little boys would follow in groups to hear him cuss the niggers, and the niggers sing-ing in time to the rise and fall of picks. Pretty soon he knew everybody in town. Whenever you heard a lot of laughing anywhere about the square, Homer Barron would be in the center of the group. Presently we began to see him and Miss Emily on Sunday afternoons driving in the yellow-wheeled buggy and the matched team of bays from the livery stable.

At first we were glad that Miss Emily would have an in-terest, because the ladies all said, "Of course a Grierson would not think seriously of a Northerner, a day laborer." But there were still others, older people, who said that even grief could not cause a real lady to forget *noblesse oblige*—without calling it *noblesse oblige*. They just said, "Poor Emily. Her kinsfolk should come to her." She had some kin in Alabama; but years ago her father had fallen out with them over the estate of old lady Wyatt, the crazy woman, and there was no communication between the two families. They had not even been represented at the funeral.

And as soon as the old people said, "Poor Emily," the whispering began. "Do you suppose it's really so?" they said to one another. "Of course it is. What else could . . ." This behind their hands; rustling of craned silk and satin behind jalousies closed upon the sun of Sunday afternoon as the thin, swift clop-clop-clop of the matched team passed: "Poor Emily."

She carried her head high enough—even when we be-lieved that she was fallen. It was as if she demanded more than ever the recognition of her dignity as the last Grierson; as if it had wanted that touch of earthiness to reaffirm her im-perviousness. Like when she bought the rat poison, the arsenic. That was over a year after they had begun to say "Poor Emily," and while the two female cousins were visiting her.

"I want some poison," she said to the druggist. She was over thirty then, still a slight woman, though thinner than usual, with cold, haughty black eyes in a face the flesh of which was strained across the temples and about the eye-sockets as you imagine a lighthouse-keeper's face ought to look. "I want some poison," she said.

"Yes, Miss Emily. What kind? For rats and such? I'd recom—"

"I want the best you have. I don't care what kind."

The druggist named several. "They'll kill anything up to an elephant. But what you want is—"

"Arsenic," Miss Emily said. "Is that a good one?"

"Is . . . arsenic? Yes, ma'am. But what you want—"

"I want arsenic."

The druggist looked down at her. She looked back at him, erect, her face like a strained flag. "Why, of course," the druggist said. "If that's what you want. But the law requires you to tell what you are going to use it for."

Miss Emily just stared at him, her head tilted back in order to look him eye for eye, until he looked away and went and got the arsenic and wrapped it up. The Negro delivery boy brought her the package; the druggist didn't come back. When she opened the package at home there was written on the box, under the skull and bones: "For rats."

IV

So the next day we all said, "She will kill herself"; and we said it would be the best thing. When she had first begun to be seen with Homer Barron, we had said, "She will marry him." Then we said, "She will persuade him yet," because Homer himself had remarked—he liked men, and it was known that he drank with the younger men in the Elks' Club—that he was not a marrying man. Later we said, "Poor Emily" be-hind the jalousies as they passed on Sunday afternoon in the glittering buggy, Miss Emily with her head high and Homer Barron with his hat cocked and a cigar in his teeth, reins and whip in a yellow glove.

Then some of the ladies began to say that it was a disgrace to the town and a bad example to the young people. The men did not want to interfere, but at last the ladies forced the Baptist minister—Miss Emily's people were Episcopal— to call upon her. He would never divulge what happened during that interview, but he refused to go back again. The next Sunday they again drove about the streets, and the following day the minister's wife wrote to Miss Emily's relations in Alabama.

So she had blood-kin under her roof again and we sat back to watch developments. At first nothing happened. Then we were sure that they were to be married. We learned that Miss Emily had been to the jeweler's and ordered a man's toilet set in silver, with the letters H. B. on each piece. Two days later we learned that she had bought a complete outfit of men's clothing, including a nightshirt, and we said, "They are married." We were really glad. We were glad because the two female cousins were even more Grierson than Miss Emily had ever been.

So we were not surprised when Homer Barron—the streets had been finished some time since—was gone. We were a little disappointed that there was not a public blowing-off, but we believed that he had gone on to prepare for Miss Emily's coming, or to give her a chance to get rid of the cousins. (By that time it was a cabal, and we were all Miss Emily's allies to help circumvent the cousins.) Sure enough, after another week they departed. And, as we had expected all along, within three days Homer Barron was back in town. A neighbor saw the Negro man admit him at the kitchen door at dusk one evening.

And that was the last we saw of Homer Barron. And of Miss Emily for some time. The Negro man went in and out with the market basket, but the front door remained closed.

Now and then we would see her at a window for a moment, as the men did that night when they sprinkled the lime, but for almost six months she did not appear on the streets. Then we knew that this was to be expected too; as if that quality of her father which had thwarted her woman's life so many times had been too virulent and too furious to die.

When we next saw Miss Emily, she had grown fat and her hair was turning gray. During the next few years it grew grayer and grayer until it attained an even pepper-and-salt iron-gray, when it ceased turning. Up to the day of her death at seventy-four it was still that vigorous iron-gray, like the hair of an active man.

From that time on her front door remained closed, save for a period of six or seven years, when she was about forty, during which she gave lessons in china-painting. She fitted up a studio in one of the downstairs rooms, where the daughters and granddaughters of Colonel Sartoris' contemporaries were sent to her with the same regularity and in the same spirit that they were sent to church on Sundays with a twenty-five cent piece for the collection plate. Meanwhile her taxes had been remitted.

Then the newer generation became the backbone and the spirit of the town, and the painting pupils grew up and fell away and did not send their children to her with boxes of color and tedious brushes and pictures cut from the ladies' magazines. The front door closed upon the last one and remained closed for good. When the town got free postal delivery, Miss Emily alone refused to let them fasten the metal numbers above her door and attach a mailbox to it. She would not listen to them.

Daily, monthly, yearly we watched the Negro grow grayer and more stooped, going in and out with the market basket. Each December we sent her a tax notice, which would be returned by the post office a week later, unclaimed. Now and then we would see her in one of the downstairs windows—she had evidently shut up the top floor of the house—like the carven torso of an idol in a niche, looking or not looking at us, we could never tell which. Thus she passed from generation to generation—dear, inescapable, impervious, tranquil, and perverse.

And so she died. Fell ill in the house filled with dust and shadows, with only a doddering Negro man to wait on her. We did not even know she was sick; we had long since given up trying to get any information from the Negro. He talked to no one, probably not even to her, for his voice had grown harsh and rusty, as if from disuse.

She died in one of the downstairs rooms, in a heavy walnut bed with a curtain, her gray head propped on a pillow yellow and moldy with age and lack of sunlight.

V

The Negro met the first of the ladies at the front door and let them in, with their hushed, sibilant voices and their quick, curious glances, and then he disappeared. He walked right through the house and out the back and was not seen again.

The two female cousins came at once. They held the funeral on the second day, with the town coming to look at Miss Emily beneath a mass of bought flowers, with the crayon face of her father musing profoundly above the bier and the ladies sibilant and macabre; and the very old men—some in their brushed Confederate uniforms—on the porch and the lawn, talking of Miss Emily as if she had been a contemporary of theirs, believing that they had danced with her and courted her perhaps, confusing time with its mathematical progression, as the old do, to whom all the past is not a diminishing road but, instead, a huge meadow which no winter ever quite touches, divided from them now by the narrow bottle-neck of the most recent decade of years.

Already we knew that there was one room in that region above stairs which no one had seen in forty years, and which would have to be forced. They waited until Miss Emily was decently in the ground before they opened it.

The violence of breaking down the door seemed to fill this room with pervading dust. A thin, acrid pall as of the tomb seemed to lie everywhere upon this room decked and furnished as for a bridal: upon the valence curtains of faded rose color, upon the rose-shaded lights, upon the dressing table, upon the delicate array of crystal and the man's toilet things backed with tarnished silver, silver so tarnished that the monogram was obscured. Among them lay a collar and tie, as if they had just been removed, which, lifted, left upon the surface a pale crescent in the dust. Upon a chair hung the suit, carefully folded; beneath it the two mute shoes and the discarded socks.

The man himself lay in the bed.

For a long while we just stood there, looking down at the profound and fleshless grin. The body had apparently once lain in the attitude of an embrace, but now the long sleep that outlasts love, that conquers even the grimace of love, had cuckolded him. What was left of him, rotted beneath what was left of the nightshirt, had become inextricable from the bed in which he lay; and upon him and upon the pillow beside him lay that even coating of the patient and biding dust.

Then we noticed that in the second pillow was the indentation of a head. One of us lifted something from it, and leaning forward, that faint and invisible dust dry and acrid in the nostrils, we saw a long strand of iron-gray hair.

Julian Green

CHRISTINE

"She was a phantom of delight
When first she gleamed upon my sight;
A lovely apparition sent
To be a moment's ornament."
                                        —*Wordsworth*

THE FORT HOPE road runs almost exactly parallel to the
black lines of the reefs from which it is separated by bands of
bare, flat ground. A dull sky hangs heavy over the cheerless
landscape, which is unrelieved by the bright colors of any
vegetation except, in places, the faint greenness of a languish-
ing grass. In the distance can be seen a long, glittering, gray
line. It is the sea.

We were in the habit of passing the summer there in a
house built on an eminence at some distance back from the
road. In America, where antiquity is of recent date, the
house was considered very ancient and, as a matter of fact,
there was an inscription in the center of the façade certifying
that it was built in 1640, at the time when the Pilgrims, at the
points of their muskets, were establishing the Kingdom of
God in these barbarous regions. Firmly set in the natural
rock, it opposed to the frenzy of the winds which blew from
the sea solid walls of smooth stone and a rudimental gable
which made one think of the prow of a boat. Below the little
round window in the gable, these words could be read,
carved in Rhode Island flint, the hardest material in the
world: IN GOD WE TRUST.

There is not an aspect of the old Puritan house of which
my mind has not kept a distinct image, not a piece of furniture the secrets and defects of which my hand could not
find without hesitation; and I should experience, I think,

the same joys as those of former days, as well as the same terrors, in following the long corridors with their arched ceilings, and in reading again above those doors which a child could move only with difficulty, the mottoes, in Old English lettering, taken from the Psalms.

I remember that all the rooms were so spacious that they seemed empty and that in them the human voice had a sound which it did not have in the city, in the apartment where we lived in Boston. Was it an echo? The voice seemed to strike against the walls and you had the impression that some one beside you was repeating the last part of your sentence. It amused me at first. When I mentioned it to mother, she advised me to pay no attention to it; but I had occasion to observe that in this house she herself spoke less than was usual with her, and more quietly.

II

The summer of my thirteenth year was marked by a rather peculiar incident, so distressing that I have never been able to decide to clear up the whole mystery, for it seems to me that it must have been still more pathetic than I thought at the time. Is it not better sometimes not to attempt to seek out the truth? And if such prudence is not always commendable, it is certainly wiser in cases such as the one I am about to relate than an audacious spirit of investigation.

I was nearly thirteen years old when mother announced to me, one August morning, the arrival of Aunt Judith. She was a more or less enigmatic person whom we almost never saw because she lived at a great distance from us, in Washington. I knew that she had had a very unhappy life and that, for some unexplained reason, she had not been able to marry. I was not fond of her. Her fixed stare made me lower my eyes and she had a gloomy manner which I did not like. Her features were as regular as my mother's, but more severe, and a singular expression of displeasure kept the corners of her mouth continually raised in a bitter half-smile.

368

Going down to the parlor a few days later, I found my aunt in conversation with mother. She had not come alone: a little girl of about my own age was at her side, but back to the light, so that at first I could not distinguish her features. My aunt seemed vexed to see me and, turning brusquely to my mother, she said a few rapid words which I did not catch. Then she touched the shoulder of the little girl, who took a step forward and dropped me a curtsy.

"Christine," said mother, "this is my little boy. His name is John. John, shake hands with Christine and kiss your aunt."

As I approached the little girl, I had to restrain myself in order not to utter a cry of admiration. Beauty—and even at the age I was then—has always moved me to the strongest and the most diverse feelings. The result is a sort of internal struggle which makes me pass in the space of a single moment from joy to desire and from desire to despair. For that reason I hope, and at the same time fear, to discover that beauty which will torment and delight me; and I seek it out, but with a painful anxiety and the secret hope that I shall not find it. Christine's beauty transported me. With the light behind her, her eyes seemed black, made larger by the shadows about them. The forceful lines of her mouth stood out strongly in the smoothness and the spotless perfection of her skin. An immense aureole of blond hair seemed to gather into its depths all the light which came from the window and gave an almost supernatural color to her cheeks and forehead. I gazed in silence at that little girl whom I should have been ready to believe an apparition if I had not already grasped in mine the hand which she extended to me. My stare did not cause her to lower her eyes; she seemed, in fact, not to see me, but to be fixing her gaze obstinately upon some one or something behind me. That impression was borne in upon me so strongly that I turned around. Mother's voice brought me back to myself and I kissed my aunt, who then withdrew with Christine.

369

Even today it is difficult for me to believe that the events which I am about to relate actually happened; and, nevertheless, my memory is trustworthy and I am inventing nothing. I never saw Christine again or, in any case, I saw her only once or twice more and in the most imperfect manner. My aunt came downstairs alone. We took our meal without Christine and the afternoon passed without her returning to the parlor.

Toward evening mother sent for me and told me that I was to sleep not on the second floor as I had up to that time, but on the third and far, consequently, from the guest-chambers where Christine and my aunt were. I cannot tell what took place within me. I should have been willing to believe that I had had a dream. With what joy I should have learned that it was all only an illusion and the little girl I thought I had seen did not exist! For it was cruel in a very different way to think that she was living in the same house with me and that I was deprived of the opportunity of seeing her.

I begged mother to tell me why Christine had not come down to lunch, but she immediately assumed a serious manner and replied that I had no need to know and that I was never to mention Christine again to anyone. Those strange instructions amazed me, and I wondered for a moment whether mother had lost her senses or I mine, but without being able to arrive at any other explanation for it than a malicious desire on her part to torment me.

At dinner my mother and aunt, so that I would not understand, began to speak in French, a language they knew well but of which I did not understand a word. I realized, however, that they were talking about Christine, for her name occurred rather often in the course of their conversation. Finally, yielding to my impatience, I bluntly asked what had become of the little girl and why she did not appear at either lunch or dinner. The answer came in the form of a box on the ear from my mother, who took that way of recalling to my mind the instructions she had given me. As for my aunt, she frowned in a way which rendered her in my eyes very awful to look upon. I said no more.

Who, then, was the little girl? If I had been more observing and not quite so young, I should certainly have noticed the peculiarity of her expression. Was I not already familiar with that fixed stare? Had I seen no one with that indefinable little grimace which resembled a smile and yet was not? But I was very far from thinking of studying my aunt's face, and I was too innocent to discover a relationship between Christine and that woman who at the time seemed monstrous to me.

III

I shall pass rapidly over the two weeks which followed in order to come at once to the most curious part of the story. The reader will imagine without difficulty all the tediousness of my solitude, which, formerly so tranquil, was now unendurable, and my sorrow at feeling myself separated from one for whom I felt I should have willingly sacrificed my life. Several times while I was wandering about the house, the idea came to me to attract Christine's attention and make her come to the window, but I had no sooner thrown some pebbles up against her windows than a severe voice called me back into the parlor. A strict watch was kept over me and my plan always failed.

I changed. I became somber and no longer took any pleasure in anything. I could not even read or undertake anything which required concentration. I was obsessed by a single idea—to see Christine again. I arranged things so as to be on the stairs when mother, my aunt, or Dinah, the maid, passed carrying Christine her luncheon or her dinner. Of course I was not allowed to follow them, but I experienced a melancholy pleasure in listening to the sound of those steps which went to her.

My aunt was displeased at this innocent maneuver and she

suspected in me, I think, more intentions than I was conscious of myself. One evening she told me an awful story concerning the part of the house which she occupied with Christine. She confided to me that she had seen some one pass by close to her in the hall which led to their room. Was it a man or a woman? She could not say, but she was sure of one thing: she had felt a warm breath against her face. And then for some moments she watched my expression attentively as if to measure the effect of her words upon me. I must have grown pale under her gaze. It was easy to terrify me with such tales, and this one seemed horrible to me, for my aunt had planned it well and she told me neither too much nor too little. So, far from thinking of going as far as Christine's room, I hesitated from that time on even to venture upon the stairs after nightfall.

From the time of my aunt's arrival, mother had taken the habit of sending me to Fort Hope every afternoon, on the pretext that she wanted me to buy a newspaper there; but, in reality, I am sure it was to get me away from the house at an hour when Christine was to go out for a walk.

Things remained thus for two long weeks. I lost my color and purple shadows began to appear around my eyes. Mother looked at me closely when I went to see her in the morning, and occasionally, seizing me abruptly by the wrist, she would say to me in a voice which trembled a little:

"Wretched child!"

But her anger and her sadness did not move me. All I cared about was Christine.

The vacation was drawing to a close and I had lost all hope of ever seeing her again, when an event which I did not expect gave an unforeseen turn to the adventure and, at the same time, brought it to a sudden end.

One evening at the beginning of September we had a thunderstorm after a day of overwhelming heat. The first drops of rain were splashing against the windows as I went upstairs to my room, and it was then, while on my way from

372

the second to the third floor, that I heard a peculiar noise I can compare to nothing except the rolling of a drum. My aunt's story came back to my mind and I began to dash rapidly up the stairs, when all at once I was stopped by a loud cry. It was neither mother's voice nor my aunt's, but a voice so piercing, so high, and of so strange a tone that it made me think of the call of an animal. A sort of vertigo seized me. I leaned against the wall. For nothing in the world would I have taken a step back, but it was equally impossible for me to go on, and I remained where I was, senseless from terror. A moment later the noise redoubled in violence and then I understood that it was some one, Christine beyond a doubt, who, for reasons I did not understand, was pounding on a door with her fists. Finally I mustered sufficient courage, not to find out what it was and go to Christine's aid, but rather to dash upstairs as fast as I could. Once in my room, imagining that I still heard the rolling of a drum and the same cry of a moment before, I fell on my knees and, putting my fingers in my ears, began to pray aloud.

IV

The next morning, in the parlor, I found my aunt in tears and mother beside her, talking to her and holding her hands in hers. They both seemed greatly excited and did not notice me. I did not fail to take advantage of circumstances which seemed so promising for finally learning something about what had happened to Christine, for they must be talking about her; and I stealthily took a seat just behind them. In that way I found out in a few moments that the storm of the night before had had a very serious effect upon the little girl. Seized with terror at the first rumblings of thunder, she had called, tried to get out of her room, and finally had fainted away.

"I ought never to have brought her here," exclaimed my aunt. And she added without a transition, but with an accent which I cannot describe and as if the words were killing her, "She tried to say something to me!"

I was in my room two hours later when mother entered with a long Paisley shawl and the hood she wore when she was going out. I had never seen her look so serious.

"John," she said, "Christine, the little girl you saw the other day your aunt arrived, is not well and we are anxious. Listen. We are both going to Providence this afternoon to consult a doctor and we are going to bring him back here with us. Christine is to remain here and Dinah will look after her. Will you promise me that you will not go near Christine's room while we are away?"

I promised.

"It is a very serious matter, but I have confidence in you," she continued, looking at me suspiciously. "Could you swear to me on the Bible that you will not go upstairs while we are gone?"

I nodded. Shortly after lunch, mother and my aunt departed.

My first impulse was to go up to Christine's room immediately, but after a moment's reflection I hesitated, for I was by nature faithful to my word. Finally, the temptation was too strong and, after making sure that Dinah, who had carried Christine her lunch an hour before, had really returned to the kitchen, I went up to the second floor.

When I reached the haunted hall, or, rather, the hall Aunt Judith claimed was haunted, my heart began to beat violently. It was long, with several turns, and very dark. Over the entrance there was a Biblical inscription which at that moment assumed a special meaning in my mind: "Yea, though I walk in the Valley of the Shadow of Death, I will fear no evil." That verse which I read mechanically made me remember that I had given my word of honor not to do what I was doing at that very moment. I had not, however, actually sworn upon the Bible and my conscience was for that reason a bit pacified.

I had gone scarcely three or four feet before I had to do my utmost to control my imagination in order not to retrace my steps, overcome with fear. The thought that perhaps I would see the little girl again and touch her hand once more kept up my courage. I began to run on my toes, holding my breath, frightened by the length of that interminable corridor; and, as I could no longer see my way before me, in a moment I ran headlong into Christine's door. In my excitement I did not think of knocking and I tried to open the door. But it was locked. I could hear Christine walking about in the room. At the noise I made she had moved toward the door. I waited, hoping that she would open, but she stopped and remained still.

In vain I knocked, gently at first, then more and more loudly. I called Christine, I spoke to her, I told her that I was Aunt Judith's nephew, that I was charged with a message for her and that she must open. Finally, giving up hope of getting any reply, I knelt down before the door and looked through the keyhole. Christine was standing some distance away, watching the door attentively. A long nightdress covered her, falling to her feet. I could see her bare toes beneath it. Her hair, no longer held in place by any comb, spread about her head like a mane. I noticed that her cheeks were flushed. Her eyes, of a brilliant blue in the light that struck her face, had that motionless stare which I had not forgotten, and the singular feeling came over me that she could see me through the wood of the door and that she was watching me. She looked even more beautiful than I had believed and I was beside myself at seeing her so near and not being able to throw myself at her feet. Finally, overcome by an emotion so long contained, I suddenly burst into tears and, striking my head against the door, gave myself up to despair.

After a certain length of time an idea came to my mind which brought back my courage, an idea which I considered

375

ingenious, because its imprudence did not then occur to me. I scrawled in big letters on a piece of paper:

"Christine, open the door for me. I love you."

And I slipped it under the door.

Looking through the keyhole, I saw her fall upon the paper and turn it over and over in every direction with an air of great curiosity, but without appearing to understand what I had written on it. All at once she dropped it and went into a part of the room where my glance could not follow her. In my distraction I called to her as loudly as I could and, without realizing any longer what I was saying, I promised to give her a present if she would consent to open the door. Those words, which came to me on the spur of the moment, gave me the idea of a new scheme.

In all haste I went upstairs to my room and hunted about in the drawers of my bureau to find something which I could use as a present; but I had nothing. I then dashed into mother's room and went carefully through the contents of all her chests of drawers, but I saw nothing there, either, which seemed to me worthy of Christine. Finally I perceived, pushed up against the wall and behind a piece of furniture, the trunk that my aunt had brought with her. Doubtless they had thought that it would not be safe in the same room with a curious little girl. In any case, the trunk happened to be unlocked and I had only to raise the lid to plunge into it my feverish hands. After searching for some time, I discovered a little shark-skin case carefully hidden under some linen. How well I remember it! Lined with watered silk, it contained some colored ribbons and a few rings, to one of which I took a liking at once. It was a very splendid gold ring with a small sapphire. A roll of letters had been passed through it like a paper finger and I pulled them out, tearing them in the process.

I went back immediately to Christine's chamber and called to her again, but with no other result than to make her come close to the door as she had done the first time. Then I slipped the ring under the door, saying:

"Christine, here is your present. Open the door for me."

And I knocked with the flat of my hand on the bottom of the door to attract her attention. She had, however, already seen the ring and seized it. For a moment she held it in the hollow of her hand, examining it. Then she tried to put it on her thumb, but the ring was too small and stopped a little below the nail. She stamped her foot and tried to push it on by force. I cried to her:

"No! Not on that finger!"

But either she did not hear me or she did not understand. She suddenly waved her hand; the ring had gone on. She gazed at it in admiration for a few minutes and then tried to take it off. She pulled with all her might, but in vain; the ring resisted. Then she bit it with rage. Finally, after a series of desperate efforts to dislodge it, she threw herself on the bed with loud and angry cries. I fled.

When, three hours later, mother and my aunt returned, accompanied by a doctor from Providence, I was in my room, a prey to a nameless fear. I did not dare to go downstairs at dinner-time, and when darkness came I went to sleep.

V

Toward five o'clock the next morning a noise of wheels drew me to the window, and I saw a two-horse carriage drawing up before our door. Everything that happened after that gave me the impression of being a bad dream. I saw the maid help the coachman to load my aunt's trunk on top of the carriage; then my aunt appeared, supported by mother. They kissed several times. A man followed them—I suppose it was the doctor from Providence who had spent the night at our house—holding Christine by the hand. She wore a great hood which concealed her face and on the thumb of her right hand glittered the ring she had been unable to re-move.

Neither mother nor my aunt, whom I saw again alone some months later, told me a word about the whole affair, and I really thought that I had dreamed it. Is it credible? I actually forgot it. The human heart is indeed strange.

The following summer, my aunt did not come on; but a few days before Christmas, as she was passing through Boston, she made us an hour's visit. Mother and I were in the parlor and I was looking out the window, watching the city men throwing shovelfuls of sand upon the icy sidewalks, when my aunt suddenly made her appearance. She stopped a moment on the parlor threshold, mechanically removing her gloves. Then, without a word, she threw herself, sobbing, into mother's arms. On her ungloved hand shone the little sapphire.

Outside, the sand fell with mournful thuds upon the pavement.

Eudora Welty

PETRIFIED MAN

REACH in my purse and git me a cigarette without no powder in it if you kin, Mrs. Fletcher, honey," said Leota to her ten o'clock shampoo-and-set customer. "I don't like no perfumed cigarettes."

Mrs. Fletcher gladly reached over to the lavender shelf under the lavender-framed mirror, shook a hair net loose from the clasp of the patent-leather bag, and slapped her hand down quickly on a powder puff which burst out when the purse was opened.

"Why, look at the peanuts, Leota!" said Mrs. Fletcher in her marveling voice.

"Honey, them goobers has been in my purse a week if they's been in it a day. Mrs. Pike bought them peanuts."

"Who's Mrs. Pike?" asked Mrs. Fletcher, settling back. Hidden in this den of curling fluid and henna packs, separated by a lavender swing door from the other customers, who were being gratified in other booths, she could give her curiosity its freedom. She looked expectantly at the black part in Leota's yellow curls as she bent to light the cigarette.

"Mrs. Pike is this lady from New Orleans," said Leota, puffing, and pressing into Mrs. Fletcher's scalp with strong red-nailed fingers. "A friend, not a customer. You see, like maybe I told you last time, me and Fred and Sal and Joe all had us a fuss, so Sal and Joe up and moved out, so we didn't do a thing but rent out their room. So we rented it to Mrs. Pike. And Mr. Pike." She flicked an ash into the basket of dirty towels. "Mrs. Pike is a very decided blonde. *She* bought me the peanuts."

"She must be cute," said Mrs. Fletcher.

"Honey, 'cute' ain't the word for what she is. I'm tellin' you, Mrs. Pike is attractive. She has her a good time. She's got a sharp eye out, Mrs. Pike has."

She dashed the comb through the air, and paused dramatically as a cloud of Mrs. Fletcher's hennaed hair floated out of the lavender teeth like a small storm cloud.

"Hair fallin'."

"Aw, Leota."

"Uh-huh, commencin' to fall out," said Leota, combing again, and letting fall another cloud.

"Is it any dandruff in it?" Mrs. Fletcher was frowning, her hair-line eyebrows diving down toward her nose, and

379

her wrinkled, beady-lashed eyelids batting with concentration.

"Nope." She combed again. "Just fallin' out."

"Bet it was that last perm'nent you gave me that did it," Mrs. Fletcher said cruelly. "Remember you cooked me fourteen minutes."

"You had fourteen minutes comin' to you," said Leota with finality.

"Bound to be somethin'," persisted Mrs. Fletcher. "Dandruff, dandruff. I couldn't of caught a thing like that from Mr. Fletcher, could I?"

"Well," Leota answered at last, "you know what I heard in here yestiddy, one of Thelma's ladies was settin' over yonder in Thelma's booth gittin' a machineless, and I don't mean to insist or insinuate or anything, Mrs. Fletcher, but Thelma's lady just happ'med to throw out—I forgotten what she was talkin' about at the time—that you was p-r-e-g., and lots of times that'll make your hair do awful funny, fall out and God knows what all. It just ain't our fault, is the way I look at it."

There was a pause. The women stared at each other in the mirror.

"Who was it?" demanded Mrs. Fletcher.

"Honey, I really couldn't say," said Leota. "Not that you look it."

"Where's Thelma? I'll get it out of her," said Mrs. Fletcher.

"Now, honey, I wouldn't go and git mad over a little thing like that," Leota said, combing hastily, as though to hold Mrs. Fletcher down by the hair. "I'm sure it was somebody didn't mean no harm in the world. How far gone are you?"

"Just wait," said Mrs. Fletcher, and shrieked for Thelma, who came in and took a drag from Leota's cigarette.

"Thelma, honey, throw your mind back to yestiddy if you kin," said Leota, drenching Mrs. Fletcher's hair with a thick fluid and catching the overflow in a cold wet towel at her neck.

"Well, I got my lady half wound for a spiral," said Thelma doubtfully.

"This won't take but a minute," said Leota. "Who is it you got in there, old Horse Face? Just cast your mind back and try to remember who your lady was yestiddy who happ'm to mention that my customer was pregnant, that's all. She's dead to know."

Thelma drooped her blood-red lips and looked over Mrs. Fletcher's head into the mirror. "Why, honey, I ain't got the faintest," she breathed. "I really don't recollect the faintest. But I'm sure she meant no harm. I declare, I forgot my hair finally got combed and thought it was a stranger behind me."

"Was it that Mrs. Hutchinson?" Mrs. Fletcher was tensely polite.

"Mrs. Hutchinson? Oh, Mrs. Hutchinson." Thelma batted her eyes. "Naw, precious, she come on Thursday and didn't ev'm mention your name. I doubt if she ev'm knows you're on the way."

"Thelma!" cried Leota staunchly.

"All I know is, whoever it is 'll be sorry some day. Why, I just barely knew it myself!" cried Mrs. Fletcher. "Just let her wait!"

"Why? What 're you gonna do to her?"

It was a child's voice, and the women looked down. A little boy was making tents with aluminum wave pinchers on the floor under the sink.

"Billy Boy, hon, mustn't bother nice ladies," Leota smiled. She slapped him brightly and behind her back waved Thelma out of the booth. "Ain't Billy Boy a sight? Only three years old and already just nuts about the beauty-parlor business."

"I never saw him here before," said Mrs. Fletcher, still unmollified.

"He ain't been here before, that's how come," said Leota.

"He belongs to Mrs. Pike. She got her a job but it was Fay's Millinery. He oughtn't to try on those ladies' hats, they come down over his eyes like I don't know what. They just git to look ridiculous, that's what, an' of course he's gonna put 'em on: hats. They tole Mrs. Pike they didn't appreciate him hangin' around there. Here, he couldn't hurt a thing."

"Well! I don't like children that much," said Mrs. Fletcher.

"Well!" said Leota moodily.

"Well! I'm almost tempted not to have this one," said Mrs. Fletcher. "That Mrs. Hutchinson! Just looks straight through you when she sees you on the street and then spits at you behind your back."

"Mr. Fletcher would beat you on the head if you didn't have it now," said Leota reasonably. "After going this far."

Mrs. Fletcher sat up straight. "Mr. Fletcher can't do a thing with me."

"He can't!" Leota winked at herself in the mirror.

"No siree, he can't. If he so much as raises his voice against me, he knows good and well I'll have one of my sick headaches, and then I'm just not fit to live with. And if I really look that pregnant already—"

"Well, now, honey, I just want you to know—I habm't told any of my ladies and I ain't goin' to tell 'em—even that you're losin' your hair. You just get you one of those Stork-a-Lure dresses and stop worryin'. What people don't know don't hurt nobody, as Mrs. Pike says."

"Did you tell Mrs. Pike?" asked Mrs. Fletcher sulkily.

"Well, Mrs. Fletcher, look, you ain't ever goin' to lay eyes on Mrs. Pike or her lay eyes on you, so what diffunce does it make in the long run?"

"I knew it!" Mrs. Fletcher deliberately nodded her head so as to destroy a ringlet Leota was working on behind her ear. "Mrs. Pike!"

Leota sighed. "I reckon I might as well tell you. It wasn't

382

any more Thelma's lady tole me you was pregnant than a bat."

"Not Mrs. Hutchinson?"

"Naw, Lord! It was Mrs. Pike."

"Mrs. Pike!" Mrs. Fletcher could only sputter and let curling fluid roll into her ear. "How could Mrs. Pike possibly know I was pregnant or otherwise, when she doesn't even know me? The nerve of some people!"

"Well, here's how it was. Remember Sunday?"

"Yes," said Mrs. Fletcher.

"Sunday, Mrs. Pike an' me was all by ourself. Mr. Pike and Fred had gone over to Eagle Lake, sayin' they was goin' to catch 'em some fish, but they didn't, a course. So we was settin' in Mrs. Pike's car, is a 1939 Dodge—"

"1939, eh," said Mrs. Fletcher.

"—An' we was gettin' us a Jax beer apiece—that's the beer that Mrs. Pike says is made right in N.O., so she won't drink no other kind. So I seen you drive up to the drugstore an' run in for just a secont, leavin' I reckon Mr. Fletcher in the car, an' come runnin' out with looked like a perscription. So I says to Mrs. Pike, just to be makin' talk, 'Right yonder's Mrs. Fletcher, and I reckon that's Mr. Fletcher—she's one of my regular customers,' I says."

"I had on a figured print," said Mrs. Fletcher tentatively.

"You sure did," agreed Leota. "So Mrs. Pike, she give you a good look—she's very observant, a good judge of character, cute as a minute, you know—and she says, 'I bet you another Jax that lady's three months on the way.'"

"What gall!" said Mrs. Fletcher. "Mrs. Pike!"

"Mrs. Pike ain't goin' to bite you," said Leota. "Mrs. Pike is a lovely girl, you'd be crazy about her, Mrs. Fletcher. But she can't sit still a minute. We went to the travelin' freak show yestiddy after work. I got through early—nine o'clock. In the vacant store next door? What, you ain't been?"

"No, I despise freaks," declared Mrs. Fletcher.

"Aw. Well, honey, talkin' about bein' pregnant an' all,

you ought to see those twins in a bottle, you really owe it to yourself."

"What twins?" asked Mrs. Fletcher out of the side of her mouth.

"Well, honey, they got these two twins in a bottle, see? Born joined plumb together—dead a course." Leota dropped her voice into a soft lyrical hum. "They was about this long—pardon—must of been full time, all right, wouldn't you say?—an' they had these two heads an' two faces an' four arms an' four legs, all kind of joined *here*. See, this face looked this-a-way, and the other face looked that-a-way, over their shoulder, see. Kinda pathetic."

"Glah!" said Mrs. Fletcher disapprovingly.

"Well, ugly? Honey, I mean to tell you—their parents was first cousins and all like that. Billy Boy, git me a fresh towel from off Teeny's stack—this 'n's wringin' wet—an' quit ticklin' my ankles with that curler. I declare! He don't miss nothin'."

"Me and Mr. Fletcher aren't one speck of kin, or he could never of had me," said Mrs. Fletcher placidly.

"Of course not!" protested Leota. "Neither is me an' Fred, not that we know of. Well, honey, what Mrs. Pike liked was the pygmies. They've got these pygmies down there, too, an' Mrs. Pike was just wild about 'em. You know, the tee-niniest men in the universe? Well honey, they can just rest back on their little bohunkus an' roll around an' you can't hardly tell if they're sittin' or standin'. That'll give you some idea. They're about forty-two years old. Just suppose it was your husband!"

"Well, Mr. Fletcher is five foot nine and one half," said Mrs. Fletcher quickly.

"Fred's five foot ten," said Leota, "but I tell him he's still a shrimp, account of I'm so tall." She made a deep wave over Mrs. Fletcher's other temple with the comb. "Well, these pygmies are a kind of a dark brown, Mrs. Fletcher. Not bad lookin' for what they are, you know."

"I wouldn't care for them," said Mrs. Fletcher. "What does that Mrs. Pike see in them?"

"Aw, I don't know," said Leota. "She's just cute, that's all. But they got this man, this petrified man, that ever'-thing ever since he was nine years old, when it goes through his digestion, see, somehow Mrs. Pike says it goes to his joints and has been turning to stone."

"How awful!" said Mrs. Fletcher.

"He's forty-two too. That looks like a bad age."

"Who said so, that Mrs. Pike? I bet she's forty-two," said Mrs. Fletcher.

"Naw," said Leota, "Mrs. Pike's thirty-three, born in January, an Aquarian. He could move his head—like this. A course his head and mind ain't a joint, so to speak, and I guess his stomach ain't, either—not yet anyways. But see—his food, he eats it, and it goes down, see, and then he digests it"—Leota rose on her toes for an instant—"and it goes out to his joints and before you can say 'Jack Robinson,' it's stone—pure stone. He's turning to stone. How'd you like to be married to a guy like that? All he can do, he can move his head just a quarter of an inch. A course he *looks* just *terrible*."

"I should think he would," said Mrs. Fletcher frostily. "Mr. Fletcher takes bending exercises every night of the world. I make him."

"All Fred does is lay around the house like a rug. I wouldn't be surprised if he woke up some day and couldn't move. The petrified man just sat there moving his quarter of an inch though," said Leota reminiscently.

"Did Mrs. Pike like the petrified man?" asked Mrs. Fletcher.

"Not as much as she did the others," said Leota deprecatingly. "And then she likes a man to be a good dresser, and all that."

"Is Mr. Pike a good dresser?" asked Mrs. Fletcher skeptically.

"Oh, well, yeah," said Leota, "but he's twelve-fourteen years older 'n her. She ast Lady Evangeline about him."

"Who's Lady Evangeline?" asked Mrs. Fletcher.

"Well, it's this mind reader they got in the freak show," said Leota. "Was real good. Lady Evangeline is her name, and if I had another dollar I wouldn't do a thing but have my other palm read. She had what Mrs. Pike said was the 'sixth mind' but she had the worst manicure I ever saw on a living person."

"What did she tell Mrs. Pike?" asked Mrs. Fletcher.

"She told her Mr. Pike was as true to her as he could be and besides, would come into some money."

"Humph!" said Mrs. Fletcher. "What does he do?"

"I can't tell," said Leota, "because he don't work. Lady Evangeline didn't tell me near enough about my nature or anything. And I would like to go back and find out some more about this boy. Used to go with this boy got married to this girl. Oh, shoot, that was about three and a half years ago, when you was still goin' to the Robert E. Lee Beauty Shop in Jackson. He married her for her money. Another fortune teller tole me that at the time. So I'm not in love with him any more, anyway, besides being married to Fred, but Mrs. Pike thought, just for the hell of it, see, to ask Lady Evangeline was he happy."

"Does Mrs. Pike know everything about you already?" asked Mrs. Fletcher unbelievingly. "Mercy!"

"Oh yeah, I tole her ever'thing about ever'thing, from now on back to I don't know when—to when I first started goin' out," said Leota. "So I ast Lady Evangeline for one of my questions, was he happily married, and she says, just like she was glad I ask her, 'Honey,' she says, 'naw, he isn't. You write down this day, March 8, 1941,' she says, 'and mock it down: three years from today him and her won't be occupyin' the same bed.' There it is, up on the wall with them other dates—see, Mrs. Fletcher? And she says, 'Child, you ought to be glad you didn't git him, because he's so mer-

386

cenary.' So I'm glad I married Fred. He sure ain't mercenary, money don't mean a thing to him. But I sure would like to go back and have my other palm read."

"Did Mrs. Pike believe in what the fortune teller said?" asked Mrs. Fletcher in a superior tone of voice.

"Lord, yes, she's from New Orleans. Ever'body in New Orleans believes ever'thing spooky. One of 'em in New Orleans before it was raided says to Mrs. Pike one summer she was goin' to go from state to state and meet some grayheaded men, and, sure enough, she says she went on a beautician convention up to Chicago. . . ."

"Oh!" said Mrs. Fletcher. "Oh, is Mrs. Pike a beautician too?"

"Sure she is," protested Leota. "She's a beautician. I'm goin' to git her in here if I can. Before she married. But it don't leave you. She says sure enough, there was three men who was a very large part of making her trip what it was, and they all three had gray in their hair and they went in six states. Got Christmas cards from 'em. Billy Boy, go see if Thelma's got any dry cotton. Look how Mrs. Fletcher's a-drippin'."

"Where did Mrs. Pike meet Mr. Pike?" asked Mrs. Fletcher primly.

"On another train," said Leota.

"I met Mr. Fletcher, or rather he met me, in a rental library," said Mrs. Fletcher with dignity, as she watched the net come down over her head.

"Honey, me an' Fred, we met in a rumble seat eight months ago and we was practically on what you might call the way to the altar inside of a half an hour," said Leota in a guttural voice, and bit a bobby pin open. "Course it don't last. Mrs. Pike says nothin' like that ever lasts."

"Mr. Fletcher and myself are as much in love as the day we married," said Mrs. Fletcher belligerently as Leota stuffed cotton into her ears.

"Mrs. Pike says it don't last," repeated Leota in a louder

387

voice. "Now go git under the dryer. You can turn yourself on can't you? I'll be back to comb you out. Durin' lunch I promised to give Mrs. Pike a facial. You know—free. Her bein' in the business, so to speak."

"I bet she needs one," said Mrs. Fletcher, letting the swing door fly back against Leota. "Oh, pardon me."

A week later, on time for her appointment, Mrs. Fletcher sank heavily into Leota's chair after first removing a drugstore rental book, called *Life Is Like That*, from the seat. She stared in a discouraged way into the mirror.

"You can tell it when I'm sitting down, all right," she said.

Leota seemed preoccupied and stood shaking out a lavender cloth. She began to pin it around Mrs. Fletcher's neck in silence.

"I said you sure can tell it when I'm sitting straight on and coming at you this way," Mrs. Fletcher said.

"Why, honey, naw you can't," said Leota gloomily. "Why, I'd never know. If somebody was to come up to me on the street and say, 'Mrs. Fletcher is pregnant!' I'd say, 'Heck, she don't look it to me.' "

"If a certain party hadn't found it out and spread it around, it wouldn't be too late even now," said Mrs. Fletcher frostily, but Leota was almost choking her with the cloth, pinning it so tight, and she couldn't speak clearly. She paddled her hands in the air until Leota wearily loosened her.

"Listen, honey, you're just a virgin compared to Mrs. Montjoy," Leota was going on, still absent-minded. She bent Mrs. Fletcher back in the chair and, sighing, tossed liquid from a teacup onto her head and dug both hands into her scalp. "You know Mrs. Montjoy—her husband's that premature-gray-headed fella?"

"She's in the Trojan Garden Club, is all I know," said Mrs. Fletcher.

"Well, honey," said Leota, but in a weary voice, "she come in here not the week before and not the day before

388

she had her baby—she come in here the very selfsame day, I mean to tell you. Child, we was all plumb scared to death. There she was! Come for her shampoo an' set. Why, Mrs. Fletcher, in a hour an' twenty minutes she was layin' up there in the Babtist Hospital with a seb'm-pound son. It was that close a shave. I declare, if I hadn't been so tired I would of drank up a bottle of gin that night."

"What gall," said Mrs. Fletcher. "I never knew her at all well."

"See, her husband was waitin' outside in the car, and her bags was all packed an' in the back seat, an' she was all ready, 'cept she wanted her shampoo an' set. An' havin' one pain right after another. Her husband kep' comin' in here, scared-like, but couldn't do nothin' with her a course. She yelled bloody murder, too, but she always yelled her head off when I give her a perm'nent."

"She must of been crazy," said Mrs. Fletcher. "How did she look?"

"Shoot!" said Leota.

"Well, I can guess," said Mrs. Fletcher. "Awful."

"Just wanted to look pretty while she was havin' her baby, is all," said Leota airily. "Course, we was glad to give the lady what she was after—that's our motto—but I bet a hour later she wasn't payin' no mind to them little end curls. I bet she wasn't thinkin' about she ought to have on a net. It wouldn't of done her no good if she had."

"No, I don't suppose it would," said Mrs. Fletcher.

"Yeah man! She was a-yellin'. Just like when I give her her perm'nent."

"Her husband ought to could make her behave. Don't it seem that way to you?" asked Mrs. Fletcher. "He ought to put his foot down."

"Ha," said Leota. "A lot he could do. Maybe some women is soft."

"Oh, you mistake me, I don't mean for her to get soft—far from it! Women have to stand up for themselves, or there's

389

just no telling. But now you take me—I ask Mr. Fletcher's advice now and then, and he appreciates it, especially on something important, like is it time for a permanent—not that I've told him about the baby. He says, 'Why dear, go ahead!' Just ask their *advice*."

"Huh! If I ever ast Fred's advice we'd be floatin' down the Yazoo River on a houseboat or somethin' by this time," said Leota. "I'm sick of Fred. I tole him to go over to Vicksburg."

"Is he going?" demanded Mrs. Fletcher.

"Sure. See, the fortune teller—I went back and had my other palm read, since we've got to rent the room agin—said my lover was goin' to work in Vicksburg, so I don't know who she could mean, unless she meant Fred. And Fred ain't workin' here—that much is so."

"Is he going to work in Vicksburg?" asked Mrs. Fletcher. "And—"

"Sure, Lady Evangeline said so. Said the future is going to be brighter than the present. He don't want to go, but I ain't gonna put up with nothin' like that. Lays around the house an' bulls—did bull—with that good-for-nothin' Mr. Pike. He says if he goes who'll cook, but I says I never get to eat anyway—not meals. Billy Boy, take Mrs. Grover that *Screen Secrets* and leg it."

Mrs. Fletcher heard stamping feet go out the door.

"Is that that Mrs. Pike's little boy here again?" she asked, sitting up gingerly.

"Yeah, that's still him." Leota stuck out her tongue.

Mrs. Fletcher could hardly believe her eyes. "Well! How's Mrs. Pike, your attractive new friend with the sharp eyes who spreads it around town that perfect strangers are pregnant?" she asked in a sweetened tone.

"Oh, Mizziz Pike." Leota combed Mrs. Fletcher's hair with heavy strokes.

"You act like you're tired," said Mrs. Fletcher.

"Tired? Feel like it's four o'clock in the afternoon

already," said Leota. "I ain't told you the awful luck we had, me and Fred? It's the worst thing you ever heard of. Maybe *you* think Mrs. Pike's got sharp eyes. Shoot, there's a limit! Well, you know, we rented out our room to this Mr. and Mrs. Pike from New Orleans when Sal an' Joe Fentress got mad at us 'cause they drank up some home-brew we had in the closet—Sal an' Joe did. So, a week ago Sat'day Mr. and Mrs. Pike moved in. Well, I kinda fixed up the room, you know—put a sofa pillow on the couch and picked some ragged robbins and put in a vase, but they never did say they appreciated it. Anyway, then I put some old magazines on the table."

"I think that was lovely," said Mrs. Fletcher.

"Wait. So, come night 'fore last, Fred and this Mr. Pike, who Fred just took up with, was back from they said they was fishin', bein' as neither one of 'em has got a job to his name, and we was all settin' around in their room. So Mrs. Pike was settin' there, readin' a old *Startling G-Man Tales* that was mine, mind you, I'd bought it myself, and all of a sudden she jumps!—into the air—you'd 'a' thought she'd set on a spider—an' says, 'Canfield'—ain't that silly, that's Mr. Pike—'Canfield, my God A'mighty,' she says, 'honey,' she says, 'we're rich, and you won't have to work.' Not that he turned one hand anyway. Well, me and Fred rushes over to her, and Mr. Pike, too, and there she sets, pointin' her finger at a photo in my copy of *Startling G-Man.* 'See that man?' yells Mrs. Pike. 'Remember him, Canfield?' 'Never forget a face,' says Mr. Pike. 'It's Mr. Petrie, that we stayed with him in the apartment next to ours in Toulouse Street in N.O. for six weeks. Mr. Petrie.' 'Well,' says Mrs. Pike, like she can't hold out one secont longer, 'Mr. Petrie is wanted for five hunderd dollars cash, for rapin' four women in California, and I know where he is.' "

"Mercy!" said Mrs. Fletcher. "Where was he?"

At some time Leota had washed her hair and now she yanked her up by the back locks and sat her up.

"Know where he was?"

"I certainly don't," Mrs. Fletcher said. Her scalp hurt all over.

Leota flung a towel around the top of her customer's head. "Nowhere else but in that freak show! I saw him just as plain as Mrs. Pike. *He* was the petrified man!"

"Who would ever have thought that!" cried Mrs. Fletcher sympathetically.

"So Mr. Pike says, 'Well whatta you know about that,' an' he looks real hard at the photo and whistles. And she starts dancin' and singin' about their good luck. She meant our bad luck! I made a point of tellin' that fortune teller the next time I saw her. I said, 'Listen, that magazine was layin' around the house for a month, and there was five hunderd dollars in it for somebody. An' there was the freak show runnin' night an' day, not two steps away from my own beauty parlor, with Mr. Petrie just settin' there waitin'. An' it had to be Mr. and Mrs. Pike, almost perfect strangers.'"

"What gall," said Mrs. Fletcher. She was only sitting there, wrapped in a turban, but she did not mind.

"Fortune tellers don't care. And Mrs. Pike, she goes around actin' like she thinks she was Mrs. God," said Leota. "So they're goin' to leave tomorrow, Mr. and Mrs. Pike. And in the meantime I got to keep that mean, bad little ole kid here, gettin' under my feet ever' minute of the day an' talkin' back too."

"Have they gotten the five hundred dollars' reward already?" asked Mrs. Fletcher.

"Well," said Leota, "at first Mr. Pike didn't want to do anything about it. Can you feature that? Said he kinda liked that ole bird and said he was real nice to 'em, lent 'em money or somethin'. But Mrs. Pike simply tole him he could just go to hell, and I can see her point. She says, 'You ain't worked a lick in six months, and here I make five hunderd dollars in two seconts, and what thanks do I get for it? You go to hell, Canfield,' she says. So," Leota went on in a

392

despondent voice, "they called up the cops and they caught the ole bird, all right, right there in the freak show where I saw him with my own eyes, thinkin' he was petrified. He's the one. Did it under his real name—Mr. Petrie. Four women in California, all in the month of August. So Mrs. Pike gits five hunderd dollars. And my magazine, and right next door to my beauty parlor. I cried all night, but Fred said it wasn't a bit of use and to go to sleep, because the whole thing was just a sort of coincidence—you know: can't do nothin' about it. He says it put him clean out of the notion of goin' to Vicksburg for a few days till we rent out the room agin—no tellin' who we'll git this time."

"But can you imagine anybody knowing this old man, that's raped four women?" persisted Mrs. Fletcher, and she shuddered audibly. "Did Mrs. Pike *speak* to him when she met him in the freak show?"

Leota had begun to comb Mrs. Fletcher's hair. "I says to her, I says, 'I didn't notice you fallin' on his neck when he was the petrified man—don't tell me you didn't recognize your fine friend?' And she says, 'I didn't recognize him with that white powder all over his face. He just looked familiar,' Mrs. Pike says, 'and lots of people look familiar.' But she says that ole petrified man did put her in mind of somebody. She wondered who it was! Kep' her awake, which man she'd ever knew it reminded her of. So when she seen the photo, it all come to her. Like a flash. Mr. Petrie. The way he'd turn his head and look at her when she took him in his breakfast."

"Took him in his breakfast!" shrieked Mrs. Fletcher. "Listen—don't tell me. I'd 'a' felt something."

"Four women. I guess those women didn't have the faintest notion at the time they'd be worth a hunderd an' twenty-five bucks apiece someday to Mrs. Pike. We ast her how old the fella was then, an' she says he musta had one foot in the grave, at least. Can you beat it?"

"Not really petrified at all, of course," said Mrs. Fletcher meditatively. She drew herself up. "I'd 'a' felt something," she said proudly.

"Shoot! I did feel somethin'," said Leota. "I tole Fred when I got home I felt so funny. I said, 'Fred, that ole petrified man sure did leave me with a funny feelin'.' He says, 'Funny-haha or funny-peculiar?' and I says, 'Funny-peculiar.'" She pointed her comb into the air emphatically.

"I'll bet you did," said Mrs. Fletcher.

They both heard a crackling noise.

Leota screamed, "Billy Boy! What you doin' in my purse?"

"Aw, I'm just eatin' these ole stale peanuts up," said Billy Boy.

"You come here to me!" screamed Leota, recklessly flinging down the comb, which scattered a whole ash tray full of bobby pins and knocked down a row of Coca-Cola bottles. "This is the last straw!"

"I caught him! I caught him!" giggled Mrs. Fletcher. "I'll hold him on my lap. You bad, bad boy, you! I guess I better learn how to spank little old bad boys," she said.

Leota's eleven o'clock customer pushed open the swing door upon Leota paddling him heartily with the brush, while he gave angry but belittling screams which penetrated beyond the booth and filled the whole curious beauty parlor. From everywhere ladies began to gather round to watch the paddling. Billy Boy kicked both Leota and Mrs. Fletcher as hard as he could, Mrs. Fletcher with her new fixed smile.

"There, my little man!" gasped Leota. "You won't be able to set down for a week if I knew what I was doin'."

Billy Boy stomped through the group of wild-haired ladies and went out the door, but flung back the words, "If you're so smart, why ain't you rich?"

William Saroyan

THE SUMMER OF THE BEAUTIFUL
WHITE HORSE

ONE DAY back there in the good old days when I was nine
and the world was full of every imaginable kind of magnificence, and life was still a delightful and mysterious dream,
my cousin Mourad, who was considered crazy by everybody who knew him except me, came to my house at four
in the morning and woke me up by tapping on the window
of my room.

Aram, he said.

I jumped out of bed and looked out the window.

I couldn't believe what I saw.

It wasn't morning yet, but it was summer and with daybreak not many minutes around the corner of the world it
was light enough for me to know I wasn't dreaming.

My cousin Mourad was sitting on a beautiful white horse.

I stuck my head out of the window and rubbed my eyes.

Yes, he said in Armenian. It's a horse. You're not dreaming. Make it quick if you want to ride.

I knew my cousin Mourad enjoyed being alive more than
anybody else who had ever fallen into the world by mistake, but this was more than even I could believe.

In the first place, my earliest memories had been memories
of horses and my first longings had been longings to ride.

This was the wonderful part.

In the second place, we were poor.

This was the part that wouldn't permit me to believe what
I saw.

We were poor. We had no money. Our whole tribe was
poverty-stricken. Every branch of the Garoghlanian family

was living in the most amazing and comical poverty in the world. Nobody could understand where we ever got money enough to keep us with food in our bellies, not even the old men of the family. Most important of all, though, we were famous for our honesty. We had been famous for our honesty for something like eleven centuries, even when we had been the wealthiest family in what we liked to think was the world. We were proud first, honest next, and after that we believed in right and wrong. None of us would take advantage of anybody in the world, let alone steal.

Consequently, even though I could *see* the horse, so magnificent; even though I could *smell* it, so lovely; even though I could *hear* it breathing, so exciting; I couldn't *believe* the horse had anything to do with my cousin Mourad or with me or with any of the other members of our family, asleep or awake, because I *knew* my cousin Mourad couldn't have *bought* the horse, and if he couldn't have bought it he must have *stolen* it, and I refused to believe he had stolen it.

No member of the Garoghlanian family could be a thief.

I stared first at my cousin and then at the horse. There was a pious stillness and humor in each of them which on the one hand delighted me and on the other frightened me.

Mourad, I said, where did you steal this horse?

Leap out of the window, he said, if you want to ride.

It was true, then. He *had* stolen the horse. There was no question about it. He had come to invite me to ride or not, as I chose.

Well, it seemed to me stealing a horse for a ride was not the same thing as stealing something else, such as money. For all I knew, maybe it wasn't stealing at all. If you were crazy about horses the way my cousin Mourad and I were, it wasn't stealing. It wouldn't become stealing until we offered to sell the horse, which of course I knew we would never do.

Let me put on some clothes, I said.

All right, he said, but hurry.

396

I leaped into my clothes.

I jumped down to the yard from the window and leaped up onto the horse behind my cousin Mourad.

That year we lived at the edge of town, on Walnut Avenue. Behind our house was the country: vineyards, orchards, irrigation ditches, and country roads. In less than three minutes we were on Olive Avenue, and then the horse began to trot. The air was new and lovely to breathe. The feel of the horse running was wonderful. My cousin Mourad who was considered one of the craziest members of our family began to sing. I mean, he began to roar.

Every family has a crazy streak in it somewhere, and my cousin Mourad was considered the natural descendant of the crazy streak in our tribe. Before him was our uncle Khosrove, an enormous man with a powerful head of black hair and the largest mustache in the San Joaquin Valley, a man so furious in temper, so irritable, so impatient that he stopped anyone from talking by roaring, *It is no harm; pay no attention to it.*

That was all, no matter what anybody happened to be talking about. Once it was his own son Arak running eight blocks to the barber shop where his father was having his mustache trimmed to tell him their house was on fire. This man Khosrove sat up in the chair and roared, It is no harm; pay no attention to it. The barber said, But the boy says your house is on fire. So Khosrove roared, Enough, it is no harm, I say.

My cousin Mourad was considered the natural descendant of this man, although Mourad's father was Zorab, who was practical and nothing else. That's how it was in our tribe. A man could be the father of his son's flesh, but that did not mean that he was also the father of his spirit. The distribution of the various kinds of spirit of our tribe had been from the beginning capricious and vagrant.

We rode and my cousin Mourad sang. For all anybody knew we were still in the old country where, at least according to some of our neighbors, we belonged. We let the horse run as long as it felt like running.

At last my cousin Mourad said, Get down. I want to ride alone.

Will you let me ride alone? I said.

That is up to the horse, my cousin said. Get down.

The *horse* will let me ride, I said.

We shall see, he said. Don't forget that I have a way with a horse.

Well, I said, any way you have with a horse, I have also.

For the sake of your safety, he said, let us hope so. Get down.

All right, I said, but remember you've got to let me try to ride alone.

I got down and my cousin Mourad kicked his heels into the horse and shouted, *Vazire*, run. The horse stood on its hind legs, snorted, and burst into a fury of speed that was the loveliest thing I had ever seen. My cousin Mourad raced the horse across a field of dry grass to an irrigation ditch, crossed the ditch on the horse, and five minutes later returned, dripping wet.

The sun was coming up.

Now it's my turn to ride, I said.

My cousin Mourad got off the horse.

Ride, he said.

I leaped to the back of the horse and for a moment knew the awfulest fear imaginable. The horse did not move.

Kick into his muscles, my cousin Mourad said. What are you waiting for? We've got to take him back before everybody in the world is up and about.

I kicked into the muscles of the horse. Once again it reared and snorted. Then it began to run. I didn't know what to do. Instead of running across the field to the irrigation ditch the horse ran down the road to the vineyard of Dikran Halabian where it began to leap over vines. The horse leaped over seven vines before I fell. Then it continued running.

My cousin Mourad came running down the road.

I'm not worried about you, he shouted. We've got to get that horse. You go this way and I'll go this way. If you come upon him, be kindly. I'll be near.

I continued down the road and my cousin Mourad went across the field toward the irrigation ditch.

It took him half an hour to find the horse and bring him back.

All right, he said, jump on. The whole world is awake now.

What will we do? I said.

Well, he said, we'll either take him back or hide him until tomorrow morning.

He didn't sound worried and I knew he'd hide him and not take him back. Not for a while, at any rate.

Where will we hide him? I said.

I know a place, he said.

How long ago did you steal this horse? I said.

It suddenly dawned on me that he had been taking these early morning rides for some time and had come for me this morning only because he knew how much I longed to ride.

Who said anything about stealing a horse? he said.

Anyhow, I said, how long ago did you begin riding every morning?

Not until this morning, he said.

Are you telling the truth? I said.

Of course not, he said, but if we are found out, that's what you're to say. I don't want both of us to be liars. All you know is that we started riding this morning.

All right, I said.

He walked the horse quietly to the barn of a deserted vineyard which at one time had been the pride of a farmer named Fetvajian. There were some oats and dry alfalfa in the barn.

We began walking home.

It wasn't easy, he said, to get the horse to behave so nicely.

At first it wanted to run wild, but, as I've told you, I have a way with a horse. I can get it to want to do anything *I* want it to do. Horses understand me.

How do you do it? I said.

I have an understanding with a horse, he said.

Yes, but what sort of an understanding? I said.

A simple and honest one, he said.

Well, I said, I wish I knew how to reach an understanding like that with a horse.

You're still a small boy, he said. When you get to be thirteen you'll know how to do it.

I went home and ate a hearty breakfast.

That afternoon my uncle Khosrove came to our house for coffee and cigarettes. He sat in the parlor, sipping and smoking and remembering the old country. Then another visitor arrived, a farmer named John Byro, an Assyrian who, out of loneliness, had learned to speak Armenian. My mother brought the lonely visitor coffee and tobacco and he rolled a cigarette and sipped and smoked, and then at last, sighing sadly, he said, My white horse which was stolen last month is still gone. I cannot understand it.

My uncle Khosrove became very irritated and shouted, It's no harm. What is the loss of a horse? Haven't we all lost the homeland? What is this crying over a horse?

That may be all right for you, a city dweller, to say, John Byro said, but what of my surrey? What good is a surrey without a horse?

Pay no attention to it, my uncle Khosrove roared.

I walked ten miles to get here, John Byro said.

You have legs, my uncle Khosrove shouted.

My left leg pains me, the farmer said.

Pay no attention to it, my uncle Khosrove roared.

That horse cost me sixty dollars, the farmer said.

I spit on money, my uncle Khosrove said.

He got up and stalked out of the house, slamming the screen door.

400

My mother explained.

He has a gentle heart, she said. It is simply that he is homesick and such a large man.

The farmer went away and I ran over to my cousin Mourad's house.

He was sitting under a peach tree, trying to repair the hurt wing of a young robin which could not fly. He was talking to the bird.

What is it? he said.

The farmer, John Byro, I said. He visited our house. He wants his horse. You've had it a month. I want you to promise not to take it back until I learn to ride.

It will take you *a year* to learn to ride, my cousin Mourad said.

We could keep the horse a year, I said.

My cousin Mourad leaped to his feet.

What? he roared. Are you inviting a member of the Garoghlanian family to steal? The horse must go back to its true owner.

When? I said.

In six months at the latest, he said.

He threw the bird into the air. The bird tried hard, almost fell twice, but at last flew away, high and straight.

Early every morning for two weeks my cousin Mourad and I took the horse out of the barn of the deserted vineyard where we were hiding it and rode it, and every morning the horse, when it was my turn to ride alone, leaped over grape vines and small trees and threw me and ran away. Nevertheless, I hoped in time to learn to ride the way my cousin Mourad rode.

One morning on the way to Fetvajian's deserted vineyard we ran into the farmer John Byro who was on his way to town.

Let me do the talking, my cousin Mourad said. I have a way with farmers.

Good morning, John Byro, my cousin Mourad said to the farmer.

The farmer studied the horse eagerly.

Good morning, sons of my friends, he said. What is the name of your horse?

My Heart, my cousin Mourad said in Armenian.

A lovely name, John Byro said, for a lovely horse. I could swear it is the horse that was stolen from me many weeks ago. May I look into its mouth?

Of course, Mourad said.

The farmer looked into the mouth of the horse.

Tooth for tooth, he said. I would swear it *is* my horse if I didn't know your parents. The fame of your family for honesty is well known to me. Yet the horse is the twin of my horse. A suspicious man would believe his eyes instead of his heart. Good day, my young friends.

Good day, John Byro, my cousin Mourad said.

Early the following morning we took the horse to John Byro's vineyard and put it in the barn. The dogs followed us around without making a sound.

The dogs, I whispered to my cousin Mourad. I thought they would bark.

They would at somebody else, he said. I have a way with dogs.

My cousin Mourad put his arms around the horse, pressed his nose into the horse's nose, patted it, and then we went away.

That afternoon John Byro came to our house in his surrey and showed my mother the horse that had been stolen and returned.

I do not know what to think, he said. The horse is stronger than ever. Better-tempered, too. I thank God.

My uncle Khosrove, who was in the parlor, became irritated and shouted, Quiet, man, quiet. Your horse has been returned. Pay no attention to it.

V

ACKNOWLEDGMENTS

Archibald MacLeish, Preface from CONQUISTADOR, copyright 1932 by Houghton Mifflin Co.; John Peale Bishop, ODE and PERSPECTIVES ARE PRECIPICES from "Selected Poems," copyright 1941 by Charles Scribner's Sons; Hart Crane, TO BROOKLYN BRIDGE and VOYAGES II from "Collected Poems," copyright 1933 by Liveright, Inc.; E. E. Cummings, TWO SONNETS from "Selected Poems," copyright 1938 by E. E. Cummings (Harcourt, Brace & Co., Inc.); Conrad Aiken, TETELESTAI from "Selected Poems," copyright 1928, 1929, 1931, 1932, 1933, 1934 by Conrad Aiken (Charles Scribner's Sons); Allen Tate, ODE TO THE CONFEDERATE DEAD and AENEAS AT WASHINGTON from "Selected Poems," copyright 1937 by Charles Scribner's Sons; John Crowe Ransom, CAPTAIN CARPENTER from "Chills and Fever," and BLUE GIRLS from "Two Gentlemen in Bonds," copyright 1927 and 1939 by Alfred A. Knopf, Inc.; Carl Sandburg, COOL TOMBS from "Selected Poems," copyright 1926 by Henry Holt & Co., Inc., and LOSERS from "Smoke and Steel," copyright 1920 by Harcourt, Brace & Co., Inc.; William Carlos Williams, THE BOTTICELLIAN TREES and POEM I from "Complete Collected Poems," copyright 1938 by William Carlos Williams; Karl Shapiro, SCYROS from "Five Young American Poets," copyright 1941 by New Directions; Delmore Schwartz, IN THE NAKED BED, IN PLATO'S CAVE from "In Dreams Begin Responsibilities," copyright 1938 by Delmore Schwartz (New Directions).

Archibald MacLeish

CONQUISTADOR

Bernál Díaz' Preface

'THAT which I have myself seen and the fighting'. . . .

And I am an ignorant man: and this priest this
Gómara with the school-taught skip to his writing

The pompous Latin the appropriate feasts
The big names the imperial decorations
The beautiful battles and the brave deceased

The onward marches the wild Indian nations
The conquests sieges sorties wars campaigns
(And one eye always on the live relations)—

He with his famous history of New Spain—
This priest is a learned man: is not ignorant:
And I am poor: without gold: gainless:

My lands deserts in Guatemala: my fig-tree the
Spiked bush: my grapes thorns: my children
Half-grown: sons with beards: the big one

Breaking the small of his back in the brothel thills
And a girl to be married and all of them snarling at home
With the Indian look in their eyes like a cat killing:

And this Professor Francisco López de Gómara
Childless; not poor: and I am old: over eighty:
Stupid with sleepless nights: unused to the combing of

Words clean of the wool while the tale waits:
And he is a youthful man: a sound one: lightened with
Good sleep: skilled in the pen's plaiting—

I am an ignorant old sick man: blind with the
Shadow of death on my face and my hands to lead me:
And he not ignorant: not sick—

                            but I

Fought in those battles! These were my own deeds!
These names he writes of mouthing them out as a man would
Names in Herodotus—dead and their wars to read—

These were my friends: these dead my companions:
I: Bernál Díaz: called del Castíllo:
Called in the time of my first fights El Galán:

I here in the turn of the day in the feel of
Darkness to come now: moving my chair with the change:
Thinking too much these times how the doves would wheel at

Evening over my youth and the air's strangeness:
Thinking too much of my old town of Medina
And the Spanish dust and the smell of the true rain:

I: poor: blind in the sun: I have seen
With these eyes those battles: I saw Montezúma:
I saw the armies of Mexico marching the leaning

Wind in their garments: the painted faces: the plumes
Blown on the light air: I saw that city:
I walked at night on those stones: in the shadowy rooms

406

I have heard the chink of my heel and the bats twittering:
I: poor as I am: I was young in that country:
These words were my life: these letters written

Cold on the page with the spilt ink and the shunt of the
Stubborn thumb: these marks at my fingers:
These are the shape of my own life. . . .

                          and I hunted the

Unknown birds in the west with their beautiful wings!

Old men should die with their time's span:
The sad thing is not death: the sad thing

Is the life's loss out of earth when the living vanish:
All that was good in the throat: the hard going:
The marching singing in sunshine: the showery land:

The quick loves: the sleep: the waking: the blowing of
Winds over us: all this that we knew:
All this goes out at the end as the flowing of

Water carries the leaves down: and the few—
Three or four there are of us still that remember it—
Perish: and that time's stopt like a stale tune:

And the bright young masters with their bitter treble
Understanding it all like an old game!
And the pucker of art on their lips like the pip of a lemon!—

'The tedious veteran jealous of his fame!'
What is my fame or the fame of these my companions?
Their tombs are the bellies of Indians: theirs are the shameful

Graves in the wild earth: in the Godless sand:
None know the place of their bones: as for mine
Strangers will dig my grave in a stony land:

Even my sons have the strangeness of dark kind in them:
Indian dogs will bark at dusk by my sepulchre:
What is my fame! But those days: the shine of the

Sun in that time: the wind then: the step
Of the moon over those leaf-fallen nights: the sleet in the
Dry grass: the smell of the dust where we slept—

These things were real: these suns had heat in them:
This was brine in the mouth: bitterest foam:
Earth: water to drink: bread to be eaten—

Not the sound of a word like the writing of Gómara:
Not a past time: a year: the name of a
Battle lost—'and the Emperor Charles came home

'That year: and that was the year the same
'They fought in Flanders and the Duke was hung—'
The dates of empire: the dry skull of fame!

No but our lives: the days of our lives: we were young then:
The strong sun was standing in deep trees:
We drank at the springs: the thongs of our swords unslung
     to it:

We saw that city on the inland sea:
Towers between: and the green-crowned Montezúma
Walking the gardens of shade: and the staggering bees:

And the girls bearing the woven baskets of bloom on their
Black hair: their breasts alive: and the hunters
Shouldering dangling herons with their ruffled plumes:

We were the first that found that famous country:
We marched by a king's name: we crossed the sierras:
Unknown hardships we suffered: hunger:

Death by the stone knife: thirst: we fared by the
Bitter streams: we came at last to that water:
Towers were steep upon the fluttering air:

We were the lords of it all . . .
                              Now time has taught us:
Death has mastered us most; sorrow and pain
Sickness and evil days are our lives' lot:

Now even the time of our youth has been taken:
Now are our deeds words: our lives chronicles:
Afterwards none will think of the night rain. . . .

How shall a man endure the will of God and the
Days and the silence!
                    In the world before us
Neither in Cuba nor the isles beyond—

Not Fonséca himself the sagging whore—
Not the Council the Audience even the Indians—
Knew of a land to the west: they skirted the Floridas:

They ran the islands on the bare-pole winds:
They touched the Old Main and the midland shores:
They saw the sun go down at the gulf's beginning:

None had sailed to the west and returned till Córdova:
I went in that ship: Alvarez handled her:
Trusting to luck: keeping the evening before him:

Sighting after the third week land
And no report of a land there in that ocean:
The Indians clean: wearing the delicate bands:

Cape Catoche we called it: 'conès catoche'—
So they cried to us over the sea flood:
Many idols they had for their devotion

Some of women: some coupled in sodomy
So we sailed on: we came to Campéchè:
There by the sweet pool they kindled the wood-fire:

Words they were saying like 'Castilán' in their speech:
They warned us by signs to be gone when the logs charred:
So we turned from them down to the smooth beaches:

The boats followed us close in: we departed:
Afterwards there was a nortë with fine haze:
We stood for Potonchán through the boil of the narrows:

There they attacked us crossing the green of the maize fields:
Me they struck thrice and they killed fifty
And all were hurt and two taken crazy with

Much pain and it blew and the dust lifted
And the thirst cracked the tongues in our mouths and before
        us the
Sea-corrupted pools where the river drifts:

And we turned back and the wind drove us to Florida:
There in the scooped sand in the withered bed—
There by the sea they encountered us threatening war:

So we returned to the islands half dead:
And Córdova did die: and we wrote to Velásquez—
Diégo the Governor—writing it out: and we said—

'Excellence: there are lands in the west: the pass is
'Clean sailing: the scuts of the men are covered:
'The houses are masonry: gold they have: baskets

'Painted with herbs: the women are chaste in love'—
Much else of the kind I cannot remember:
And Velásquez took the credit for this discovery:

410

And all we had was our wounds: and enough of them:
And Fonséca Bishop of Búrgos (for so he was called)
President of the Council: he wrote to the Emperor

Telling the wonderful news in a mule's volley
And not a word of our deeds or our pains or our battles:
And Charles gone: and Joanna the poor queen stalled

In Tordesíllas shaking the peas in a rattle:
And Barbarossa licking his chin in Algiers:
And trouble enough in Spain with all that

And the Cardinal dying and Sicily over the ears—
Trouble enough without new lands to be conquered and
Naked Indians taken and wild sheep sheared:

But as for us that returned from that westward country—
We could not lie in our towns for the sound of the sea:
We could not rest at all in our thoughts: we were young then:

We looked to the west: we remembered the foreign trees
Borne out on the tide from the unknown rivers
And the clouds like hills in the air our eyes had seen:

And Grijálva sailed next and we that were living—
We that had gear to our flesh and the gold to find
And an old pike in the stall with the haft to it slivered—

We signed on and we sailed by the first tide:
And we fought at Potonchán that voyage: I remember
The locusts covered the earth like a false shine to it:

They flew with a shrill sound like the arrow stem:
Often we took the whir of the darts for the locusts:
Often we left our shields from our mouths as they came:

I remember our fighting was much marred by the locusts:
And that voyage we came to the river Tabasco:
We saw the nets as we came in and the smoke of the

Sea over the bar: and we filled the casks there:
There first we heard of the farther land—
'Colúa' they said 'Méjico'—we that were asking the

Gold there on that shore on the evening sand—
'Colúa' they said: pointing on toward the sunset:
They made a sign on the air with their solemn hands:

Afterward: north: on the sea: and the ships running
We saw the steep snow mountain on the sky:
We stared as dream-awakened men in wonder:

And that voyage it was we came to the Island:
Well I remember the shore and the sound of that place
And the smoke smell on the dunes and the wind dying:

Well I remember the walls and the rusty taste of the
New-spilled blood in the air: many among us
Seeing the priests with their small and arrogant faces:

Seeing the dead boys' breasts and the idols hung with the
Dried shells of the hearts like the husks of cicadas
And their human eyeballs and their painted tongues

Cried out to the Holy Mother of God for it:
And some that stood there bore themselves the stone:
And some were eaten of wild beasts of their bodies:

And none of us all but had his heart foreknown the
Evil to come would have turned from the land then:
But the lives of men are covered and not shown—

Only late to the old at their time's ending
The land shows backward and the way is there:
And the next day we sailed and the sea was against us

And our bread was dirty with weevils and grown scarce and
        the
Rains began and the beans stank in the ovens
And we soldiers were thoroughly tired of sea-faring:

So we returned from that voyage with God's love:
And they talked about nothing else in the whole of Cuba:
And gentlemen sold their farms to go on discoveries:

And we that had fought in the marshes with no food—
We sat by the palms in the square in the green gloaming
With the delicate girls on our knees and the night to lose:

We that had fought in those lands. . . .
                   and the eloquent Gómara:
The quilled professors: the taught tongues of fame:
What have they written of us: the poor soldiers:

We that were wounded often for no pay:
We that died and were dumped cold in the bread sacks:
Bellies up: the birds at us: floating for days

And none remembering which it was that was dead there
Whether of Búrgos or Yúste or Villalár:
Where have they written our names? What have they said of
        us?

They call the towns for the kings that bear no scars:
They keep the names of the great for time to stare at—
The bishops rich-men generals cocks-at-arms:

Those with the glaze in their eyes and the fine bearing:
The born leaders of men: the resonant voices:
They give them the lands for their tombs: they call it
     America!

(And who has heard of Vespucci in this soil
Or down by the lee of the coast or toward the Havana?)
And we that fought here: that with heavy toil

Earthed up the powerful cities of this land—
What are we? When will our fame come?
An old man in a hill town
                  a handful of
Dust under the dry grass at Otúmba

Unknown names
            hands vanished
                     faces

Many gone from the day
              unspeakable numbers
Lives forgotten
           deeds honored in strangers

'That which I have myself seen and the fighting' . . .

John Peale Bishop

ODE

WHY WILL they never sleep
Those great women who sit
Peering at me with parrot eyes?
They sit with grave knees; they keep
Perpetual stare; and their hands move
As though hands could be aware—
Forward and back, to begin again—
As though on tumultuous shuttles of wind they wove
Shrouds out of air.

The three are sisters. There is one
Who sits divine in weeping stone
On a small chair of skeleton
And is most inescapable.
I have walked through many mirrors
But always accompanied.
I have been as many men, as many ghosts,
As there were days. The boy was seen
Always at rainfall, mistily, not lost.
I have tried changing shapes
But always, alone, I have heard
Her shadow coming nearer, and known
The awful grasp of striding hands
Goddess! upon
The screaming metamorphosis.

One has a face burned hard
As the red Cretan clay,
Who wears a white torso scarred
With figures like a calendar.

She sits among broken shafts
Of stone; she is and still will be
Who feeds on cities, gods and men,
Weapons of bronze and curious ornaments,
Reckoning the evens as the odds,
Her least movement recalls the sea.

The last has idiot teeth
And a brow not made
For any thought but suffering.
Tired, she repeats
In idiot singing
A song shaped like a ring:
"Now is now and never Then
Dead Virgins will bear no men
And now that we speak of love, of love,
The woman's beneath
That's burdened with love
And the man's above
While the thing is done and done.
One is one and Three is three
Children may come from a spark in the sun
But One is one and never Three
And never a Virgin shall bear a Son
While the shadow lasts of the gray ashtree!"

Phantasmal marbles!

There was One who might have saved
Me from these grave dissolute stones
And parrot eyes. But He is dead,
Christ is dead. And in a grave
Dark as a sightless skull He lies
And of His bones are charnels made.

John Peale Bishop

PERSPECTIVES ARE PRECIPICES

Sister Anne, Sister Anne,
Do you see anybody coming?

> I see a distance of black yews
> Long as the history of the Jews

> I see a road sunned with white sand
> Wide plains surrounding silence. And

> Far-off, a broken colonnade
> That overthrows the sun with shade.

Sister Anne, Sister Anne,
Do you see nobody coming?

                            A man

> Upon that road a man who goes
> Dragging a shadow by its toes.

> Diminishing he goes, head bare
> Of any covering even hair.

> A pitcher depending from one hand
> Goes mouth down. And dry is sand

Sister Anne, Sister Anne,
What do you see?

> His dwindling stride. And he seems blind
> Or worse to the prone man behind.

I see a road. Beyond nowhere
Defined by cirrus and blue air.

I saw a man but he is gone
His shadow gone into the sun.

§

Hart Crane

TO BROOKLYN BRIDGE

How many dawns, chill from his rippling rest
The seagull's wings shall dip and pivot him,
Shedding white rings of tumult, building high
Over the chained bay waters Liberty—

Then, with inviolate curve, forsake our eyes
As apparitional as sails that cross
Some page of figures to be filed away;
—Till elevators drop us from our day . . .

I think of cinemas, panoramic sleights
With multitudes bent toward some flashing scene
Never disclosed, but hastened to again,
Foretold to other eyes on the same screen;

And Thee, across the harbor, silver-paced
As though the sun took step of thee, yet left
Some motion ever unspent in thy stride,—
Implicitly thy freedom staying thee!

Out of some subway scuttle, cell or loft
A bedlamite speeds to thy parapets,
Tilting there momently, shrill shirt ballooning,
A jest falls from the speechless caravan.

Down Wall, from girder into street noon leaks,
A rip-tooth of the sky's acetylene;
All afternoon the cloud-flown derricks turn . . .
Thy cables breathe the North Atlantic still.

And obscure as that heaven of the Jews,
Thy guerdon . . . Accolade thou dost bestow
Of anonymity time cannot raise:
Vibrant reprieve and pardon thou dost show.

O harp and altar, of the fury fused, .
(How could mere toil align thy choiring strings!)
Terrific threshold of the prophet's pledge,
Prayer of pariah, and the lover's cry,—

Again the traffic lights that skim thy swift
Unfractioned idiom, immaculate sigh of stars,
Beading thy path—condense eternity:
And we have seen night lifted in thine arms.

Under thy shadow by the piers I waited;
Only in darkness is thy shadow clear.
The City's fiery parcels all undone,
Already snow submerges an iron year . . .

O Sleepless as the river under thee,
Vaulting the sea, the prairies' dreaming sod,
Unto us lowliest sometime sweep, descend
And of the curveship lend a myth to God.

Hart Crane

VOYAGES

II

And yet this great wink of eternity,
Of rimless floods, unfettered leewardings,
Samite sheeted and processioned where
Her undinal vast belly moonward bends,
Laughing the rapt inflections of our love;

Take this Sea, whose diapason knells
On scrolls of silver snowy sentences,
The sceptred terror of whose sessions rends
As her demeanors motion well or ill,
All but the pieties of lovers' hands.

And onward, as bells off San Salvador
Salute the crocus lustres of the stars,
In these poinsettia meadows of her tides,—
Adagios of islands, O my Prodigal,
Complete the dark confessions her veins spell.

Mark how her turning shoulders wind the hours,
And hasten while her penniless rich palms
Pass superscription of bent foam and wave,—
Hasten, while they are true,—sleep, death, desire,
Close round one instant in one floating flower.

Bind us in time, O Seasons clear, and awe.
O minstrel galleons of Carib fire,
Bequeath us to no earthly shore until
Is answered in the vortex of our grave
The seal's wide spindrift gaze toward paradise.

E. E. Cummings

TWO SONNETS

if i should sleep with a lady called death
get another man with firmer lips
to take your new mouth in his teeth
(hips pumping pleasure into hips).

Seeing how the limp huddling string
of your smile over his body squirms
kissingly, i will bring you every spring
handfuls of little normal worms.

Dress deftly your body in stupid stuffs,
phrase the immense weapon of your hair.
Understanding why his eye laughs
i will bring you every year

something which is worth the whole,
an inch of nothing for your soul.

it is funny, you will be dead some day.
By you the mouth, hair eyes, and i mean
the unique and nervously obscene

Need; it's funny. They will all be dead

knead of lustfulhunched deeplytoplay
lips and stare the gross fuzzy-pash
—dead—and the dark gold delicately smash . . .
grass, and the stars, of my shoulder in stead.

421

It is a funny, thing. And you will be
and i and all the days and nights that matter
knocked by sun moon jabbed jerked with ecstasy
.... tremble (not knowing how much better

than me will you like the rain's face and

the rich improbable hands of the Wind)

❦

Conrad Aiken

TETÉLESTAI

I

How SHALL we praise the magnificence of the dead,
The great man humbled, the haughty brought to dust?
Is there a horn we should not blow as proudly
For the meanest of us all, who creeps his days,
Guarding his heart from blows, to die obscurely?
I am no king, have laid no kingdoms waste,
Taken no princes captive, led no triumphs
Of weeping women through long walls of trumpets;
Say rather, I am no one, or an atom;
Say rather, two great gods, in a vault of starlight,
Play ponderingly at chess, and at the game's end
One of the pieces, shaken, falls to the floor
And runs to the darkest corner; and that piece
Forgotten there, left motionless, is I....
Say that I have no name, no gifts, no power,
Am only one of millions, mostly silent;

One who came with eyes and hands and a heart,
Looked on beauty, and loved it, and then left it.
Say that the fates of time and space obscured me,
Led me a thousand ways to pain, bemused me,
Wrapped me in ugliness; and like great spiders
Dispatched me at their leisure. . . . Well, what then?
Should I not hear, as I lie down in dust,
The horns of glory blowing above my burial?

II

Morning and evening opened and closed above me:
Houses were built above me; trees let fall
Yellowing leaves upon me, hands of ghosts;
Rain has showered its arrows of silver upon me
Seeking my heart; winds have roared and tossed me;
Music in long blue waves of sound has borne me
A helpless weed to shores of unthought silence;
Time, above me, within me, crashed its gongs
Of terrible warning, sifting the dust of death;
And here I lie. Blow now your horns of glory
Harshly over my flesh, you trees, you waters!
You stars and suns, Canopus, Deneb, Rigel,
Let me, as I lie down, here in this dust,
Hear, far off, your whispered salutation!
Roar now above my decaying flesh, you winds,
Whirl out your earth-scents over this body, tell me
Of ferns and stagnant pools, wild roses, hillsides!
Anoint me, rain, let crash your silver arrows
On this hard flesh! I am the one who named you,
I lived in you, and now I die in you.
I your son, your daughter, treader of music,
Lie broken, conquered . . . Let me not fall in silence.

III

I, the restless one; the circler of circles;
Herdsman and roper of stars, who could not capture

The secret of self; I who was tyrant to weaklings,
Striker of children; destroyer of women; corrupter
Of innocent dreamers, and laugher at beauty; I,
Too easily brought to tears and weakness by music,
Baffled and broken by love, the helpless beholder
Of the war in my heart of desire with desire, the struggle
Of hatred with love, terror with hunger; I
Who laughed without knowing the cause of my laughter,
    who grew
Without wishing to grow, a servant to my own body;
Loved without reason the laughter and flesh of a woman,
Enduring such torments to find her! I who at last
Grow weaker, struggle more feebly, relent in my purpose,
Choose for my triumph an easier end, look backward
At earlier conquests; or, caught in the web, cry out
In a sudden and empty despair, 'Tetélestai!'
Pity me, now! I, who was arrogant, beg you!
Tell me, as I lie down, that I was courageous.
Blow horns of victory now, as I reel and am vanquished.
Shatter the sky with trumpets above my grave.

IV

... Look! this flesh how it crumbles to dust and is blown!
These bones, how they grind in the granite of frost and are
    nothing!
This skull, how it yawns for a flicker of time in the dark-
    ness,
Yet laughs not and sees not! It is crushed by a hammer of
    sunlight,
And the hands are destroyed. . . . Press down through the
    leaves of the jasmine,
Dig through the interlaced roots—nevermore will you find
    me;
I was no better than dust, yet you cannot replace me. . . .
Take the soft dust in your hand—does it stir: does it sing?
Has it lips and a heart? Does it open its eyes to the sun?

424

Does it run, does it dream, does it burn with a secret, or
      tremble
In terror of death? Or ache with tremendous decisions? . . .
Listen! . . . It says: 'I lean by the river. The willows
Are yellowed with bud. White clouds roar up from the south
And darken the ripples; but they cannot darken my heart,
Nor the face like a star in my heart! . . . Rain falls on the
      water
And pelts it, and rings it with silver. The willow trees glisten,
The sparrows chirp under the eaves; but the face in my
      heart
Is a secret of music. . . . I wait in the rain and am silent.'
Listen again! . . . It says: 'I have worked, I am tired,
The pencil dulls in my hand: I see through the window
Walls upon walls of windows with faces behind them,
Smoke floating up to the sky, an ascension of sea-gulls.
I am tired. I have struggled in vain, my decision was fruitless,
Why then do I wait? with darkness, so easy, at hand! . . .
But tomorrow, perhaps . . . I will wait and endure till to-
      morrow!' . . .
Or again: 'It is dark. The decision is made. I am vanquished
By terror of life. The walls mount slowly about me
In coldness. I had not the courage. I was forsaken.
I cried out, was answered by silence . . . Tetélestai! . . .'

V

Hear how it babbles!—Blow the dust out of your hand,
With its voices and visions, tread on it, forget it, turn home-
      ward
With dreams in your brain. . . . This, then, is the humble,
      the nameless,—
The lover, the husband and father, the struggler with
      shadows,
The one who went down under shoutings of chaos, the weak-
      ling

Who cried his 'forsaken!' like Christ on the darkening hill
    top! . . .
This, then, is the one who implores, as he dwindles to silence,
A fanfare of glory. . . . And which of us dares to deny him?

Allen Tate

ODE TO THE CONFEDERATE DEAD

Row AFTER row with strict impunity
The headstones yield their names to the element,
The wind whirrs without recollection;
In the riven troughs the splayed leaves
Pile up, of nature the casual sacrament
To the seasonal eternity of death;
Then driven by the fierce scrutiny
Of heaven to their election in the vast breath,
They sough the rumor of mortality.

Autumn is desolation in the plot
Of a thousand acres where these memories grow
From the inexhaustible bodies that are not
Dead, but feed the grass row after rich row.
Think of the autumns that have come and gone!—
Ambitious November with the humors of the year,
With a particular zeal for every slab,
Staining the uncomfortable angels that rot
On the slabs, a wing chipped here, an arm there:
The brute curiosity of an angel's stare
Turns you, like them, to stone,

Transforms the heaving air
Till plunged to a heavier world below
You shift your sea-space blindly
Heaving, turning like the blind crab.

     Dazed by the wind, only the wind
     The leaves flying, plunge

You know who have waited by the wall
The twilight certainty of an animal,
Those midnight restitutions of the blood
You know—the immitigable pines, the smoky frieze
Of the sky, the sudden call: you know the rage,
The cold pool left by the mounting flood,
Of muted Zeno and Parmenides.
You who have waited for the angry resolution
Of those desires that should be yours tomorrow,
You know the unimportant shrift of death
And praise the vision
And praise the arrogant circumstance
Of those who fall
Rank upon rank, hurried beyond decision—
Here by the sagging gate, stopped by the wall.

     Seeing, seeing only the leaves
     Flying, plunge and expire

Turn your eyes to the immoderate past,
Turn to the inscrutable infantry rising
Demons out of the earth—they will not last.
Stonewall, Stonewall, and the sunken fields of hemp,
Shiloh, Antietam, Malvern Hill, Bull Run.
Lost in that orient of the thick and fast
You will curse the setting sun.

     Cursing only the leaves crying
     Like an old man in a storm

You hear the shout, the crazy hemlocks point
With troubled fingers to the silence which
Smothers you, a mummy, in time.

                                   The hound bitch
Toothless and dying, in a musty cellar
Hears the wind only.

                             Now that the salt of their blood
Stiffens the saltier oblivion of the sea,
Seals the malignant purity of the flood,
What shall we who count our days and bow
Our heads with a commemorial woe
In the ribboned coats of grim felicity,
What shall we say of the bones, unclean,
Whose verdurous anonymity will grow?
The ragged arms, the ragged heads and eyes
Lost in these acres of the insane green?
The gray lean spiders come, they come and go;
In a tangle of willows without light
The singular screech-owl's tight
Invisible lyric seeds the mind
With the furious murmur of their chivalry.

        We shall say only the leaves
        Flying, plunge and expire

We shall say only the leaves whispering
In the improbable mist of nightfall
That flies on multiple wing:
Night is the beginning and the end
And in between the ends of distraction
Waits mute speculation, the patient curse
That stones the eyes, or like the jaguar leaps
For his own image in a jungle pool, his victim.

What shall we say who have knowledge
Carried to the heart? Shall we take the act
To the grave? Shall we, more hopeful, set up the grave
In the house? The ravenous grave?

                              Leave now
The shut gate and the decomposing wall:
The gentle serpent, green in the mulberry bush,
Riots with his tongue through the hush—
Sentinel of the grave who counts us all!

1926-1936

Allen Tate

AENEAS AT WASHINGTON

I MYSELF saw furious with blood
Neoptolemus, at his side the black Atridae,
Hecuba and the hundred daughters, Priam
Cut down, his filth drenching the holy fires.
In that extremity I bore me well
A true gentleman, valorous in arms,
Disinterested and honorable. Then fled:
That was a time when civilization
Run by the few fell to the many, and
Crashed to the shout of men, the clang of arms:
Cold victualing I seized, I hoisted up
The old man my father upon my back,
In the smoke made by sea for a new world
Saving little—a mind imperishable

If time is, a love of past things tenuous
As the hesitation of receding love.

(To the reduction of uncited littorals
We brought chiefly the vigor of prophecy
Our hunger breeding calculation
And fixed triumphs)

           The thirsty dove I saw
In the glowing fields of Troy, hemp ripening
And tawny corn, the thickening Blue Grass
All lying rich forever in the green sun.
I see all things apart, the towers that men
Contrive I too contrived long, long ago.
Now I demand little. The singular passion
Abides its object and consumes desire
In the circling shadow of its appetite.
There was a time when the young eyes were slow,
Their flame steady beyond the firstling fire,
I stood in the rain, far from home at nightfall
By the Potomac, the great Dome lit the water,
The city my blood had built I knew no more
While the screech-owl whistled his new delight
Consecutively dark.

           Stuck in the wet mire
Four thousand leagues from the ninth buried city
I thought of Troy, what we had built her for.

John Crowe Ransom

CAPTAIN CARPENTER

CAPTAIN Carpenter rose up in his prime
Put on his pistols and went riding out
But had got wellnigh nowhere at that time
Till he fell in with ladies in a rout.

It was a pretty lady and all her train
That played with him so sweetly but before
An hour she'd taken a sword with all her main
And twined him of his nose for evermore.

Captain Carpenter mounted up one day
And rode straightway into a stranger rogue
That looked unchristian but be that as it may
The Captain did not wait upon prologue.

But drew upon him out of his great heart
The other swung against him with a club
And cracked his two legs at the shinny part
And let him roll and stick like any tub.

Captain Carpenter rode many a time
From male and female took he sundry harms
He met the wife of Satan crying "I'm
The she-wolf bids you shall bear no more arms."

Their strokes and counters whistled in the wind
I wish he had delivered half his blows
But where she should have made off like a hind
The bitch bit off his arms at the elbows.

And Captain Carpenter parted with his ears
To a black devil that used him in this wise
O jesus ere his threescore and ten years
Another had plucked out his sweet blue eyes.

Captain Carpenter got up on his roan
And sallied from the gate in hell's despite
I heard him asking in the grimmest tone
If any enemy yet there was to fight?

"To any adversary it is fame
If he risk to be wounded by my tongue
Or burnt in two beneath my red heart's flame
Such are the perils he is cast among.

"But if he can he has a pretty choice
From an anatomy with little to lose
Whether he cut my tongue and take my voice
Or whether it be my round red heart he choose."

It was the neatest knave that ever was seen
Stepping in perfume from his lady's bower
Who at this word put in his merry mien
And fell on Captain Carpenter like a tower.

I would not knock old fellows in the dust
But there lay Captain Carpenter on his back
His weapons were the old heart in his bust
And a blade shook between rotten teeth alack.

The rogue in scarlet and gray soon knew his mind
He wished to get his trophy and depart;
With gentle apology and touch refined
He pierced him and produced the Captain's heart.

God's mercy rest on Captain Carpenter now
I thought him Sirs an honest gentleman

Citizen husband soldier and scholar enow
Let jangling kites eat of him if they can.

But God's deep curses follow after those
That shore him of his goodly nose and ears
His legs and strong arms at the two elbows
And eyes that had not watered seventy years.

The curse of hell upon the sleek upstart
Who got the Captain finally on his back
And took the red red vitals of his heart
And made the kites to whet their beaks clack clack.

John Crowe Ransom

BLUE GIRLS

TWIRLING your blue skirts, traveling the sward
Under the towers of your seminary,
Go listen to your teachers old and contrary
Without believing a word.

Tie the white fillets then about your lustrous hair
And think no more of what will come to pass
Than bluebirds that go walking on the grass
And chattering on the air.

Practice your beauty, blue girls, before it fail;
And I will cry with my loud lips and publish
Beauty which all our power shall never establish,
It is so frail.

433

For I could tell you a story which is true:
I know a lady with a terrible tongue,
Blear eyes fallen from blue,
All her perfections tarnished—and yet it is not long
Since she was lovelier than any of you.

Carl Sandburg

COOL TOMBS

WHEN Abraham Lincoln was shovelled into the tombs, he
    forgot the copperheads and the assassin . . . in the
    dust, in the cool tombs.

And Ulysses Grant lost all thought of con men and Wall
    Street, cash and collateral turned ashes . . . in the dust,
    in the cool tombs.

Pocahontas' body, lovely as a poplar, sweet as a red haw in
    November or a pawpaw in May, did she wonder? does
    she remember? . . . in the dust, in the cool tombs?

Take any streetful of people buying clothes and groceries,
    cheering a hero or throwing confetti and blowing tin
    horns . . . tell me if the lovers are losers . . . tell me
    if any get more than the lovers . . . in the dust . . .
    in the cool tombs.

Carl Sandburg

LOSERS

IF I should pass the tomb of Jonah
I would stop there and sit for awhile;
Because I was swallowed one time deep in the dark
And came out alive after all.

If I pass the burial spot of Nero
I shall say to the wind, "Well, well!"—
I who have fiddled in a world on fire,
I who have done so many stunts not worth doing.

I am looking for the grave of Sindbad too.
I want to shake his ghost-hand and say,
"Neither of us died very early, did we?"

And the last sleeping-place of Nebuchadnezzar—
When I arrive there I shall tell the wind:
"You ate grass; I have eaten crow—
Who is better off now or next year?"

Jack Cade, John Brown, Jesse James,
There too I could sit down and stop for awhile.
I think I could tell their headstones:
"God, let us remember all good losers."

I could ask people to throw ashes on their heads
In the name of that sergeant at Belleau Wood,
Walking into the drumfires, calling his men,
"Come on, you . . . Do you want to live for ever?"

William Carlos Williams

THE BOTTICELLIAN TREES

THE ALPHABET of
the trees

is fading in the
song of the leaves

the crossing
bars of the thin

letters that spelled
winter

and the cold
have been illumined

with
pointed green

by the rain and sun—
The strict simple

principles of

straight branches
are being modified
by pinched out

ifs of color, devout
conditions

the smiles of love—

. . . .

until the stript
sentences

move as a woman's
limbs under cloth

and praise from secrecy
with hot ardor

love's ascendancy
in summer—

In summer the song
sings itself

above the muffled words—

❧

William Carlos Williams

POEM I

FROM *Spring and All*

BY THE road to the contagious hospital
under the surge of the blue
mottled clouds driven from the
northeast—a cold wind. Beyond, the
waste of broad, muddy fields
brown with dried weeds, standing and fallen

437

patches of standing water
the scattering of tall trees

All along the road the reddish
purplish, forked, upstanding, twiggy
stuff of bushes and small trees
with dead, brown leaves under them
leafless vines—

Lifeless in appearance, sluggish
dazed spring approaches—

They enter the new world naked,
cold, uncertain of all
save that they enter. All about them
the cold, familiar wind—

Now the grass, tomorrow
the stiff curl of wildcarrot leaf

One by one objects are defined—
It quickens: clarity, outline of leaf

But now the stark dignity of
entrance—Still, the profound change
has come upon them: rooted they
grip down and begin to awaken

Karl Shapiro

SCYROS

Snuffle and sniff and handkerchief

THE DOCTOR punched my vein
The captain called me Cain
Upon my belly sat the sow of fear
    With coins on either eye
    The President came by
And whispered to the braid what none could hear

    High over where the storm
    Stood steadfast cruciform
The golden eagle sank in wounded wheels
    White Negroes laughing still
    Crept fiercely on Brazil
Turning the navies upward on their keels

    Now one by one the trees
    Stripped to their naked knees
To dance upon the heaps of shrunken dead
    The roof of England fell
    Great Paris tolled her bell
And China staunched her milk and wept for bread

    No island singly lay
    But lost its name that day
The Ainu dived across the plunging sands
    From dawn to dawn to dawn
    King George's birds came on
Strafing the tulips from his children's hands

Thus in the classic sea
Southeast from Thessaly
The dynamited mermen washed ashore
And tritons dressed in steel
Trolled heads with rod and reel
And dredged potatoes from the Aegean floor

Hot is the sky and green
Where Germans have been seen
The moon leaks metal on the Atlantic fields
Pink boys in birthday shrouds
Loop lightly through the clouds
Or coast the peaks of Finland in their shields

That prophet year by year
Lay still but could not hear
Where scholars tapped to find his new remains
Gog and Magog ate pork
In vertical New York
And war began next Wednesday on the Danes

Delmore Schwartz

IN THE NAKED BED,

IN PLATO'S CAVE

In the naked bed, in Plato's cave,
Reflected headlights slowly slid the wall,
Carpenters hammered under the shaded window,
Wind troubled the window curtains all night long,

A fleet of trucks strained uphill, grinding,
Their freights covered, as usual.
The ceiling lightened again, the slanting diagram
Slid slowly forth.
              Hearing the milkman's clop,
His striving up the stair, the bottle's chink,
I rose from bed, lit a cigarette,
And walked to the window. The stony street
Displayed the stillness in which buildings stand,
The street-lamp's vigil and the horse's patience.
The winter sky's pure capital
Turned me back to bed with exhausted eyes.

Strangeness grew in the motionless air. The loose
Film grayed. Shaking wagons, hooves' waterfalls,
Sounded far off, increasing, louder and nearer.
A car coughed, starting. Morning, softly
Melting the air, lifted the half-covered chair
From underseas, kindled the looking-glass,
Distinguished the dresser and the white wall.
The bird called tentatively, whistled, called,
Bubbled and whistled, so! Perplexed, still wet
With sleep, affectionate, hungry and cold. So, so,
O son of man, the ignorant night, the travail
Of early morning, the mystery of beginning
Again and again,
             while History is unforgiven.

VI

ACKNOWLEDGMENTS

Caroline Gordon, THE CAPTIVE, 1789, by permission of Caroline Gordon (The Hound and Horn); Katherine Anne Porter, FLOWERING JUDAS from "Flowering Judas," copyright 1935 by Harcourt, Brace & Co., Inc.; John Steinbeck, THE RED PONY, copyright 1937 by The Viking Press, Inc.

Caroline Gordon

THE CAPTIVE

(1 7 8 9)

WE WERE up long before daybreak and were loading the horses at first dawn-streak. Even then Tom was a mind not to go.

"This ginseng it don't have to get to the station," he said, "and as for the money it'll bring we can git along without that."

"We've been without salt for three weeks now," I told him.

"Thar's worse things than doing without salt," Tom said.

I knowed if he got to studying about it he wouldn't go and I was bound he should make the trip, Indians or no Indians. I slapped the lead horse on the rump. "G' long," I said, "I'd as soon be scalped now and have done with it as keep on thinking about it all the time."

Tom rode off without saying anything more and I went on in the house and set about my morning work. The children was all stirring by that time. Joe, he felt mighty big to be the only man on the place and he was telling 'em what He'd do if any Indians was to come.

"You better hush that up," I says. "Can't you git your mind off them Indians a minute?"

All that morning, though, I was thinking about what Tom had said and wishing he hadn't had to go. Seems like I was riding with him most of the day.

"Now he's at West Fork," I'd say to myself and then after I'd done some more chores, "He'll be about at the crossroads now or maybe Sayler's tavern." I knowed, though, it

445

warn't much use to be following him that way in my mind. It'd be good dark before he could git home and my thinking about it wouldn't hurry him none.

It was around ten o'clock that I heard the first owl hooting. Over on the mountain it seemed like. Joe was in the yard feeding the chickens and he stopped stock still when he heard it and throwed back his head.

"You hear that, Mammy?" he said.

I knowed then thar must be something wrong with the call, or a boy like Joe wouldn't have noticed it.

I spoke up sharp, though. "I heard it," I says, "and I could hear a heap of other things ef'n I had time to stand around with my years open. How long you reckon it's going to take you to git them chickens fed?"

We both went on about our business without more talk, but all the time I was saying to myself that ef'n I could git through this day, git through this day and see Tom Wiley riding in at the gate one more time I'd be content to bide without salt the rest of my natural life. I knowed it wouldn't do to let down before the children, though, and I kept 'em all busy doing one thing and another till dinner time. It began to rain while we was eating our dinner and it rained a long time. After it stopped raining the fog settled down, so thick you could hardly see your hand before you. And all the time the owls was calling. Calling back and forth from one mountain to the other. My littlest girl, Martha, got scared so I made all the children stay in the house and play by the fire whilst I started in on a piece of cloth I'd had in the loom a long time and never could seem to finish. Red it was with a stripe running through it. I aimed to make both the girls a dress out of that piece before the winter set in.

By that time the fog had risen as high as the top of the ridges and the whole house was swallowed up in it. The children kept teasing, saying it was good dark now and couldn't they have a candle.

446

"Yes," I said, "we here all by ourselves and you want to go lighting candles, so they can't help finding the house."

One of the gals got to crying. "Who's coming?" she said, "Mammy, who you think's coming?"

I seen then I'd got 'em stirred up and I'd have to settle 'em for seems like I couldn't stand to be worrying like I was and the children crying too. I give them all a lump of sugar around and got 'em started on a play-party. I made out I had the headache and if they was going to sing they'd have to sing low. Hog Drovers it was they was playing.

> Hog-drovers, hog-drovers, hog-drovers we air
> A-courtin' your darter so sweet and so fair,
> Kin we git lodgin' here, O here,
> Kin we git lodgin' here?

I got 'em started to frolicking and playing and then I went back to my work. But I couldn't git my mind off something a man said to me once when we was out hunting on the Hurricane, and I made him go right in on a bear without waiting for the other men folks to come up.

"You're brash, Jinny," he said, "you're brash and you always been lucky but one of these times you going to be too brash."

Sitting there listening to them owls calling and wondering how much longer it'd be before Tom got home, I got to thinking that maybe this was the time I was too brash. For I knowed well thar warn't another woman in the settlements would have undertook to stay on that place all day with nothing but a passel of children. Still I said to myself it's done now and thar ain't no undoing it. And the first thing I know Tom will be back and tomorrow morning it'll fair up, and I'll be thinking what a goose I was to get so scared over nothing.

The children was still singing.

> Oh, this is my darter that sets by my lap
> No pig-stealin' drover kin git her from pap,

447

You can't git lodgin' here, O here
You can't git lodgin' here.

I got up and looked out the window. Seemed to me the fog was lifting a little. A man was coming up the path. I knew it was a white man by the walk, but I didn't know it was John Borders till he stepped up on the porch.

The first thing he asked was where was Tom.

"Gone to the station with a load of ginseng," I told him. "I'm looking for him back now any minute."

He stood there looking off towards the mountain. "How long them owls been calling?" he asked.

"Off and on all evening," I said, "but owls'll hoot, dark days like this."

"Yes," he said, "and some owls'll holler like wolves and gobble like turkeys and ever' other kind of varmint. Jinny, you better git them children and come over to our house. Ain't no telling when Tom'll be back."

Just then an owl hooted and another one answered him from somewhere on top of the ridge. We both listened hard. It sounded like a real owl calling to his mate, but I was good and scared by that time and I thought I'd best go over to the Borderses. It was my judgment, though, that thar warn't any hurry. Indians hardly ever come round before nightfall.

I told John that if he'd wait till I'd fastened up the stock I'd go back with him. He said that while I was doing that he'd walk out in the woods a little way. He'd been looking all day for some strayed sheep and hadn't found no trace of them, but he thought they might be herded up in that gulley by the spring. He went off down the path and I fastened the front door and went out the back way. I didn't fasten the back door but I kept my eye on it all the time I was worrying with the cattle. Joe, he was along helping me. The cow was standing there at the pen so I stopped and milked her while Joe went up in the triangle to look for the heifer. He found her all right and brought her up to the cow

448

pen just as I finished milking. We fastened both cows up in the stable and Joe went over and saw that all the chickens was up and fastened the door on them. Then we started back to the house with the milk.

We were halfway up the path when we heard the Indians holler. We started for the house on a dead run. I could see Indians in the yard and one Indian was coming around to the house to the back door. I ran faster and slipped in the door ahead of him. Joe was right behind me. The room was so full of Indians that at first I couldn't see any of my children. The Indians was dancing around and hollering and hacking with their tomahawks. I heard one of the children screaming but I didn't know which one it was. An Indian caught me around the waist but I got away from him. I thought I have got to do something. I fell down on my knees and crawled around between the Indians' legs, they striking at me all the time, till I found Martha, my littlest one, in the corner of the loom. She was dead and I crawled on a little way and found Sadie. She was dead, too, with her skull split open. The baby was just sitting there holding on to the bar of the loom. I caught him in my bosom and held him up to me tight, then I got to my feet. Joe was right behind me all the time and he stood up when I did. But an Indian come up and brained him with a tomahawk. I seen him go down and I knowed I couldn't git any more help from him. I couldn't think of anything to do so I worked my way over towards the door, but there was two or three Indians standing on the porch and I knowed there was no use running for it. I just stood there holding the baby while the Indians pulled burning logs out of the fire on to the floor. When the blaze had sprung up they all come out on to the porch.

I made a break and got some way down the path but an Indian run after me and caught me. He stood there, holding me tight till the other Indians come up, then he laid his hand on my head and he touched the baby too. It seemed he was claiming me for his prisoner. He had rings on his arms and

449

ankles and trinkets in his ears. I knew he was a chief and I thought he must be a Shawnee. I could understand some of what he said.

He was telling them they better hurry and git away before Tice Harman come home. Another Indian stepped up. I knew him. A Cherokee that come sometimes to the station. Mad Dog they called him. Tice Harman had killed his son. It come to me that they had been thinking all along that they was at Tice Harman's. I jerked my arm away from the Shawnee chief.

"You think you're burning Tice Harman's house," I said, "This ain't Tice Harman's house. It's Tom Wiley's. Tom Wiley. Tom Wiley never killed any Indians."

They looked at each other and I think they was feared. Feared because they had burned the wrong house, but feared too of Tice Harman. Mad Dog said something and laid his hand on his tomahawk but the old chief shook his head and took hold of my arm again. He spoke, too, but so fast I couldn't tell what he was saying. The Cherokee looked mad but he turned around after a minute and called to the other Indians and they all left the house and started off through the woods. Mad Dog went first and half a dozen young Indians after him. The old chief and I came last. He had hold of my arm and was hurrying me along and all the time he kept talking, telling me that he had saved my life, that I was to go with him to his town to be a daughter to him to take the place of a daughter that had died.

I didn't take in much that he was saying. I kept looking back towards the burning house, thinking maybe they wasn't all dead before the Indians set fire to it. Finally I couldn't stand it no longer and I asked the old Shawnee. He pointed to one of the young Indians who was going up the ridge ahead of us. I seen something dangling from his belt and I looked away quick. I knowed it was the scalps of my children.

We went up over the ridge and then struck north through the woods. I didn't take much notice of where we was going. I had all I could do to keep Dinny quiet—he warn't but ten months old. I let him suck all the way but it didn't do much good. We went so fast it'd jolt out of his mouth and he'd cry louder than ever. The Shawnee would grab my arm and say the other Indians would kill him sure if he kept that up. Finally I got his head down inside the waist of my dress and I helt him up against me so tight he couldn't cry and then I was scared he'd smother, but the Shawnee wouldn't let me stop to find out.

We went on, up one valley and down another, till finally we come out on level land at the foot of a mountain. The old chief made me go first, right up the mountainside. It was worse there than it was in the woods. The laurel and the ivy was so thick that sometimes he'd have to reach ahead of me and break a way through. My arms got numb and wouldn't hold the baby up. It was lucky for me I was crawling up a mountain. I would put him up ahead of me and then crawl to him and in this way my arms would get a little ease of the burden. The old chief didn't like this, though, and ever' time it happened he'd slap me and tell me to go faster, go faster or they would surely kill the baby.

We got to the top of the mountain, somehow, and started down. My legs were hurting me now worse than my arms. It was going so straight down the mountainside. The back of my legs got stiff and would jerk me up every time I set my foot down, what they call stifled in a horse. I got on, somehow, though, all through that night and for most of the next day. It was near sundown when we stopped, in a rockhouse * at the head of a creek. The Indians must have thought they was too far for any white men to follow them. They

* A rockhouse is not a cave but a place sheltered by an overhanging ledge of rock.

made up a big fire and walked around it pretty careless. Two of the young Indians went off in the woods. I heard a shot and they come back dragging a little deer. They butchered it and sliced it down the middle, and slung the two haunches over the fire on forked sticks. The tenderer parts they broiled on rocks that they heated red hot in the coals. A young buck squatted down by the fire and kept the venison turning. Soon the smell of rich meat cooking rose up in the air. The juices begun dripping down into the blaze and I thought it was a shame for all that gravy to go to waste. I asked the Shawnee to lend me a little kittle he had and I hung it on a forked stick and caught the juices as they fell and then poured them back over the meat. When they turned brown and rich I caught the gravy in the little kittle and sopped my fingers in it and let the baby suck them.

The old chief, Crowmocker, smiled like he thought a lot of me. "White woman know," he said. "White woman teach Indian women. You make rum?"

I said I didn't know how to make rum, but there was plenty in the settlements and if he would take me back, take me just within a mile or two of the clearing I'd undertake to furnish him and his men with all the rum they could drink.

He laughed. "White people promise," he said, "You in your cabin you forget poor Indian."

The Cherokee, Mad Dog, had been sitting there broiling the deer nose on a rock that he had got red hot in the flames. When it was brown he brought it over and gave it to me. Then he went back and sat down, sullen like, not saying anything. The fire shone on his black eyes and on his long beak of a nose. When he moved you could see the muscles moving, too, in his big chest and up and down his nekkid legs. An Indian woman would have thought him a fine looking man, tall and well formed in every way, but it frightened me to look at him. I was glad it was the old chief and not him that had taken me prisoner. I was glad, too, that the chief was old. I'd heard tell how particular the Indians was

452

about things like that and I thought the old chief would likely do what he said and keep me for his daughter, but if it was Mad Dog he would have me for his wife.

I thought the meat never would get done but it finally did. The Indians give me a good sized piece off the haunch and I ate it all, except a little piece I put in Dinny's mouth. He spit it out but I kept putting it back till he got some good of it. Then I took him down to the creek and scooped up water in my hands for him. He'd been fretting because my milk was giving out but the water and the juice from the meat quieted him a little. After we'd both had all the water we could drink I went back up the hill and sat down on a log with Dinny laying across my knees. It felt good to have his weight off my arms but I was afraid to take my hands off him. I was feared one of them might come up and snatch him away from me any minute.

He laid there a while a-fretting and then he put his little hand up and felt my face.

"Sadie . . ." he said, "Sadie . . ."

Sadie was the oldest girl. She played with him a lot and fondled him. He's go to her any time out of my arms.

I hugged him up close and sang him the song Sadie used to get him to sleep by. "Lord Lovell, he stood at the castle gate," I sang and the tears a-running down my face.

"Hush, my pretty," I said, "hush. Sadie's gone, but Mammy's here. Mammy's here with baby."

He cried, though, for Sadie and wouldn't nothing I could do comfort him. He cried himself hoarse and then he'd keep opening his little mouth but wouldn't no sound come. I felt him and he was hot to the touch. I was feared he'd fret himself into a fever, but there wasn't nothing I could do. I helt his arms and legs to the blaze and got him as warm as I could and then I went off from the fire a little way and laid down with him in my arms.

The Indians kept putting fresh wood to the fire till it blazed up and lit the whole hollow. They squatted around

453

it, talking. After a while half a dozen of them got up and went off in the woods. The light fell far out through the trees. I could see their nekkid legs moving between the black trunks. Some of them was dragging up down timber for the fire and some kept reaching up and tearing boughs off the trees. They come back trailing the green boughs behind them. Two or three other Indians come over and they all squatted down and begun stripping the leaves off the switches and binding them into hoops. An Indian took one of the scalps off his belt, Sadie's light hair, curling a little at the ends and specked now all over with blood. I watched it fall across the bough of maple. I watched till they began stretching the scalp on the hoop and then I shut my eyes.

After a while Crowmocker come over and tied me with some rawhide thongs that he took off his belt. He tied me up tight and it felt good to have the keen thongs cutting into me. I strained against them for a while and then I must have dropped off to sleep. I woke up hollering. I thought at first it was the Indians hollering and then I knew it was me. I tried to stop but I couldn't. It would start way down inside me and I would fight to hold it in but before I knew it my mouth would be wide open and as soon as I'd loose one shriek another would start working its way up and there wasn't nothing I could do to hold it back. I was shaking, too, so hard that the baby rolled out of my arms and started crying.

The old chief got up from where he was sleeping and come over. He stood there looking down at me and then he lighted a torch and went off in the woods a little way. He brought some leaves back with him and he put them to boil in his little kittle. He made me drink some tea from the leaves and he gave the baby some too and after a while we both went off to sleep.

III

I woke with the old chief shaking me by the arm and telling me it was time to get up. I was still sort of light headed and for a minute I didn't know where I was. It was raining hard and so dark you couldn't tell whether it was good day. The Indians had built a fire up under the ledge and was broiling the rest of the venison. I laid there and I saw the light shine on their nekkid legs and the tomahawks hanging from their belts and I knew where I was and all that had happened.

The old chief untied the thongs and I stood up with Dinny in my arms. They gave me a little piece of venison and some parched corn. My lips was so swelled I couldn't chew but I swallowed the corn and I put the meat in my mouth and sucked it till it went away. I felt milk in my breasts and I was glad for the baby. I gave him his dinny but he wouldn't suck. He wouldn't hardly open his eyes. I thought that was from the tea the old Indian had given us and I was feared he'd got too much. He was still hot to the touch and I thought he might have got a fever from laying out all night in the rain. I tore off part of my top skirt and I made a sort of sling that I put around my shoulders to carry him in and I made a cover, too, out of part of the cloth to keep the rain off his little face.

Soon as we had finished eating the Indians stomped out the fire and scattered the ashes so you couldn't have told there had ever been a camp there, and we started off through the woods.

We hadn't gone far before two of the young Indians left us. I thought they was most likely going back over the trail to watch if anybody was following us. I heard them saying that the folks at the settlement would be sure to send out a party. Some of the Indians thought it wouldn't do no good because the heavy rains had washed out the trail so nobody could find it. But Mad Dog said Tice Harman could follow any trail. I never knew before the Indians was so feared of Harman. They said he was the best hunter among the Long Knives, that he could go as far and stand as much as any Indian and that they would like for him to come and live with them and be one of their warriors. Mad Dog said now that the only thing was to go so fast and go so far that even Tice Harman couldn't come up with us. He said "O-hi-yo" several times and I judged they meant to make for one of the towns on the river.

It stopped raining after a while but it didn't do much good. It was level ground we was travelling over and the water was standing everywhere, so that half the time you was wading. I knew we was some place high up in the hills, but afterwards I couldn't have told what country I had passed over. I went with my head down most of the time, not seeing anything but the black trunks of the trees going by and the yellow leaves floating in the puddles. Beech-woods we must have been in because the leaves was all yellow and little.

We went on like that all day, not stopping to eat anything except some parched corn that the old chief took out of his bag and handed around to us still travelling. Late that evening we come to a water hole. One of the Indians shot a bear and we stopped and built a fire under a cliff. The Indians hadn't no more'n butchered the meat when two scouts come running into camp. They said that white men were following us, on horseback. The Indians all looked scared at this. Crowmocker stood there talking to Mad Dog about what we had best do. I went over and stood by them. Mad Dog said they ought to kill the child and change the course, that they would have to go faster than ever now and I couldn't keep up, carrying the baby. Crowmocker showed him the sling I had made and said the baby wasn't no burden to me now. He said he had brought me this far and he was going to carry me on to his town to teach his women how to weave cloth like the dress I had on.

456

He told Mad Dog that and then he motioned to me and said "Go!" I started off, top speed, through the trees. Behind me I could hear the Indians stomping around in the leaves to cover up the signs of the fire. I went on as fast as I could, but every now and then an Indian would shoot past me. Pretty soon they was all ahead except the old chief.

We went down hill towards a hollow that had a little branch running through it. Mad Dog was in the lead, the other Indians right on his heels, jumping over down logs and bushes quick as cats. The old chief stayed by me and when I'd slow up getting over a log or fall down in the bushes he'd jerk me onto my feet again.

The branch was narrow but running deep with the rains. Mad Dog started wading down stream and the other Indians after him, single file. They hadn't slowed up much and the water splashed high. I could see their legs moving through the splashing water. The old chief by my side was breathing hard. I knowed he was winded but I thought he would wind quicker than the others. I thought I would keep moving as long as I saw the Indians' legs going on.

The Indian that was in front of me stepped in a hole up to his waist. When he come out of it he took two three steps and stood still. I knowed then that Mad Dog had stopped and I knowed he would be coming back down the line. I looked up but the sides of the gulley was too steep. I turned and ran back up stream fast as I could. I heard the breathing close behind me and I knowed it was the old chief and then there was a splashing and I knowed Mad Dog was after me.

I left the water and ran sideways up the gulley. The breathing was closer now. I tried to run faster and I caught my foot in a root. They was on me as soon as I went down. Mad Dog grabbed me by both arms. Crowmocker got there a second after but Mad Dog already had hold of Dinny. I caught at his legs and tried to push them out from under him but he kicked me away. I got up and went at him again but he kicked me down. He kicked me again and then he

457

went on up the side of the gulley till he come to a big tree and he held the baby by the feet and dashed his brains out.

I rolled over on my face and I laid there flat on the ground till the old chief come up. He pulled me to my feet and said we would have to run on fast, that the white men were following us on horses. I said no, I wouldn't go, I would stay there with my baby, but he and another Indian took me by the arms and drug me down the stream spite of all I could do.

We went on down the branch a good way. Towards dark we came out on the banks of a river. Water was standing halfway up the trunks of big trees. I saw the current, running fast and covered with black drift, and I didn't believe even an Indian could get across that raging river. But they didn't stop a minute. Crowmocker fell back and two young Indians took hold of my arms and carried me out into the water. The current caught us and swept us off our feet. I couldn't swim much on account of my clothes but the two young Indians held on to my wrists and carried me on between them. The other Indians come right in after us. They held their guns up high over their heads and swum like boys treading water. I could see their heads bobbing all around me through the black drift and I couldn't see nothing to keep all of us from drowning. They managed to keep out of the drift somehow, though, and all the time they was working towards the other bank till finally we come out in dead water at the mouth of a creek. The Indians that was holding me up stopped swimming all of a sudden and I knowed then that we must have got across. It was so dark by that time that I couldn't see nothing hardly. I got out of the water as best I could and a little way up the creek bank. I fell down there 'mongst some willows. I saw the Indians come out of the water shaking themselves like dogs and I saw them falling down all around me and then my eyes went shut.

IV

The old chief woke me up at the first dawn streak. I heard him and I felt him shaking me but I didn't get up. As soon as I opened my eyes the pain in my feet started up. I touched one foot to the ground and it throbbed worse'n toothache. I knew I couldn't travel any that day and I didn't care. I turned over on my back and laid there looking up at the sky. It had cleared off during the night and the stars was shining. The sky was all a pale gray except for one long sulphur colored streak where day was getting ready to break. Behind me the Indians was looking to their guns and settling their tomahawks in their belts. I watched their heads and shoulders moving against that yellow light and I saw one of them take his tomahawk out and heft it and then try the blade with his finger. I thought that if I just kept on laying there that maybe he would be the one to finish me off and then I thought Mad Dog was quicker and would beat him to it.

The old chief was still shaking me. "Get up, Jinny. Day come."

"No," I said, "I ain't going to get up."

He took me by the shoulders and tried to pull me to my feet but I slumped back on the ground. I spoke to him in Shawnee.

"My feet bleed and I cannot travel. Let me die."

He leaned over and looked at my feet and then he called to one of the young Indians to bring him some white oak bark. When the bark come he boiled it over the fire and then he took the liquor from the bark and cooled it with more water and poured it over my feet.

The other Indians had finished scattering the fire and was starting out through the willows but Crowmocker just sat there pouring that stuff on my feet. I could feel the swelling going down and after a while I touched my foot to the ground. It didn't hurt nothing like it had, and I got up and

459

we started off. He give me some parched corn and I ate it, walking. He said we would have to travel fast to catch up with the other Indians. I asked him if the white people was still following us and he laughed and said no white men could get across that river. I owned to myself that they couldn't and I didn't think any more about them coming after me. I thought the Indians would probably take me so far away that I'd never see a white face.

We caught up with the other Indians towards dark. That night we slept in a canebrake by a little river. A buffalo was wallowing in the river as we come up. One of the Indians shot him. They butchered him there in the water and drug big slabs of the meat up the bank with ropes cut from the hide. We must have been in Indian country by this time. They didn't seem to think it made no difference how much noise they made. They made up a big fire to one side of the brake and they was half the night cooking the meat and eating. I went to sleep under a tree with them singing and yelling all around me.

When I woke up the next morning they was having a council. They talked till the sun was high and then they split up into two parties. Mad Dog and three of the young bucks left us and swum across the river. The rest of us kept on up the bank. We travelled all that day through the cane and then we struck a divide and followed it into another valley. We had run out of everything to eat by this time except the strings of jerked meat that they all carried slung around their necks. We stayed two three days at a buffalo lick, hoping to kill some game but none came and we went on.

Most of the leaves was off the trees by this time and the nights was real cold. I knew it was some time in October that the Indians come and burned our house but I didn't know how long we'd been on the trail and I didn't have no idea what country we was in.

One morning we come out in some deep narrows just

460

above where two creeks flowed together. A wild looking place with tumbling falls and big rocks laying around everywhere. I looked up at the cliffs over our heads and I couldn't believe my eyes. They was painted: deer and buffalo and turtles big as a man, painted in red and in black on the rock. Some of the young Indians acted like they had never been there before either. They would keep walking around looking at things and sometimes stand and stare at the pictures of wild beasts that was painted everywhere on the smooth rock.

The old chief took a way up the side of the cliffs, the rest of us following. The young Indians went up like deer but I had to pull myself up by the laurel and ivy that grew down in between the rocks. We walked along a narrow ledge and come to a rockhouse. It was the biggest rockhouse ever I seen, run all along one side of the cliff. The old chief uncovered an iron pot from where it was hid in a lot of trash in one corner of the cave and showed me how to set it up on forked sticks. He said that I would have to do all the work around the camp from now on the way Indian women did and when the spring rains come and melted the snows he would take me to his town on the Tenassee and I would learn more about Indian ways and be adopted into the tribe in place of his dead daughter.

I thought if he took me there I would never get away and I had it in mind to make a break for it first chance I got. I got hold of two strings of jerked meat and I kept them tied around my waist so I'd be ready when the time came. I thought I would wait, though, and maybe I would find out how far it was to the settlements. I would lie there in my corner of the cave at night, making out I was asleep and listen to them talking around the fire. I heard them call the names of the creeks that flowed through that valley, Big Paint and Little Mudlick and further off was another creek, Big Mudlick where they went sometimes to hunt. The names was strange to me and I never could tell from their talk how

461

far it was to the settlements or even which way to go. I had an idea that the place I was in was secret to the Indians, for it was a wonder to see and yet I had never heard any white body tell of it. I asked Crowmocker what the pictures of deer and buffalo and bear was for and he said they was the Indians' fathers and that I would learn about them when I was adopted into the tribe. Once he pointed some mounds out to me and said they was graves. He said that he and his people always stopped when they come this way to visit the graves of their fathers that was all over the valley.

A spell of fine weather come, late in the fall. Indian summer they call it. We looked out one day and bees was swarming on the cliffside. Crowmocker was mad when he saw them. He said it meant that the white people were coming, that when bees swarmed out of season they was running away from the white people who had scared all the game out of the country and made it so that even bees couldn't live in it. I asked would the white people find their way into this valley and he said they couldn't, that it was a way known only to Indians, that if a white man ever set foot in it the great bear would come down off the wall and crush him in his paws. He said, though, that there would be fighting soon over all the land and a lot of bloodshed.

I knowed that was all foolishness about the bear, but I thought likely as not there would be fighting and I wanted to get away worse than ever. One morning I was down in the hollow by myself, gathering wood and I thought that was the time. Three of the Indians had gone off hunting and I knowed the others was laying up in the cave asleep. I didn't think anybody would be following me, for a while, anyhow. I started off, slipping from tree to tree and I got quite a ways up the hollow. I knowed wasn't nobody following me but I would keep looking back over my shoulder all the time. I got to thinking. I didn't have no way to kill no game and nothing to eat but them two strings of jerked meat. I didn't even know how far I'd have to go before I came to any settlement. Worst of all I didn't even know which way to take. Likely as not I'd starve to death in the woods, or freeze if the weather turned. I'd better stay with the Indians, where at least I could sleep warm and eat, if it wasn't nothing but parched corn. I picked up my load of wood and I got back to camp quick as I could and didn't none of them ever know I'd been away.

I never tried it again, but sometimes I'd sit there on the edge of the cliff and pick out the way I'd take if I did go. There was a ridge covered with black pines rose up right in front of the rockhouse. I thought if I could once get up there I could get down into the valley easy. I hadn't never been over there but I knew what the country would be like. I saw myself slipping along through that divide, around the foot of the mountain and over some more mountains till I'd come out on a clearing. I'd slip up to some cabin, towards dark. They'd think I was an Indian at first, maybe, and then they'd see my eyes was light and they'd take me in and keep me till I could get back to my own folks again.

We stayed in that rockhouse a long time. The leaves all fell off the trees and one or two light snows fell but the real cold weather was late coming. The Indians hunted just enough to keep us in meat. They said the pelts was thin that year and not worth taking. Sometimes they would take me along to bring in the game but mostly they left me to work by myself. When cold weather set in we built big fires in the cave and it was warm inside like a house. When the Indians wasn't hunting they would lie around on buffalo skins and sleep. The smoke was terrible and the smell of Indians was all over everything. At first it bothered me but after a while I got so I didn't notice it.

I wasn't in the cave much, even in bad weather. I had to gather all the firewood. The Indians didn't have no axe and I couldn't get nothing but dead branches. There wasn't much down timber on the cliff-side so I'd mostly go up over the cliffs when I was hunting wood. There was a barren

463

there, flat as the palm of your hand and covered with a thin kind of grass. It had plenty of trees on it but they was all twisty and stunted by the wind. The only sizeable tree was a big elm. It was peeled for thirty or forty feet and had a rattlesnake painted on it, a monster snake coiling up around the trunk. You could see that snake from everywhere on the barren. I was feared to look at it. The Indians seemed to think a lot of it. Sometimes they would go up there at night and I would hear them singing and dancing and calling to the snake.

Somewhere on that barren there was lead mines. The Indians never let me go to them but they would go off and stay two three hours and come back with big balls of lead. They made me smelt it out for bullets. I had to have a mighty fire. It would take me days and days to get up enough wood. I would heap it up in a big pile and then I would kindle the fire and keep it going for hours. When the lead melted it ran down through little ditches into holes that I had dug to form the bullets. It would take the lead a long time to melt. Sometimes I would be up on the barren from sunup to sundown.

I would sit there and think about my husband and my children. I would wonder whether Tom went out in the woods hunting ginseng the way he used to do and was he still looking for me or had give me up for dead. When I thought of Tom the house would be there, too, not burning down the way it was last time I saw it, but standing with the rooms just the way they always was. I could see both rooms plain, even to the hole that was burnt in the floor when a big log fell out one night. The children would be playing in and out of the house like they did. It was like they was all living; it was only me that was gone away.

I would think back, too, over things that happened long before ever I was grown and married to Tom Wiley. There was a man named Rayburn stayed at the settlement one winter. Lance Rayburn. A big, strong man and a mighty hunter.

464

We ate bear of his shooting all that fall. He was handy with snares, too, and took over a hundred beaver down in the bottom. He courted me some that winter, sitting in front of the fire after the old folks was in bed. I laughed and went on with him but Tom Wiley had just started a-courting me and all the time my mind was on him more'n it was on the stranger.

Come time for Rayburn to pack up his pelts to take to the station he saved one out for me. Beaver, and extra fine and soft. He give it to my sister, Sarah, and told her to hand it to me when I come to the house. She made one of the children bring it down to the creek where I was boiling clothes. I laid it there on the grass and I would stop and look at it as I went back and forth with my clothes and sometimes I would wipe my hands dry and lay them on the soft fur for pleasure in the feel. But all the time I knowed I wasn't going to keep it. When Rayburn come towards me through the willows I went to meet him with the pelt in my hands.

"Keep this," I said, "and give it to some girl where you're going."

"Don't you want it?" he asked.

"I ain't taking nothing from you."

He stood there looking at me and all of a sudden his eyes narrowed up like a cat's. "You're full young to be marrying," he said.

"I ain't too young to know my own mind," I told him and before I thought I laughed.

He come towards me and before I knowed what he was up to he was on me and trying to bear me to the ground. He was a strong man but I was stout, too, and I stood up to him. We was rassling around in the bushes quite some while before he got me down and then he had to keep both his hands on my chest. I laid there right still, looking up at him.

"What you reckon my pappy'll say when I tell him about this?" I asked.

He laughed. "I ain't a-feared of no Sellards that ever

465

walked," he said, "but that Tom Wiley ain't no manner of man for you," he said.

"You can talk against Tom Wiley and you can hold me here till Doomsday," I told him, "but it ain't going to do you no good. I ain't going to have none of you no matter what happens."

His face kind of changed. Looked like it hurt him to hear me say it. He got up off me right away and he picked the beaver pelt up from where it lay in the grass and he throwed it hard as he could into the creek.

"It'll git to my girl that way fast as any other," he said.

I watched the pelt floating down the water and on to a rock and then off again. When I turned around he was out of sight and he was gone when I got back to the house. He stayed at the station a while and then he went off in the mountains hunting bear and wasn't never heard of again. Some said he was killed by wild beasts. A rifle and a cap that they said was his'n was found up in the hills. The man that found the rifle kept it but they give the cap to the Borderses. Wouldn't nobody wear it and Sally hung it up in the dog alley. I used to look at it ever' time I passed and wonder whether it had ever been on Lance Rayburn's head and was he dead or still living. And sometimes I'd wonder how it'd been if I'd married him instead of Tom, but I knowed all the time I wouldn't never have married nobody but Tom because he was the one I fancied from the time I was a chap, living neighbor to the Wileys, back to the Roanoke country.

I thought about Lance Rayburn and I thought about a lot of other folks that had come to the settlement and stayed and then gone on and wouldn't anybody know whether they was living still or dead. And I thought about people dead long ago, my old granny back in Carolina, ninety-eight years old and turned simple. She'd sit in the chimney corner all day long singing the likeliest tunes!

"Pa'tridge in the pea patch," she'd sing and call me to her and fondle me, liking gals, she said, always better than boys.

> "Pa'tridge in the pea patch
> Pickin' up the peas
> 'Long comes the bell cow
> Kickin' up her heels. . . ."

"Oh . . . h, the bell cow," she'd sing and catch me by my little shimmy tail. "O . . O . . hh, the bell cow . . ." and hist me up over the arm of her chair. "O . . O . . hh, the bell cow, kickin' up her heels. Call the little gal to milk her in the pail."

I used to call those songs to mind when I had to go down to the lick for salt. It was a place I didn't like to go. A deep hollow with three sulphur springs and a lick that covered nigh an acre of ground. The biggest lick ever I seen in my life. The way was white with the bones of beasts and in between the piled up bones the long furrows that the buffalo made licking the ground for salt. I would walk down those furrows to the spring and fill my bucket with the salty water and go back up the hill to where my kettle was slung between two little birches. Sitting there waiting for the water to boil I couldn't keep my eyes off the bones. I would take them up in my hand and turn them over and over, wondering what manner of beasts they had belonged to.

Once I made myself a little beast, laying all the bones out on some lacy moss, the front feet stiff like it was galloping off in the woods, the hind legs drawn up under him. A hare it might have been or a little fawn. Or maybe a beast that nobody ever heard of before.

They was beasts come to that lick one time or another not known to men. Bigger'n buffalo they must have been. One thigh bone, I mind, longer'n I was and twice as big around as two good sized men.

I thought of a man used to be around the station, Vard Wiley, second cousin to Tom. Folks said he was the biggest liar in the settlements. He would stay off in the woods hunting day after day and never bring in no game except maybe a brace of wild turkeys. And he told tall tales about a lick bigger'n any lick around those parts where the beasts come up in tens of thousands. He would lay up in a tree all day and watch 'em he said and not take a shot for wonder. There was beasts used there he said ten times the size of buffalo. He offered to take anybody there and show them the bones and when they asked him why he didn't bring them back to the settlement he said couldn't no man carry them, nor no two horses.

Folks laughed at him and the children round the settlement used to sing a song:

"Vard Wiley's gone west, Vard Wiley's gone east,
A-huntin' the woods for a monster beast.

He'll make him a tent out of the wild beast's hide
And all the king's horses can stable inside.

He'll make him a wagon out of solid bone
And it'll take ten oxen to draw it home."

I called that song to mind and I thought how if I ever saw Vard Wiley again I'd go up to him and say I knew him to be a truth teller and all the people would laugh at me maybe, the way they did Vard Wiley but all the time I would be knowing it was the truth.

I thought, too, of other tales he told and of jokes he played. Of the time he borrowed my dress and sunbonnet and shawl and went and sat on the creek bank when the schoolmaster was in swimming. He sat there all evening with the sunbonnet hiding his face and old Mister Daugherty shaking his fist at him. "You hussy! You brazen hussy! Don't you know I'm nekkid?" and finally when he come up out of the water nekkid as the day he was born Vard took out after him and run him clean to the house. Old Mister Daugherty went around saying they was a woman ought to be run

468

out of the settlements and Vard would talk to him and make out it was me. But Old Man Daugherty knowed wouldn't none of Hezekiah Sellards' daughters be carrying on like that. He was bound it was a woman from Ab's Valley.

I would think about 'em sitting there and arguing about how the hussy ought to be run out of the settlements and I would laugh all by myself there in the woods. Throw back my head and laugh and then feel silly when the woods give back the echo.

I done a lot of work while I was with the Indians. It was hard on me at first but I got used to it. It was better after Mad Dog left us. The old chief was like a father to me and the young ones knowed I belonged to him and didn't bother me none. I slept off by myself in a fur corner of the cave and he would wake me up at daybreak and tell me what there was to do that day. He took pains to show me how to flesh pelts and cure them and he showed me how to split a deer sinew for thread and how to make a whistle to call deer out of birch bark and sticks. And after I got so I could sew skins good he had me make him a pair of leggings and trim them with porcupine quills, porcupine quills colored with some roots he got out of the woods.

It bothered him the way I looked and he made me paint my face the way the Indians did. Fixed me up some of the red root mixed with bear's grease and after I'd been putting it on my face for a while you couldn't told me from an Indian woman, except for my light eyes.

He'd stay in the cave with me sometimes all day, his buffalo hide wrapped around him so tight that his knees was up against him like a chair. He'd sit there and rock back and forth on his heels and talk while I worked. Down in the hollow the young braves would be practising their war whoops. He would listen to them and laugh.

"Our young men give the war whoop loudly to cover up their fear of the enemy. It was not so when I was young. There was joy in the war whoop then."

He said he was a chief but he might have been something better. He might have been a medicine man. He had the gift of it from his grandmother. His own mother died when he was born, he said, and his old granny raised him. He told me about how she would take him into the woods with her looking for yarbs and roots and how she knew where everything grew and which roots would be good to take and which had no strength in them. He said that after I was adopted into the tribe he would tell some of her secrets to me but the spirit would be angry if a white woman knew them.

I asked him wouldn't I still be a white woman after I was adopted into the tribe but he said no, the white blood would go out of me and the Spirit would send Indian blood to take its place and then I would feel like an Indian and know all the Indian ways and maybe get to be a wise woman like his old granny.

He told me about his youngest daughter and how she come by her death, following what she thought was a fawn bleating. They found her days afterward, three enemy arrows in her. Her death had been paid for, with three scalps of warriors, and he would say that he didn't grieve over her but I knew he did. I got to feeling sorry for him sometimes to have lost his daughter that meant so much to him and then I would think how I had lost all my children and my husband and I would cry, dropping tears on the skin I was sewing.

I got so after a while that the Indian way of doing things seemed natural to me. I thought nothing of seeing dark faces around me all the time, but in the night sometimes I would dream of white faces. White faces coming towards me through the trees. Or sometimes I would be in a house again and look up all of a sudden and all the faces in the room would be white.

One white face was always coming to me in my dreams: Tice Harman, the man whose house the Indians thought they was burning the day they burned ours. I always thought that if anybody came to save me it would be Tice Harman. I could see him plain in my dreams. A little man, wouldn't weigh more'n a hundred and twenty pounds, but he had a big head. A big head and a big beak of a nose and long yellow hair down to his shoulders. His eyes was blue and in my dreams they glittered like ice. I would dream about Tice Harman and when I waked I would think what I'd heard said of him, how he could go further and stand more than any man in the settlements and how he loved to fight Indians better'n eat when he was hungry. I would think, too, of how folks said he would bring trouble on the settlements shooting that Indian down when there warn't really no use in it, and I would think that since it was him that brought all my trouble on me maybe it would be him that would get me away from the Indians. But time went on and nobody came, and after a while I got so I didn't think much about it.

One evening I was gathering wood on the cliffside and I heard a lot of whooping and hollering down near the mouth of the creek. The Indians come out from where they was sleeping back in the cave and stood looking over the falls. A long whoop came and the old chief put his hands to his mouth and answered it. There was more whooping back and forth and then Mad Dog came up the trail by the falls with about twenty Indians following him. They was painted for war and marched single file, all except the last six or eight. They was in pairs and in the middle of them a white man, walking with his hands tied behind him. A white man? A boy. Couldn't have been more'n eighteen years old.

I had to step out of the path to let them by. The dead branches rustled in my hands. The prisoner turned his head. He looked straight into my eyes. It was like he didn't know I was there. I spoke to him.

"I can't do nothing," I said, "I'm a white woman, but I can't do nothing. Christ!" I said, "there ain't nothing I can do."

He kept on looking at me but he didn't say nothing. They was hurrying him past. I dropped the branches and run after them. Mad Dog called to one of the young bucks and he caught me and held me. I fought him but he held me till they had all gone up the path.

I went on to the rockhouse and kindled up the fire. After a while Mad Dog come down and told me to cook up some meat quick as I could. There would be singing and dancing he said; they would want meat all night long.

I looked at him. "A present," I said, "A present for Kaga-hye-liske's daughter. Give me this boy. He is not good for anything but to gather wood."

His eyes was fierce. "Boy?" he said. "He has this day killed my brother." Then he laughed and smoothed my hair. "Jinny," he said, "pretty Jinny."

I made out I had to see to the fire and walked away. I put some bear meat on to boil and I told him I would call him when it was done and he went on back up the path.

There was a moon coming. I sat there waiting for the meat to boil and watched it rise over the pines. Up on the barren the Indians was dragging up all the dead branches they could find into one pile. After a while I looked up over the rock-house and saw the sky all light and I knew they had kindled the fire.

The stamping and yelling went on and every now and then a gun would go off. Then there was running around the tree. You could hear the feet pounding and the long calls. "Ai . . . yi . . . Ai . . . yi . . . Ai . . . yi . . ." One for each man that had died that day. And the sharp cry for the scalp taking. They would act it all out and the boy standing there watching. He was dazed, though; he wouldn't see it for what it was. He wouldn't know what they was doing, might not know what they was going to do. There on the path he looked at me and didn't know me for a white woman. I ought to have found out his name and where he come from. I ought to have done that much. But he wouldn't have an-

472

swered. And what good would it do his folks . . . if I ever saw white folks again? Mad Dog's hand on my hair. "Pretty Jinny . . . pretty Jinny . . ."

The flames shot up and lit the whole valley. The moon looked cold where it hung over the pines. I kept the fire up under the kittle but I couldn't sit still. I walked back and forth in the rockhouse, back and forth, back and forth, waiting for the shrieks to start.

They was a long time coming. I thought maybe it was already going on. Indians can stand there burning and not make a sound, and there have been white men that could. But this was just a boy . . .

The first shriek was long and then they come short and quick, one right after the other. I got over in a corner of the rockhouse and held on tight to a big rock. After a while I let go of the rock and put both fingers in my ears and then I was feared to take them out, thinking it might not be over yet. The Indians was still yelling and stamping. The young ones kept running down and grabbing up chunks of meat from the boiling pot and carrying them up to the barren. I could see the old chief's shadow where he stood on the edge of the cliff calling to the new moon.

When he came down to the rockhouse Mad Dog was with him. They stood there dipping meat up out of the kettle. Mad Dog talked.

"It is too much. For five hundred brooches I could buy a girl of the Wild-Cats, young and swift, a fine worker in beads. A girl like a moonbeam, daughter of a mighty warrior."

His eyes was black in the circles of paint. His tongue showed bright between his painted lips. The red lines ran from his forehead down the sides of his cheeks to make gouts of blood on his chin.

A devil. A devil come straight from hell to burn and murder. Three white men killed that day and the boy brought back to torture. It was him that killed them, him that yelled

473

the loudest when the boy was burning. Him that set fire to my house and burned my children . . .

I saw him running through the woods, white men after him. I saw him fall, a dozen bullets in him. But he wouldn't be dead. He would lay there bleeding and look at me out of his painted eyes and I would go up and stomp on him, stomp him into the dirt . . .

My hands shook so I dropped the sticks I was carrying. I was up near enough now to hear all they was saying. Mad Dog was taking little silver brooches out of a buckskin bag. He poured them out in a pile on a rock and then counted them. The old chief stood there till he got through counting, then he swept them all up into a bag he took from around his neck.

"Brother," he said, "the woman is yours."

Mad Dog had left the fire and was coming towards me. I ran over and caught hold of the old chief's arm. I called him by his Indian name.

"Kag-ahyeliske, do not give me to this man. He has killed my children and burned my house."

He looked down at me and it was like he'd never seen me before. His face, not painted, was as cruel as the Cherokee's, the eyes bloodshot and the whole face swollen from the meat he had eaten.

"The war whoop drowns sorrow," he said. "This chief is my brother and a mighty warrior. He has this day killed three white men."

I hung on to his arm. "Keep me for one of the young men of your village," I said. "The Cherokee are old women. You have said so and you have promised. You have promised to take me with you wherever you go."

He shook my hands off. "A promise," he said, "to a white coward! Go to your work."

He turned around like he was going to leave the cave. I run after him and caught hold of his knees, but he broke away. Mad Dog come and tied me up tight with thongs that

474

he cut from buffalo hide, and then they both went on up to the barren where the other Indians was still screeching and stamping.

The screeching and stamping went on far into the night. The fire under the kittle went out and it was dark except for a little light from the moon. I laid there on the floor, listening to the Indians and thinking about how it would be when Mad Dog came down to take me for his wife. I laid there, expecting him to come any minute, but the singing and dancing went on and he didn't come and after a while I went to sleep.

V

The white boy that they had burned came to me while I was asleep. He came carrying a lamp that was made from the bleached skull of a sheep. The brain hollow was filled with buffalo fat and there was a wick in it burning bright. He came walking between the trees like he didn't have need to look where he was going. His hair was light like I had seen it when he passed me there on the path, but it was long, too, like Tice Harman's. His eyes were the same eyes that had looked at me there on the path.

I said to him what I had said there. "I couldn't do nothing," I said. "There wasn't nothing I could do."

He didn't speak, only made signs for me to follow him. I got up and walked after him. The rawhide thongs was still on me but they didn't bind any more and I moved as easy and as light as he did. He went down by the falls and clomb up over the hill to where the elm tree stood that had the big rattlesnake painted on it. He walked past the elm tree and struck out through the black pines that was all over that ridge. Sometimes he would go so fast that I couldn't keep up with him and then I would stand still and after a while I would see the light flickering through the trees and I would go on to where he was waiting for me. We went on through

475

the pine woods and started down the side of the ridge. I heard water running somewhere far down below. I thought that would be Mudlick creek but when I got to it it was a branch I'd never seen before. We crossed it and went on up a path through a clearing. There was little shrubs all around like the ones up on the barren and in the middle of them was a house. It was my house and yet it wasn't. White all over and the walls so thin you could see the light from the lamp shining through the logs.

People was walking around in the yard and sitting on the door step. They moved to let me go through the door, but they didn't speak to me and I didn't speak to them.

The men that was sitting in front of the fire playing draughts didn't even look up when I came in. I went over to the hearth and tried to dry out my clothes. I stood there holding out my hands but didn't no heat come. I looked at the logs and they was white like the timbers of the house and the same light came from them. I saw that the men playing didn't have no lamp and yet there was light all around them.

People kept walking in and out of the cabin, men and women and little children. I would go up to them and look in their faces but there wasn't nobody there I knew. I walked round and round the room. Every now and then the people would move out of the way and I would catch a sight of the walls. White, with patches of green on them. I put my hand up and felt one of the logs. It was round and cold to the touch. No log at all, but bleached bone. I knew then that all the house was bone, the floor and the walls and the chimney, even the table that the men was playing on, all made from the big bones down at the lick.

One of the men at the table stretched his arm out and pulled me over to him. He had on a beaver cap and his face under it was pale like he'd been in the woods a long time.

He looked at me and I saw it was Lance Rayburn. He sang, pulling me up over the arm of his chair:

476

"Oh . . . the bell cow, kicking up her heels,
Call the little gal to milk her in the pail . . ."

Fiddling started up somewhere and all fell to dancing.
They danced to one of my old granny's tunes:

"They was an old lord lived in a northern countree,
Bowee down, bowee down . . ."   ..

There was bowing back and forth and balancing and
there was figures called, but wasn't no women dancing anywhere. I would see something going by and think it was a
woman's skirt but when I got up to it it would be fur or
feathers dangling from a belt and all the faces around was
dark, not like they was at first.

The great flames went leaping up the chimney and all of
a sudden I knew that they had built that fire to burn somebody by. I looked around for the one they was going to burn
but he wasn't there. I said they will burn me next, and I saw
what they would tie me to, the rattlesnake tree, going straight
up from the table through the roof.

I went to the door and I saw through the black trunks a
light flickering. I run and Mad Dog and the old chief was
after me the way they was that day in the hollow. I thought
they will kill me now when I go down and I run faster and
then they was both gone away and I was walking through
pine woods, the light flickering on ahead of me.

I walked on and come to a creek that ran along between
wide banks of cane. The light shone on the water and made
it light as mist. I stepped in, not knowing whether it was
water or mist and I could feel it coming up around my knees,
water and yet not water. I moved along through it light as
the wind till I come to where the creek forked. I could see
the two forks and the white trunks of the sycamores along
the bank but I didn't know which way to go.

The light was all around me. I could see it shining on the
reeds and on the little leaves of the cane and on the water

477

where it broke on the rocks. Behind me there was voices talking.

"Jinny Wiley . . . Jinny Wiley, that was stolen and lived with the Indians. . . ."

And then it was the old chief talking to the new moon:

"The white people. . . . The white people are all over the land. The beaver makes no more dams and the buffalo does not come to the lick. And bees swarm here in the ancient village. Bees swarm on the graves of our fathers. . . ."

The light that had been around me was gone. It was shining now through the tree trunks down a fork of the creek. I waded towards it through the light water, the voices following and then they was gone away and I was standing at the foot of a high mountain. I looked up and I saw the light flickering at the top and I clomb towards it, pulling myself up by the scrubs and holly bushes.

I got up on the mountain top but the young man wasn't there. I walked out on to the edge of a cliff and he was by my side. He said "Look, Jinny!" and the flame of his lamp leaped up and lighted the whole valley and I looked across a river and I saw a fort. I saw the roofs of the houses and the stockade and the timber burned back over the rifle range and I saw men and women walking around inside the stockade.

I said: "I'm a-going over there," but the young man wasn't with me no more and the dark that was all around was the inside of the rockhouse.

VI

When I woke up the next morning the Indians had a big fire going and was all sitting around eating. I laid there and made out I was still asleep. They had found trace of buffalo down at the lick and was making ready for a big hunt. I thought maybe they would take me along to bring in the game the way they did sometimes, and then I heard Mad Dog say they would leave me tied up in the cave till they got ready to start for their town.

478

I was laying with my face turned up and I was feared they could tell by my eyes that I wasn't asleep. I give a kind of groan and rolled over on my side. I laid there not moving while the talking went on all around me. Once footsteps come over to the corner where I was laying and I heard something slap down on the ground right by me but I didn't give any sign and the footsteps went away.

I laid there so still that I went to sleep again with the talking and the making ready for the hunt still going on. I was waked up by a kind of roaring sound. At first I thought it was the falls and then I knowed the falls wouldn't sound that loud. I opened my eyes. The Indians was all gone and there was a big storm blowing up.

I laid there watching the pine tops lash back and forth in the wind and the dream I'd had come back into my mind as plain as if it was something that had happened. I thought it was sent to me on purpose to tell me that now was the chance to get away. I knowed that if the Indians come back with any game that night they'd feast high again and was more than likely to take me up on the barren and burn me like they done that boy.

I sat up. A piece of meat was lying on the floor right by me. That meant that the Indians would be all gone all day and maybe another day. If I could only get free of the thongs I might get a long way off before they knew I was gone.

There was a knife stuck in a crack of the rock where they laid the meat. If I could only get hold of that! I rolled over and over till I got to the rock and I managed to get up on my knees, though the thongs cut into me bad. I could see the handle of the knife sticking up out of the crack and I laid my face down flat on the rock and tried to catch hold of it with my teeth. But it was too far down and all I did was get my mouth full of grit and sand. I gave up and laid down again. The wind wasn't as high as it had been, but the rain was coming down hard. It blew way back into the cave. I laid there with the big drops spattering in my face and a thought

479

came to me. I rolled over to where the rain was pouring down off the roof and I laid there till I was soaked through. All the time I kept straining at the thongs and I could feel them giving a little, the way leather does when it's wet. I kept on, getting them looser and looser till finally I worked my way out of them and stood up free.

I listened and I couldn't hear anything but the roaring of the wind and the beating of the rain on the ledge. I tiptoed to the end of the cave and looked down the path. But I couldn't see any sign of living creature. I dug the knife out from between the rocks and I took the piece of cooked meat and a little kittle that the old chief had left laying around and I went off out of the other end of the cave and along the cliffside.

I kept to the path a little way and then I struck off through the trees down the hillside. The ground was wet and slid from under my feet in big chunks. I caught on to the trees all the way to keep myself from falling. When I got to the bottom I could look back and see where I'd come, as plain as if I'd blazed a trail. I knowed I'd have to strike water. I run in among some pines and come to a wet weather branch. I waded right in. It was swift water and full of holes. I would step in one every now and then and go down but I kept on as fast as I could. I felt all the time like the Indians was after me. I knowed they had gone south towards the salt lick and I knowed the whole cliffside and the barren was between me and them but all the time I felt like they was right behind me. When I looked over my shoulder the top boughs of the rattlesnake tree showed from the barren. I was glad when I rounded a bend and it was out of sight.

When I come to where the branch flowed into the creek I didn't know which way to go and then I thought that in my dream I was following water and I struck right down the stream. It was harder going here than it was in the branch. The snows melting had filled all the dry weather branches and muddy water kept running in till you couldn't tell noth-

480

ing about the depth. It was good I was going down stream but even then the current was a hindrance to me, reaching in and sweeping me off my feet sometimes into a hole that I would have a time getting out of. More'n once I was in danger of drowning.

I kept on like this all day. When it was drawing towards dark I crawled up on the bank under some cedars and I laid there and I ate a good sized piece of the cooked meat I had brought with me. The rain had fallen off to a light drizzle and there was some color in the sky, sign of a clear day to-morrow. There was a flight of little birds over the water and then round and round the tops of the cedars. Some of them lit in the boughs of the tree I was laying under. I could hear them flying in and out and the quick cries and then the twit-tering as they settled down to roost. It was dark under the trees but the streak of light stayed on the water. I laid here and watched it fade and I wished I could stay there where the cedar boughs was like a little house. I wished I could stay there and not run no more. I thought I would maybe sleep a few minutes and then I could go on faster. But when I shut my eyes I would think I heard the Indians coming through the trees and after a little I got up and went on again.

I tried wading some more but I couldn't make it in the pitch dark. I got up on the bank of the creek and pushed my way through the bushes as best I could. Sometimes the under-growth would be so thick I couldn't make it and then I would have to get down in the water again. All the way I ,was worrying about losing time following the bending and twisting of the creek, and then I would think that was the only sure way to get out of the hill country and I had best stick to water, spite of all the bending.

Some time during the night I lost my way from the creek and wandered in the pitch dark into a marsh that was all along the creek bottom. More like a bog it was. I couldn't seem to get out of it no matter what I did. I stood there bogged to the knees and I couldn't even hear the creek run-

481

ning, nothing but the wind soughing in the trees. And I thought what a lone place it was and if I came on quicksand as was more than likely I could go down and even my bones never be found. And I thought of how Lance Rayburn's bones might have been laying all this time in some hollow of the mountain and nothing maybe but squirrels or deer ever going near the place and it seemed to me I might better have stayed with the Indians. But I knew it wouldn't be no use going back now. They would put the fire to me sure.

I stood there and I heard some wild thing passing. Pit pat pit pat it went; feet falling on dry ground. I pulled out of the muck and made towards the sound and a deer or something broke through the thicket and went off through the woods.

I followed and come out on high ground, a slope covered with pine needles. I throwed myself down flat on my face. I must have gone off to sleep. When I come to myself light was growing through the trees and all around me I could hear twigs snapping and little rustlings. I got up quick, thinking it was the Indians coming and then I felt foolish, knowing it was only game stirring at break of day. I saw two deer go by, moving slow over the brown pine needles. The air was so still they didn't get a whiff of me till they was out of the thicket. The buck wheeled, so quick he almost knocked the doe over and then they was both clattering off over the hill.

I went down to the creek bank and washed my face and let the water run over my wrists where they was scratched by the branches. I ate the last of my meat sitting there on a rock. When I got ready to go I found out that one of my strings of jerked meat had slipped off during the night. I couldn't hardly believe it at first. I stood up and felt all over my clothes time and again but it warn't there.

"Well," I said, "it's gone and they ain't no use crying over it, but I wish to God it'd a been the little piece."

I got in the water and started wading again. The creek was shallow for about half a mile and then it run into a bigger creek. The two of them run on before me and I didn't know which way to go. I stood there looking. The sun was up and it shone on the water. I watched the riffles break on the black rocks where the sun caught them and the place was not the same place I had seen in the dream and yet it was the same because of the light that was over everything.

I remembered the way I took in the dream. "Left I'll go," I said, "like it was in the dream and if it don't turn out right it's no fault of mine."

I went on, wading half the time. All that day I was thinking about something to eat. Seems like everything good I ever had to eat in my life come back to torment me that day. The smell of herrings over the coals the way children did when their mammy wouldn't give them anything else to eat between meals. I would go over it all, time and again, the herrings hanging in rows in the smoke house, like tobacco in a barn, and us climbing up on a slab of wood to get at them.

"Three," Dinny, that's my oldest brother'd say every time. "Three. You might as well get one apiece while you're at it."

I thought, too, about people wasting things, of a woman I knew used to give all her buttermilk to her pig and I thought how it was shameful to have no mind for them that might be starving. And I thought how if I could have that pig's dinner one time, or even a moldy piece of bread, the kind I'd thrown away many a time as not good enough for the dogs. And yet I'd been as wasteful as any of them in my day, worse, even, with game. I used to go hunting just for the fun of it. Seemed like there warn't nothing I liked better than sighting down a rifle.

Warn't none of the Sellards or Damron boys a better shot than I was and I could throw a knife with the best of them. That time John and Dick and me and the two Damrons went to Sinking Fork on a big hunt I shot eighteen wild gobblers and when we loaded up and they was more'n we could carry it was me that said to leave them laying, that there warn't no use in breaking yourself down and the woods full of gobblers like they was. I thought about them gobblers more'n once that day and Lord, how I wished I could git my hands on a rifle butt just one more time.

I throwed my knife once or twice at some small game, mostly rabbits, but it was a rusty old thing and not fitted to the hand the way a knife has to be to turn proper. One rabbit that I hit square in the middle got up and skittered off like nothing had happened and I seed then it was a waste of time to throw at them.

Late that evening I come on some forward wild greens in a sheltered place on the creek bank. I went down on my knees and I gathered every shoot. I found some punk and I went up to a rockhouse on the side of the hill and I built a little fire 'way in under the ledge the way I'd seen the Indians do. I knowed it was craziness to build a fire but it might be days before I'd come on any wild greens again. "I'll eat," I said, "varmints or no varmints."

I put my greens on to boil in the little kittle with a piece of the jerked meat and I sat there, thinking about how Indians would go up on a cliff to sight over the country and how the least little smoke curling up would be a sign to them. Once I was on the point of putting the fire out but I couldn't bring myself to do it. I feared to feed it much and yet I'd catch myself putting dead twigs to it. It was a long time before the bubbles started rising up in that little old kittle. I sat there rocking on my heels and talking to them.

"Bile," I said, "bile. God's sake, can't you bile no faster'n that? And me setting here starving."

I ate up ever' mite of the greens and I drank the pot liquor and licked the kittle and then I put out down the hill as fast as I could. I could feel my stomach tight under my waist band and strength coming up in me from the vittles and I run faster than I'd ever run before. It was dark under the trees but there was still light down the water courses. I thought how in some cleared place or in a town it wouldn't

484

be dark for two or three hours yet and I saw myself in such a place, moving around and talking to people but staying always in the light. And I said to myself if I ever got into such a cleared place again it'd be hard to get me to set foot in the woods.

The creek I was following was a master tumbler. Straight down it went over big rocks and the water white everywhere with its dashing. Once I thought I would leave it and strike out through the woods again and then I thought falling water'd take me out of the hills quicker'n anything else and I'd best stick to it long as I could.

I went on and then all of a sudden I come upon something that froze my guts cold: the print of a foot by the water. I knowed it would be a moccasin but I stooped down and looked at it good. I told myself it might be a white man, might be a hunter wearing moccasins like most of 'em did but I went on a little way and there was three four footprints in some wet sand and all of 'em was moccasins. I thought then the game was up or would be directly but I run on. I run on. I couldn't think of nothing else to do.

It was still light when I come out on a big rock by some little falls. I stood there looking and I couldn't believe my eyes. A broad river ran there before me and clearings here and there on the bank and right across from the rock I was standing on a fort: a blockhouse with a stockade fence around it and the timber burned back over the rifle range.

I got off the rock and I run down towards the water. A woman and some children was walking along outside the stockade. I called to the woman. She give one look at me and turned and run inside the fort, the children after her. I saw the gate swing to behind them and I knowed they had shot the bolt.

I tore off my petticoat and I waved it over my head and I yelled loud as I could.

"Let me in! Let me in, I tell you!"

I could see heads at the upper storey and one somebody

485

standing up on a stump to look over the stockade. But nobody answered and there wasn't no sign of the gate opening.

I looked over my shoulder. The woods was dark behind me and they wasn't no signs of Indians but I knowed they'd be coming any minute. I felt like I knowed the place in the woods they was at now. I saw them trotting, trotting through the trees, one after another, the way they went.

I thought I'll have to do something quick or they'll git me sure, after all my trouble. I started in to swim it but I couldn't make no headway against that current. I saw I would be drowning in a minute and I swum hard and got back to shallow water. It come to me then that the folks in the fort didn't know who I was. I stood up in the water and I yelled, loud as I could.

"I'm Jinny Wiley . . . Jinny Wiley that the Indians stole."

The echo come back to me from the woods, but there warn't no sound from the fort. Then the gate opened a little way and an old man come out with a gun in his hand. He stood there looking at me and he turned around and said something to the folks in the fort and then he started down the path. I watched him coming down over the rifle range, an old man, gray-haired and feeble enough to 'a' been my grandsire. I shouted at him.

"You can't do it. Send some young body over."

He stood over the bank and shouted back at me, his old voice quavering across the water:

"Where'd you come from?"

I jumped up and down and shrieked, top of my voice:

"God sakes, man, you going to let me die right here before your eyes? I'm white! White, I tell you!"

"All of 'em's gone but me," he said, "and they ain't no canoe."

"Make a raft," I told him.

He nodded his head up and down. I could see his old gray beard a-shaking. "You better be ready to swim for it," he said. "I don't know as I can git across."

486

He called to the women in the fort and they come and brought an axe. They was a dead mulberry tree on the bank and they went to work felling it. The old man went off in the woods and come back with some grapevine. When the tree fell it split into three logs and he tied them together with grapevine and then he and the women rolled them down to the water. They handed him two rifles and he laid them on the raft and started poling. The current caught him and he was going down stream. Yelling had started behind me somewhere in the woods. The Indians was coming.

I run down the bank till I got even with the raft and I swum out and clomb aboard. The old man poled hard. We got half way out in the river and then the vines begun to come loose and the raft was spreading apart. I knelt down and held the logs together with my hands as best as I could. The old man fell down on his knees and started praying.

" 'Tain't no use," he said, "we can't make it."

I looked over my shoulder. The Indians was swarming down towards the water. I knowed they'd be swimming directly. The old man was still praying. I took the pole away from him.

"Go on and pray, you old fool," I said, "I'm a-going to git across this river."

I put all the strength I had into it and we made some headway. The yelling was closer now. The Indians was in the water. A shot rung out. I hoped to God one of 'em was hit. I poled harder and I seen some willow boughs ahead of me. I reached out and grabbed hold of 'em and we pulled ourselves to shore.

We went up over the rifle range fast as we could. I looked back once. The Indians had left the water and was standing on the bank. I heard Mad Dog calling:

"Whoopee! . . . whoopee! . . . pretty Jinny!"

We went through the gate. I heard the bolt shoot home and I knowed I was inside the fort. I fell down on the ground and the women and children come crowding. The Indians was still yelling. I sat up and the high stockade fence was all around me.

"Lord God," I said, "I was lucky to git away from them Indians!"

❧

Katherine Anne Porter

FLOWERING JUDAS

BRAGGIONI sits heaped upon the edge of a straight-backed chair much too small for him, and sings to Laura in a furry, mournful voice. Laura has begun to find reasons for avoiding her own house until the latest possible moment, for Braggioni is there almost every night. No matter how late she is, he will be sitting there with a surly, waiting expression, pulling at his kinky yellow hair, thumbing the strings of his guitar, snarling a tune under his breath. Lupe the Indian maid meets Laura at the door, and says with a flicker of a glance towards the upper room, "He waits."

Laura wishes to lie down, she is tired of her hairpins and the feel of her long tight sleeves, but she says to him, "Have you a new song for me this evening?" If he says yes, she asks him to sing it. If he says no, she remembers his favorite one, and asks him to sing it again. Lupe brings her a cup of chocolate and a plate of rice, and Laura eats at the small table under the lamp, first inviting Braggioni, whose answer is always the same: "I have eaten, and besides, chocolate thickens the voice."

Laura says, "Sing, then," and Braggioni heaves himself

into song. He scratches the guitar familiarly as though it were a pet animal, and sings passionately off key, taking the high notes in a prolonged painful squeal. Laura, who haunts the markets listening to the ballad singers, and stops every day to hear the blind boy playing his reed-flute in Sixteenth of September Street, listens to Braggioni with pitiless courtesy, because she dares not smile at his miserable performance. Nobody dares to smile at him. Braggioni is cruel to everyone, with a kind of specialized insolence, but he is so vain of his talents, and so sensitive to slights, it would require a cruelty and vanity greater than his own to lay a finger on the vast cureless wound of his self-esteem. It would require courage, too, for it is dangerous to offend him, and nobody has this courage.

Braggioni loves himself with such tenderness and amplitude and eternal charity that his followers—for he is a leader of men, a skilled revolutionist, and his skin has been punctured in honorable warfare—warm themselves in the reflected glow, and say to each other: "He has a real nobility, a love of humanity raised above mere personal affections." The excess of this self-love has flowed out, inconveniently for her, over Laura, who, with so many others, owes her comfortable situation and her salary to him. When he is in a very good humor, he tells her, "I am tempted to forgive you for being a *gringa. Gringita!*" and Laura, burning, imagines herself leaning forward suddenly, and with a sound backhanded slap wiping the suety smile from his face. If he notices her eyes at these moments he gives no sign.

She knows what Braggioni would offer her, and she must resist tenaciously without appearing to resist, and if she could avoid it she would not admit even to herself the slow drift of his intention. During these long evenings which have spoiled a long month for her, she sits in her deep chair with an open book on her knees, resting her eyes on the consoling rigidity of the printed page when the sight and sound of Braggioni singing threaten to identify themselves with all

489

her remembered afflictions and to add their weight to her uneasy premonitions of the future. The gluttonous bulk of Braggioni has become a symbol of her many disillusions, for a revolutionist should be lean, animated by heroic faith, a vessel of abstract virtues. This is nonsense, she knows it now and is ashamed of it. Revolution must have leaders, and leadership is a career for energetic men. She is, her comrades tell her, full of romantic error, for what she defines as cynicism in them is merely "a developed sense of reality." She is almost too willing to say, "I am wrong, I suppose I don't really understand the principles," and afterward she makes a secret truce with herself, determined not to surrender her will to such expedient logic. But she cannot help feeling that she has been betrayed irreparably by the disunion between her way of living and her feeling of what life should be, and at times she is almost contented to rest in this sense of grievance as a private store of consolation. Sometimes she wishes to run away, but she stays. Now she longs to fly out of this room, down the narrow stairs, and into the street where the houses lean together like conspirators under a single mottled lamp, and leave Braggioni singing to himself.

Instead she looks at Braggioni, frankly and clearly, like a good child who understands the rules of behavior. Her knees cling together under sound blue serge, and her round white collar is not purposely nun-like. She wears the uniform of an idea, and has renounced vanities. She was born Roman Catholic, and in spite of her fear of being seen by someone who might make a scandal of it, she slips now and again into some crumbling little church, kneels on the chilly stone, and says a Hail Mary on the gold rosary she bought in Tehuantepec. It is no good and she ends by examining the altar with its tinsel flowers and ragged brocades, and feels tender about the battered doll-shape of some male saint whose white, lace-trimmed drawers hang limply around his ankles below the hieratic dignity of his velvet robe. She has encased herself in a set of principles derived from her early training, leaving no detail of gesture or of personal taste untouched, and for this reason she will not wear lace made on machines. This is her private heresy, for in her special group the machine is sacred, and will be the salvation of the workers. She loves fine lace, and there is a tiny edge of fluted cobweb on this collar, which is one of twenty precisely alike, folded in blue tissue paper in the upper drawer of her clothes chest.

Braggioni catches her glance solidly as if he had been waiting for it, leans forward, balancing his paunch between his spread knees, and sings with tremendous emphasis, weighing his words. He has, the song relates, no father and no mother, nor even a friend to console him; lonely as a wave of the sea he comes and goes, lonely as a wave. His mouth opens round and yearns sideways, his balloon cheeks grow oily with the labor of song. He bulges marvelously in his expensive garments. Over his lavender collar, crushed upon a purple necktie, held by a diamond hoop: over his ammunition belt of tooled leather worked in silver, buckled cruelly around his gasping middle: over the tops of his glossy yellow shoes Braggioni swells with ominous ripeness, his mauve silk hose stretched taut, his ankles bound with the stout leather thongs of his shoes.

When he stretches his eyelids at Laura she notes again that his eyes are the true tawny yellow cat's eyes. He is rich, not in money, he tells her, but in power, and this power brings with it the blameless ownership of things, and the right to indulge his love of small luxuries. "I have a taste for the elegant refinements," he said once, flourishing a yellow silk handkerchief before her nose. "Smell that? It is Jockey Club, imported from New York." Nonetheless he is wounded by life. He will say so presently. "It is true everything turns to dust in the hand, to gall on the tongue." He sighs and his leather belt creaks like a saddle girth. "I am disappointed in everything as it comes. Everything." He shakes his head. "You, poor thing, you will be disappointed too. You are born for it. We are more alike than you realize

491

in some things. Wait and see. Some day you will remember what I have told you, you will know that Braggioni was your friend."

Laura feels a slow chill, a purely physical sense of danger, a warning in her blood that violence, mutilation, a shocking death, wait for her with lessening patience. She has translated this fear into something homely, immediate, and sometimes hesitates before crossing the street. "My personal fate is nothing, except as the testimony of a mental attitude," she reminds herself, quoting from some forgotten philosophic primer, and is sensible enough to add, "Anyhow, I shall not be killed by an automobile if I can help it."

"It may be true I am as corrupt, in another way, as Braggioni," she thinks in spite of herself, "as callous, as incomplete," and if this is so, any kind of death seems preferable. Still she sits quietly, she does not run. Where could she go? Uninvited she has promised herself to this place; she can no longer imagine herself as living in another country, and there is no pleasure in remembering her life before she came here.

Precisely what is the nature of this devotion, its true motives, and what are its obligations? Laura cannot say. She spends part of her days in Xochimilco, near by, teaching Indian children to say in English, "The cat is on the mat." When she appears in the classroom they crowd about her with smiles on their wise, innocent, clay-colored faces, crying, "Good morning, my titcher!" in immaculate voices, and they make of her desk a fresh garden of flowers every day.

During her leisure she goes to union meetings and listens to busy important voices quarreling over tactics, methods, internal politics. She visits the prisoners of her own political faith in their cells, where they entertain themselves with counting cockroaches, repenting of their indiscretions, composing their memoirs, writing out manifestoes and plans for their comrades who are still walking about free, hands in pockets, sniffing fresh air. Laura brings them food and cigarettes and a little money, and she brings messages disguised in equivocal phrases from the men outside who dare not set foot in the prison for fear of disappearing into the cells kept empty for them. If the prisoners confuse night and day, and complain, "Dear little Laura, time doesn't pass in this infernal hole, and I won't know when it is time to sleep unless I have a reminder," she brings them their favorite narcotics, and says in a tone that does not wound them with pity, "Tonight will really be night for you," and though her Spanish amuses them, they find her comforting, useful. If they lose patience and all faith, and curse the slowness of their friends in coming to their rescue with money and influence, they trust her not to repeat everything, and if she inquires, "Where do you think we can find money, or influence?" they are certain to answer, "Well, there is Braggioni, why doesn't he do something?"

She smuggles letters from headquarters to men hiding from firing squads in back streets in mildewed houses, where they sit in tumbled beds and talk bitterly as if all Mexico were at their heels, when Laura knows positively they might appear at the band concert in the Alameda on Sunday morning, and no one would notice them. But Braggioni says, "Let them sweat a little. The next time they may be careful. It is very restful to have them out of the way for a while." She is not afraid to knock on any door in any street after midnight, and enter in the darkness, and say to one of these men who is really in danger: "They will be looking for you—seriously—tomorrow morning after six. Here is some money from Vicente. Go to Vera Cruz and wait."

She borrows money from the Roumanian agitator to give to his bitter enemy the Polish agitator. The favor of Braggioni is their disputed territory, and Braggioni holds the balance nicely, for he can use them both. The Polish agitator talks love to her over café tables, hoping to exploit what he believes is her secret sentimental preference for him, and he gives her misinformation which he begs her to repeat as the

493

solemn truth to certain persons. The Roumanian is more adroit. He is generous with his money in all good causes, and lies to her with an air of ingenuous candor, as if he were her good friend and confidant. She never repeats anything they may say. Braggioni never asks questions. He has other ways to discover all that he wishes to know about them.

Nobody touches her, but all praise her gray eyes, and the soft, round under lip which promises gayety, yet is always grave, nearly always firmly closed: and they cannot understand why she is in Mexico. She walks back and forth on her errands, with puzzled eyebrows, carrying her little folder of drawings and music and school papers. No dancer dances more beautifully than Laura walks, and she inspires some amusing, unexpected ardors, which cause little gossip, because nothing comes of them. A young captain who had been a soldier in Zapata's army attempted, during a horseback ride near Cuernavaca, to express his desire for her with the noble simplicity befitting a rude folk-hero: but gently, because he was gentle. This gentleness was his defeat, for when he alighted, and removed her foot from the stirrup, and essayed to draw her down into his arms, her horse, ordinarily a tame one, shied fiercely, reared and plunged away. The young hero's horse careered blindly after his stable-mate, and the hero did not return to the hotel until rather late that evening. At breakfast he came to her table in full charro dress, gray buckskin jacket and trousers with strings of silver buttons down the leg, and he was in a humorous, careless mood. "May I sit with you?" and "You are a wonderful rider. I was terrified that you might be thrown and dragged. I should never have forgiven myself. But I cannot admire you enough for your riding!"

"I learned to ride in Arizona," said Laura.

"If you will ride with me again this morning, I promise you a horse that will not shy with you," he said. But Laura remembered that she must return to Mexico City at noon.

Next morning the children made a celebration and spent

their playtime writing on the blackboard, "We lov ar ticher," and with tinted chalks they drew wreaths of flowers around the words. The young hero wrote her a letter: "I am a very foolish, wasteful, impulsive man. I should have first said I love you, and then you would not have run away. But you shall see me again." Laura thought, "I must send him a box of colored crayons," but she was trying to forgive herself for having spurred her horse at the wrong moment.

A brown, shock-haired youth came and stood in her patio one night and sang like a lost soul for two hours, but Laura could think of nothing to do about it. The moonlight spread a wash of gauzy silver over the clear spaces of the garden, and the shadows were cobalt blue. The scarlet blossoms of the Judas tree were dull purple, and the names of the colors repeated themselves automatically in her mind, while she watched not the boy, but his shadow, fallen like a dark garment across the fountain rim, trailing in the water. Lupe came silently and whispered expert counsel in her ear: "If you will throw him one little flower, he will sing another song or two and go away." Laura threw the flower, and he sang a last song and went away with the flower tucked in the band of his hat. Lupe said, "He is one of the organizers of the Typographers Union, and before that he sold corridos in the Merced market, and before that, he came from Guanajuato, where I was born. I would not trust any man, but I trust least those from Guanajuato."

She did not tell Laura that he would be back again the next night, and the next, nor that he would follow her at a certain fixed distance around the Merced market, through the Zócolo, up Francisco I. Madero Avenue, and so along the Paseo de la Reforma to Chapultepec Park, and into the Philosopher's Footpath, still with that flower withering in his hat, and an indivisible attention in his eyes.

Now Laura is accustomed to him, it means nothing except that he is nineteen years old and is observing a convention with all propriety, as though it were founded on a law of nature, which in the end it might well prove to be. He is beginning to write poems which he prints on a wooden press, and he leaves them stuck like handbills in her door. She is pleasantly disturbed by the abstract, unhurried watchfulness of his black eyes which will in time turn easily towards another object. She tells herself that throwing the flower was a mistake, for she is twenty-two years old and knows better; but she refuses to regret it, and persuades herself that her negation of all external events as they occur is a sign that she is gradually perfecting herself in the stoicism she strives to cultivate against that disaster she fears, though she cannot name it.

She is not at home in the world. Every day she teaches children who remain strangers to her, though she loves their tender round hands and their charming opportunist savagery. She knocks at unfamiliar doors not knowing whether a friend or a stranger shall answer, and even if a known face emerges from the sour gloom of that unknown interior, still it is the face of a stranger. No matter what this stranger says to her, nor what her message to him, the very cells of her flesh reject knowledge and kinship in one monotonous word. No. No. No. She draws her strength from this one holy talismanic word which does not suffer her to be led into evil. Denying everything, she may walk anywhere in safety, she looks at everything without amazement.

No, repeats this firm unchanging voice of her blood; and she looks at Braggioni without amazement. He is a great man, he wishes to impress this simple girl who covers her great round breasts with thick dark cloth, and who hides long, invaluably beautiful legs under a heavy skirt. She is almost thin except for the incomprehensible fullness of her breasts, like a nursing mother's, and Braggioni, who considers himself a judge of women, speculates again on the puzzle of her notorious virginity, and takes the liberty of speech which she permits without a sign of modesty, indeed, without any sort of sign, which is disconcerting.

"You think you are so cold, *gringita!* Wait and see. You will surprise yourself some day! May I be there to advise you!" He stretches his eyelids at her, and his ill-humored cat's eyes waver in a separate glance for the two points of light marking the opposite ends of a smoothly drawn path between the swollen curve of her breasts. He is not put off by that blue serge, nor by her resolutely fixed gaze. There is all the time in the world. His cheeks are bellying with the wind of song. "O girl with the dark eyes," he sings, and reconsiders. "But yours are not dark. I can change all that. O girl with the green eyes, you have stolen my heart away!" then his mind wanders to the song, and Laura feels the weight of his attention being shifted elsewhere. Singing thus, he seems harmless, he is quite harmless, there is nothing to do but sit patiently and say "No," when the moment comes. She draws a full breath, and her mind wanders also, but not far. She dares not wander too far.

Not for nothing has Braggioni taken pains to be a good revolutionist and a professional lover of humanity. He will never die of it. He has the malice, the cleverness, the wickedness, the sharpness of wit, the hardness of heart, stipulated for loving the world profitably. *He will never die of it.* He will live to see himself kicked out from his feeding trough by other hungry world-saviors. Traditionally he must sing in spite of his life which drives him to bloodshed, he tells Laura, for his father was a Tuscany peasant who drifted to Yucatan and married a Maya woman: a woman of race, an aristocrat. They gave him the love and knowledge of music, thus: and under the rip of his thumbnail, the strings of the instrument complain like exposed nerves.

Once he was called Delgadito by all the girls and married women who ran after him; he was so scrawny all his bones showed under his thin cotton clothing, and he could squeeze his emptiness to the very backbone with his two hands. He was a poet and the revolution was only a dream then; too many women loved him and sapped away his youth, and he

497

could never find enough to eat anywhere, anywhere! Now he is a leader of men, crafty men who whisper in his ear, hungry men who wait for hours outside his office for a word with him, emaciated men with wild faces who waylay him at the street gate with a timid, "Comrade, let me tell you . . ." and they blow the foul breath from their empty stomachs in his face.

He is always sympathetic. He gives them handfuls of small coins from his own pocket, he promises them work, there will be demonstrations, they must join the unions and attend the meetings, above all they must be on the watch for spies. They are closer to him than his own brothers, without them he can do nothing—until tomorrow, comrade!

Until tomorrow. "They are stupid, they are lazy, they are treacherous, they would cut my throat for nothing," he says to Laura. He has good food and abundant drink, he hires an automobile and drives in the Paseo on Sunday morning, and enjoys plenty of sleep in a soft bed beside a wife who dares not disturb him; and he sits pampering his bones in easy billows of fat, singing to Laura, who knows and thinks these things about him. When he was fifteen, he tried to drown himself because he loved a girl, his first love, and she laughed at him. "A thousand women have paid for that," and his tight little mouth turns down at the corners. Now he perfumes his hair with Jockey Club, and confides to Laura: "One woman is really as good as another for me, in the dark. I prefer them all."

His wife organizes unions among the girls in the cigarette factories, and walks in picket lines, and even speaks at meetings in the evening. But she cannot be brought to acknowledge the benefits of true liberty. "I tell her I must have my freedom, net. She does not understand my point of view." Laura has heard this many times. Braggioni scratches the guitar and meditates. "She is an instinctively virtuous woman, pure gold, no doubt of that. If she were not, I should lock her up, and she knows it."

His wife, who works so hard for the good of the factory girls, employs part of her leisure lying on the floor weeping because there are so many women in the world, and only one husband for her, and she never knows where nor when to look for him. He told her: "Unless you can learn to cry when I am not here, I must go away for good." That day he went away and took a room at the Hotel Madrid.

It is this month of separation for the sake of higher principles that has been spoiled not only for Mrs. Braggioni, whose sense of reality is beyond criticism, but for Laura, who feels herself bogged in a nightmare. Tonight Laura envies Mrs. Braggioni, who is alone, and free to weep as much as she pleases about a concrete wrong. Laura has just come from a visit to the prison, and she is waiting for tomorrow with a bitter anxiety as if tomorrow may not come, but time may be caught immovably in this hour, with herself transfixed, Braggioni singing on forever, and Eugenio's body not yet discovered by the guard.

Braggioni says: "Are you going to sleep?" Almost before she can shake her head, he begins telling her about the May-day disturbances coming on in Morelia, for the Catholics hold a festival in honor of the Blessed Virgin, and the Socialists celebrate their martyrs on that day. "There will be two independent processions, starting from either end of town, and they will march until they meet, and the rest depends . . ." He asks her to oil and load his pistols. Standing up, he unbuckles his ammunition belt, and spreads it laden across her knees. Laura sits with the shells slipping through the cleaning cloth dipped in oil, and he says again he cannot understands why she works so hard for the revolutionary idea unless she loves some man who is in it. "Are you not in love with someone?" "No," says Laura. "And no one is in love with you?" "No." "Then it is your own fault. No woman need go begging. Why, what is the matter with you? The legless beggar woman in the Alameda has a perfectly faithful lover. Did you know that?"

Laura peers down the pistol barrel and says nothing, but a long, slow faintness rises and subsides in her; Braggioni curves his swollen fingers around the throat of the guitar and softly smothers the music out of it, and when she hears him again he seems to have forgotten her, and is speaking in the hypnotic voice he uses when talking in small rooms to a listening, close-gathered crowd. Some day this world, now seemingly so composed and eternal, to the edges of every sea shall be merely a tangle of gaping trenches, of crashing walls and broken bodies. Everything must be torn from its accustomed place where it has rotted for centuries, hurled skyward and distributed, cast down again clean as rain, without separate identity. Nothing shall survive that the stiffened hands of poverty have created for the rich and no one shall be left alive except the elect spirits destined to pro-create a new world cleansed of cruelty and injustice, ruled by benevolent anarchy: "Pistols are good, I love them, cannon are even better, but in the end I pin my faith to good dynamite," he concludes, and strokes the pistol lying in her hands. "Once I dreamed of destroying this city, in case it offered resistance to General Ortíz, but it fell into his hands like an overripe pear."

He is made restless by his own words, rises and stands waiting. Laura holds up the belt to him: "Put that on, and go kill somebody in Morelia, and you will be happier," she says softly. The presence of death in the room makes her bold. "Today, I found Eugenio going into a stupor. He re-fused to allow me to call the prison doctor. He had taken all the tablets I brought him yesterday. He said he took them because he was bored."

"He is a fool, and his death is his own business," says Braggioni, fastening his belt carefully.

"I told him if he had waited only a little while longer, you would have got him set free," says Laura. "He said he did not want to wait."

"He is a fool and we are well rid of him," says Braggioni, reaching for his hat.

He goes away. Laura knows his mood has changed, she will not see him any more for a while. He will send word when he needs her to go on errands into strange streets, to speak to the strange faces that will appear, like clay masks with the power of human speech, to mutter their thanks to Braggioni for his help. Now she is free, and she thinks, I must run while there is time. But she does not go.

Braggioni enters his own house where for a month his wife has spent many hours every night weeping and tangling her hair upon her pillow. She is weeping now, and she weeps more at the sight of him, the cause of all her sorrows. He looks about the room. Nothing is changed, the smells are good and familiar, he is well acquainted with the woman who comes toward him with no reproach except grief on her face. He says to her tenderly: "You are so good, please don't cry any more, you dear good creature." She says, "Are you tired, my angel? Sit here and I will wash your feet." She brings a bowl of water, and kneeling, unlaces his shoes, and when from her knees she raises her sad eyes under her blackened lids, he is sorry for everything, and bursts into tears. "Ah, yes, I am hungry, I am tired, let us eat something together," he says, between sobs. His wife leans her head on his arm and says, "Forgive me!" and this time he is refreshed by the solemn, endless rain of her tears.

Laura takes off her serge dress and puts on a white linen nightgown and goes to bed. She turns her head a little to one side, and lying still, reminds herself that it is time to sleep. Numbers tick in her brain like little clocks, soundless doors close of themselves around her. If you would sleep, you must not remember anything, the children will say tomorrow, good morning, my teacher, the poor prisoners who come every day bringing flowers to their jailor. 1-2-3-4-5—it is monstrous to confuse love with revolution, night with day, life with death—ah, Eugenio!

The tolling of the midnight bell is a signal, but what does it mean? Get up, Laura, and follow me: come out of your sleep, out of your bed, out of this strange house. What are you doing in this house? Without a word, without fear she rose and reached for Eugenio's hand, but he eluded her with a sharp, sly smile and drifted away. This is not all, you shall see—Murderer, he said, follow me, I will show you a new country, but it is far away and we must hurry. No, said Laura, not unless you take my hand, no; and she clung first to the stair rail, and then to the topmost branch of the Judas tree that bent down slowly and set her upon the earth, and then to the rocky ledge of a cliff, and then to the jagged wave of a sea that was not water but a desert of crumbling stone. Where are you taking me, she asked in wonder but without fear. To death, and it is a long way off, and we must hurry, said Eugenio. No, said Laura, not unless you take my hand. Then eat these flowers, poor prisoner, said Eugenio in a voice of pity, take and eat: and from the Judas tree he stripped the warm bleeding flowers, and held them to her lips. She saw that his hand was fleshless, a cluster of small white petrified branches, and his eye sockets were without light, but she ate the flowers greedily for they satisfied both hunger and thirst. Murderer! said Eugenio, and Cannibal! This is my body and my blood. Laura cried No! and at the sound of her own voice, she awoke trembling, and was afraid to sleep again.

John Steinbeck

THE RED PONY

AT DAYBREAK Billy Buck emerged from the bunkhouse and stood for a moment on the porch looking up at the sky. He was a broad, bandy-legged little man with a walrus mustache, with square hands, puffed and muscled on the palms. His eyes were a contemplative, watery grey and the hair which protruded from under his Stetson hat was spiky and weathered. Billy was still stuffing his shirt into his blue jeans as he stood on the porch. He unbuckled his belt and tightened it again. The belt showed, by the worn shiny places opposite each hole, the gradual increase of Billy's middle over a period of years. When he had seen to the weather, Billy cleared each nostril by holding its mate closed with his forefinger and blowing fiercely. Then he walked down to the barn, rubbing his hands together. He curried and brushed two saddle horses in the stalls, talking quietly to them all the time; and he had hardly finished when the iron triangle started ringing at the ranch house. Billy stuck the brush and currycomb together and laid them on the rail, and went up to breakfast. His action had been so deliberate and yet so wasteless of time that he came to the house while Mrs. Tiflin was still ringing the triangle. She nodded her grey head to him and withdrew into the kitchen. Billy Buck sat down on the steps, because he was a cow-hand, and it wouldn't be fitting that he should go first into the dining-room. He heard Mr. Tiflin in the house, stamping his feet into his boots.

The high jangling note of the triangle put the boy Jody in motion. He was only a little boy, ten years old, with hair like dusty yellow grass and with shy polite grey eyes, and with a mouth that worked when he thought. The triangle picked him up out of sleep. It didn't occur to him to disobey the harsh note. He never had: no one he knew ever had. He brushed the tangled hair out of his eyes and skinned his nightgown off. In a moment he was dressed—blue chambray shirt and overalls. It was late in the summer, so of course there were no shoes to bother with. In the kitchen he waited until his mother got from in front of the sink and went back to the stove. Then he washed himself and brushed back his wet hair with his fingers. His mother turned sharply on him as he left the sink. Jody looked shyly away.

"I've got to cut your hair before long," his mother said. "Breakfast's on the table. Go on in, so Billy can come."

Jody sat at the long table which was covered with white oilcloth washed through to the fabric in some places. The fried eggs lay in rows on their platter. Jody took three eggs on his plate and followed with three thick slices of crisp bacon. He carefully scraped a spot of blood from one of the egg yolks.

Billy Buck clumped in. "That won't hurt you," Billy explained. "That's only a sign the rooster leaves."

Jody's tall stern father came in then and Jody knew from the noise on the floor that he was wearing boots, but he looked under the table anyway, to make sure. His father turned off the oil lamp over the table, for plenty of morning light now came through the windows.

Jody did not ask where his father and Billy Buck were riding that day, but he wished he might go along. His father was a disciplinarian. Jody obeyed him in everything without questions of any kind. Now, Carl Tiflin sat down and reached for the egg platter.

"Got the cows ready to go, Billy?" he asked.

"In the lower corral," Billy said. "I could just as well take them in alone."

"Sure you could. But a man needs company. Besides your throat gets pretty dry." Carl Tiflin was jovial this morning.

504

Jody's mother put her head in the door. "What time do you think to be back, Carl?"

"I can't tell. I've got to see some men in Salinas. Might be gone till dark."

The eggs and coffee and big biscuits disappeared rapidly. Jody followed the two men out of the house. He watched them mount their horses and drive six old milk cows out of the corral and start over the hill toward Salinas. They were going to sell the old cows to the butcher.

When they had disappeared over the crown of the ridge Jody walked up the hill in back of the house. The dogs trotted around the house corner hunching their shoulders and grinning horribly with pleasure. Jody patted their heads —Doubletree Mutt with the big thick tail and yellow eyes, and Smasher, the shepherd, who had killed a coyote and lost an ear in doing it. Smasher's one good ear stood up higher than a collie's ear should. Billy Buck said that always happened. After the frenzied greeting the dogs lowered their noses to the ground in a businesslike way and went ahead, looking back now and then to make sure that the boy was coming. They walked up through the chicken yard and saw the quail eating with the chickens. Smasher chased the chickens a little to keep in practice in case there should ever be sheep to herd. Jody continued on through the large vegetable patch where the green corn was higher than his head. The cow-pumpkins were green and small yet. He went on to the sagebrush line where the cold spring ran out of its pipe and fell into a round wooden tub. He leaned over and drank close to the green mossy wood where the water tasted best. Then he turned and looked back on the ranch, on the low, whitewashed house girded with red geraniums, and on the long bunkhouse by the cypress tree where Billy Buck lived alone. Jody could see the great black kettle under the cypress tree. That was where the pigs were scalded. The sun was coming over the ridge, now, glaring on the whitewash of the houses and barns, making the wet grass blaze softly. Behind him, in the tall sagebrush, the birds were scampering on the ground, making a great noise among the dry leaves; the squirrels piped shrilly on the side-hills. Jody looked along at the farm buildings. He felt an uncertainty in the air, a feeling of change and of loss and of the gain of new and unfamiliar things. Over the hillside two big black buzzards sailed low to the ground and their shadows slipped smoothly and quickly ahead of them. Some animal had died in the vicinity. Jody knew it. It might be a cow or it might be the remains of a rabbit. The buzzards overlooked nothing. Jody hated them as all decent things hate them, but they could not be hurt because they made away with carrion.

After a while the boy sauntered down hill again. The dogs had long ago given him up and gone into the brush to do things in their own way. Back through the vegetable garden he went, and he paused for a moment to smash a green muskmelon with his heel, but he was not happy about it. It was a bad thing to do, he knew perfectly well. He kicked dirt over the ruined melon to conceal it.

Back at the house his mother bent over his rough hands, inspecting his fingers and nails. It did little good to start him clean to school for too many things could happen on the way. She sighed over the black cracks on his fingers, and then gave him his books and his lunch and started him on the mile walk to school. She noticed that his mouth was working a good deal this morning.

Jody started his journey. He filled his pockets with little pieces of white quartz that lay in the road, and every so often he took a shot at a bird or at some rabbit that had stayed sunning itself in the road too long. At the crossroads over the bridge he met two friends and the three of them walked to school together, making ridiculous strides and being rather silly. School had just opened two weeks before. There was still a spirit of revolt among the pupils.

It was four o'clock in the afternoon when Jody topped

the hill and looked down on the ranch again. He looked for the saddle horses, but the corral was empty. His father was not back yet. He went slowly, then, toward the afternoon chores. At the ranch house, he found his mother sitting on the porch, mending socks.

"There's two doughnuts in the kitchen for you," she said. Jody slid to the kitchen, and returned with half of one of the doughnuts already eaten and his mouth full. His mother asked him what he had learned in school that day, but she didn't listen to his doughnut-muffled answer. She interrupted, "Jody, tonight see you fill the wood-box clear full. Last night you crossed the sticks and it wasn't only about half full. Lay the sticks flat tonight. And Jody, some of the hens are hiding eggs, or else the dogs are eating them. Look about in the grass and see if you can find any nests."

Jody, still eating, went out and did his chores. He saw the quail come down to eat with the chickens when he threw out the grain. For some reason his father was proud to have them come. He never allowed any shooting near the house for fear the quail might go away.

When the wood-box was full, Jody took his twenty-two rifle up to the cold spring at the brush line. He drank again and then aimed the gun at all manner of things, at rocks, at birds on the wing, at the big black pig kettle under the cypress tree, but he didn't shoot for he had no cartridges and wouldn't have until he was twelve. If his father had seen him aim the rifle in the direction of the house he would have put the cartridges off another year. Jody remembered this and did not point the rifle down the hill again. Two years was enough to wait for cartridges. Nearly all of his father's presents were given with reservations which hampered their value somewhat. It was good discipline.

The supper waited until dark for his father to return. When at last he came in with Billy Buck, Jody could smell the delicious brandy on their breaths. Inwardly he rejoiced, for his father sometimes talked to him when he smelled of brandy, sometimes even told things he had done in the wild days when he was a boy.

After supper, Jody sat by the fireplace and his shy polite eyes sought the room corners, and he waited for his father to tell what it was he contained, for Jody knew he had news of some sort. But he was disappointed. His father pointed a stern finger at him.

"You'd better go to bed, Jody. I'm going to need you in the morning."

That wasn't so bad. Jody liked to do the things he had to do as long as they weren't routine things. He looked at the floor and his mouth worked out a question before he spoke it. "What are we going to do in the morning, kill a pig?" he asked softly.

"Never you mind. You better get to bed."

When the door was closed behind him, Jody heard his father and Billy Buck chuckling and he knew it was a joke of some kind. And later, when he lay in bed, trying to make words out of the murmurs in the other room, he heard his father protest, "But, Ruth, I didn't give much for him."

Jody heard the hoot-owls hunting mice down by the barn, and he heard a fruit tree limb tap-tapping against the house. A cow was lowing when he went to sleep.

When the triangle sounded in the morning, Jody dressed more quickly even than usual. In the kitchen, while he washed his face and combed back his hair, his mother addressed him irritably. "Don't you go out until you get a good breakfast in you."

He went into the dining-room and sat at the long white table. He took a steaming hotcake from the platter, arranged two fried eggs on it, covered them with another hotcake and squashed the whole thing with his fork.

His father and Billy Buck came in. Jody knew from the sound on the floor that both of them were wearing flat-heeled shoes, but he peered under the table to make sure.

508

His father turned off the oil lamp, for the day had arrived, and he looked stern and disciplinary, but Billy Buck didn't look at Jody at all. He avoided the shy questioning eyes of the boy and soaked a whole piece of toast in his coffee.

Carl Tiflin said crossly, "You come with us after breakfast!"

Jody had trouble with his food then, for he felt a kind of doom in the air. After Billy had tilted his saucer and drained the coffee which had slopped into it, and had wiped his hands on his jeans, the two men stood up from the table and went out into the morning light together, and Jody respectfully followed a little behind them. He tried to keep his mind from running ahead, tried to keep it absolutely motionless.

His mother called, "Carl! Don't you let it keep him from school."

They marched past the cypress, where a single tree hung from a limb to butcher the pigs on, and past the black iron kettle, so it was not a pig killing. The sun shone over the hill and threw long, dark shadows of the trees and buildings. They crossed a stubble-field to shortcut to the barn. Jody's father unhooked the door and they went in. They had been walking toward the sun on the way down. The barn was black as night in contrast and warm from the hay and from the beasts. Jody's father moved over toward the one box stall. "Come here!" he ordered. Jody could begin to see things now. He looked into the box stall and then stepped back quickly.

A red pony colt was looking at him out of the stall. Its tense ears were forward and a light of disobedience was in its eyes. Its coat was rough and thick as an airedale's fur and its mane was long and tangled. Jody's throat collapsed in on itself and cut his breath short.

"He needs a good currying," his father said, "and if I ever hear of you not feeding him or leaving his stall dirty, I'll sell him off in a minute."

Jody couldn't bear to look at the pony's eyes any more.

509

He gazed down at his hands for a moment, and he asked very shyly, "Mine?" No one answered him. He put his hand out toward the pony. Its grey nose came close, sniffing loudly, and then the lips drew back and the strong teeth closed on Jody's fingers. The pony shook its head up and down and seemed to laugh with amusement. Jody regarded his bruised fingers. "Well," he said with pride—"Well, I guess he can bite all right." The two men laughed, somewhat in relief. Carl Tiflin went out of the barn and walked up a side-hill to be by himself, for he was embarrassed, but Billy Buck stayed. It was easier to talk to Billy Buck. Jody asked again—"Mine?"

Billy became professional in tone. "Sure! That is, if you look out for him and break him right. I'll show you how. He's just a colt. You can't ride him for some time."

Jody put out his bruised hand again, and this time the red pony let his nose be rubbed. "I ought to have a carrot," Jody said. "Where'd we get him, Billy?"

"Bought him at a sheriff's auction," Billy explained. "A show went broke in Salinas and had debts. The sheriff was selling off their stuff."

The pony stretched out his nose and shook the forelock from his wild eyes. Jody stroked the nose a little. He said softly, "There isn't a—saddle?"

Billy Buck laughed. "I'd forgot. Come along."

In the harness room he lifted down a little saddle of red morocco leather. "It's just a show saddle," Billy Buck said disparagingly. "It isn't practical for the brush, but it was cheap at the sale."

Jody couldn't trust himself to look at the saddle either, and he couldn't speak at all. He brushed the shining red leather with his fingertips, and after a long time he said, "It'll look pretty on him though." He thought of the grandest and prettiest things he knew. "If he hasn't a name already, I think I'll call him Gabilan Mountains," he said.

Billy Buck knew how he felt. "It's a pretty long name.

Why don't you just call him Gabilan? That means hawk. That would be a fine name for him." Billy felt glad. "If you will collect tail hair, I might be able to make a hair rope for you sometime. You could use it for a hackamore."

Jody wanted to go back to the box stall. "Could I lead him to school, do you think—to show the kids?"

But Billy shook his head. "He's not even halter-broke yet. We had a time getting him here. Had to almost drag him. You better be starting for school though."

"I'll bring the kids to see him here this afternoon," Jody said.

Six boys came over the hill half an hour early that afternoon, running hard, their heads down, their forearms working, their breath whistling. They swept by the house and cut across the stubble-field to the barn. And then they stood self-consciously before the pony, and then they looked at Jody with eyes in which there was a new admiration and a new respect. Before today Jody had been a boy, dressed in overalls and a blue shirt—quieter than most, even suspected of being a little cowardly. And now he was different. Out of a thousand centuries they drew the ancient admiration of the footman for the horseman. They knew instinctively that a man on a horse is spiritually as well as physically bigger than a man on foot. They knew that Jody had been miraculously lifted out of equality with them, and had been placed over them. Gabilan put his head out of the stall and sniffed them.

"Why'n't you ride him?" the boys cried. "Why'n't you braid his tail with ribbons like in the fair?" "When you going to ride him?"

Jody's courage was up. He too felt the superiority of the horseman. "He's not old enough. Nobody can ride him for a long time. I'm going to train him on the long halter. Billy Buck is going to show me how."

"Well, can't we even lead him around a little?"

"He isn't even halter-broke," Jody said. He wanted to be completely alone when he took the pony out the first time. "Come and see the saddle."

They were speechless at the red morocco saddle, completely shocked out of comment. "It isn't much use in the brush," Jody explained. "It'll look pretty on him though. Maybe I'll ride bareback when I go into the brush."

"How you going to rope a cow without a saddle horn?"

"Maybe I'll get another saddle for every day. My father might want me to help him with the stock." He let them feel the red saddle, and showed them the brass chain throat-latch on the bridle and the big brass buttons at each temple where the headstall and brow band crossed. The whole thing was too wonderful. They had to go away after a little while, and each boy, in his mind, searched among his possessions for a bribe worthy of offering in return for a ride on the red pony when the time should come.

Jody was glad when they had gone. He took brush and currycomb from the wall, took down the barrier of the box stall and stepped cautiously in. The pony's eyes glittered, and he edged around into kicking position. But Jody touched him on the shoulder and rubbed his high arched neck as he had always seen Billy Buck do, and he crooned, "So-o-o Boy," in a deep voice. The pony gradually relaxed his tenseness. Jody curried and brushed until a pile of dead hair lay in the stall and until the pony's coat had taken on a deep red shine. Each time he finished he thought it might have been done better. He braided the mane into a dozen little pigtails, and he braided the forelock, and then he undid them and brushed the hair out straight again.

Jody did not hear his mother enter the barn. She was angry when she came, but when she looked in at the pony and at Jody working over him, she felt a curious pride rise up in her. "Have you forgot the wood-box?" she asked gently. "It's not far off from dark and there's not a stick of wood in the house, and the chickens aren't fed."

Jody quickly put up his tools. "I forgot, ma'am."

"Well, after this do your chores first. Then you won't forget. I expect you'll forget lots of things now if I don't keep an eye on you."

"Can I have carrots from the garden for him, ma'am?"

She had to think about that. "Oh—I guess so, if you only take the big tough ones."

"Carrots keep the coat good," he said, and again she felt the curious rush of pride.

Jody never waited for the triangle to get him out of bed after the coming of the pony. It became his habit to creep out of bed even before his mother was awake, to slip into his clothes and to go quietly down to the barn to see Gabilan. In the grey quiet mornings when the land and the brush and the houses and the trees were silver-grey and black like a photograph negative, he stole toward the barn, past the sleeping stones and the sleeping cypress tree. The turkeys, roosting in the tree out of coyotes' reach, clicked drowsily. The fields glowed with a grey frost-like light and in the dew the tracks of rabbits and of field mice stood out sharply. The good dogs came stiffly out of their little houses, hackles up and deep growls in their throats. Then they caught Jody's scent, and their stiff tails rose up and waved a greeting— Doubletree Mutt with the big thick tail, and Smasher, the incipient shepherd—then went lazily back to their warm beds.

It was a strange time and a mysterious journey, to Jody— an extension of a dream. When he first had the pony he liked to torture himself during the trip by thinking Gabilan would not be in his stall, and worse, would never have been there. And he had other delicious little self-induced pains. He thought how the rats had gnawed ragged holes in the red saddle, and how the mice had nibbled Gabilan's tail until it was stringy and thin. He usually ran the last little way to the barn. He unlatched the rusty hasp of the barn door and stepped in, and no matter how quietly he opened the door, Gabilan was always looking at him over the barrier of the box stall and Gabilan whinnied softly and stamped his front foot, and his eyes had big sparks of red fire in them like oakwood embers.

Sometimes, if the work horses were to be used that day, Jody found Billy Buck in the barn harnessing and currying. Billy stood with him and looked long at Gabilan and he told Jody a great many things about horses. He explained that they were terribly afraid for their feet, so that one must make a practice of lifting the legs and patting the hooves and ankles to remove their terror. He told Jody how horses love conversation. He must talk to the pony all the time, and tell him the reasons for everything. Billy wasn't sure a horse could understand everything that was said to him, but it was impossible to say how much was understood. A horse never kicked up a fuss if some one he liked explained things to him. Billy could give examples, too. He had known, for instance, a horse nearly dead beat with fatigue to perk up when told it was only a little farther to his destination. And he had known a horse paralyzed with fright to come out of it when his rider told him what it was that was frightening him. While he talked in the mornings, Billy Buck cut twenty or thirty straws into neat three-inch lengths and stuck them into his hatband. Then during the whole day, if he wanted to pick his teeth or merely to chew on something, he had only to reach up for one of them.

Jody listened carefully, for he knew and the whole country knew that Billy Buck was a fine hand with horses. Billy's own horse was a stringy cayuse with a hammer head, but he nearly always won the first prizes at the stock trials. Billy could rope a steer, take a double half-hitch about the horn with his riata, and dismount, and his horse would play the steer as an angler plays a fish, keeping a tight rope until the steer was down or beaten.

Every morning, after Jody had curried and brushed the

pony, he let down the barrier of the stall, and Gabilan thrust past him and raced down the barn and into the corral. Around and around he galloped, and sometimes he jumped forward and landed on stiff legs. He stood quivering, stiff ears forward, eyes rolling so that the whites showed, pretending to be frightened. At last he walked snorting to the water-trough and buried his nose in the water up to the nostrils. Jody was proud then, for he knew that was the way to judge a horse. Poor horses only touched their lips to the water, but a fine spirited beast put his whole nose and mouth under, and only left room to breathe.

Then Jody stood and watched the pony, and he saw things he had never noticed about any other horse, the sleek, sliding flank muscles and the cords of the buttocks, which flexed like a closing fist, and the shine the sun put on the red coat. Having seen horses all his life, Jody had never looked at them very closely before. But now he noticed the moving ears which gave expression and even inflection of expression to the face. The pony talked with his ears. You could tell exactly how he felt about everything by the way his ears pointed. Sometimes they were stiff and upright and sometimes lax and sagging. They went back when he was angry or fearful, and forward when he was anxious and curious and pleased; and their exact position indicated which emotion he had.

Billy Buck kept his word. In the early fall the training began. First there was the halter-breaking, and that was the hardest because it was the first thing. Jody held a carrot and coaxed and promised and pulled on the rope. The pony set his feet like a burro when he felt the strain. But before long he learned. Jody walked all over the ranch leading him. Gradually he took to dropping the rope until the pony followed him unled wherever he went.

And then came the training on the long halter. That was slower work. Jody stood in the middle of a circle, holding

515

the long halter. He clucked with his tongue and the pony started to walk in a big circle, held in by the long rope. He clucked again to make the pony trot, and again to make him gallop. Around and around Gabilan went thundering and enjoying it immensely. Then he called, "Whoa," and the pony stopped. It was not long until Gabilan was perfect at it. But in many ways he was a bad pony. He bit Jody in the pants and stomped on Jody's feet. Now and then his ears went back and he aimed a tremendous kick at the boy. Every time he did one of these bad things, Gabilan settled back and seemed to laugh to himself.

Billy Buck worked at the hair rope in the evenings before the fireplace. Jody collected tail hair in a bag, and he sat and watched Billy slowly constructing the rope, twisting a few hairs to make a string and rolling two strings together for a cord, and then braiding a number of cords to make the rope. Billy rolled the finished rope on the floor under his foot to make it round and hard.

The long halter work rapidly approached perfection. Jody's father, watching the pony stop and start and trot and gallop, was a little bothered by it.

"He's getting to be almost a trick pony," he complained. "I don't like trick horses. It takes all the—dignity out of a horse to make him do tricks. Why, a trick horse is kind of like an actor—no dignity, no character of his own." And his father said, "I guess you better be getting him used to the saddle pretty soon."

Jody rushed for the harness-room. For some time he had been riding the saddle on a sawhorse. He changed the stirrup length over and over, and could never get it just right. Sometimes, mounted on the sawhorse in the harness-room, with collars and hames and tugs hung all about him, Jody rode out beyond the room. He carried his rifle across the pommel. He saw the fields go flying by, and he heard the beat of the galloping hoofs.

516

It was a ticklish job, saddling the pony the first time. Gabilan hunched and reared and threw the saddle off before the cinch could be tightened. It had to be replaced again and again until at last the pony let it stay. And the cinching was difficult, too. Day by day Jody tightened the girth a little more until at last the pony didn't mind the saddle at all.

Then there was the bridle. Billy explained how to use a stick of licorice for a bit until Gabilan was used to having something in his mouth. Billy explained, "Of course we could force-break him to everything, but he wouldn't be as good a horse if we did. He'd always be a little bit afraid, and he wouldn't mind because he wanted to."

The first time the pony wore the bridle he whipped his head about and worked his tongue against the bit until the blood oozed from the corners of his mouth. He tried to rub the headstall off on the manger. His ears pivoted about and his eyes turned red with fear and with general rambunctiousness. Jody rejoiced, for he knew that only a mean-souled horse does not resent training.

And Jody trembled when he thought of the time when he would first sit in the saddle. The pony would probably throw him off. There was no disgrace in that. The disgrace would come if he did not get right up and mount again. Sometimes he dreamed that he lay in the dirt and cried and couldn't make himself mount again. The shame of the dream lasted until the middle of the day.

Gabilan was growing fast. Already he had lost the long-leggedness of the colt; his mane was getting longer and blacker. Under the constant currying and brushing his coat lay as smooth and gleaming as orange-red lacquer. Jody oiled the hoofs and kept them carefully trimmed so they would not crack.

The hair rope was nearly finished. Jody's father gave him an old pair of spurs and bent in the side bars and cut down the strap and took up the chainlets until they fitted. And then one day Carl Tiflin said:

"The pony's growing faster than I thought. I guess you can ride him by Thanksgiving. Think you can stick on?"

"I don't know," Jody said shyly. Thanksgiving was only three weeks off. He hoped it wouldn't rain, for rain would spot the red saddle.

Gabilan knew and liked Jody by now. He nickered when Jody came across the stubble-field, and in the pasture he came running when his master whistled for him. There was always a carrot for him every time.

Billy Buck gave him riding instructions over and over. "Now when you get up there, just grab tight with your knees and keep your hands away from the saddle, and if you get throwed, don't let that stop you. No matter how good a man is, there's always some horse can pitch him. You just climb up again before he gets to feeling smart about it. Pretty soon, he won't throw you no more, and pretty soon he can't throw you no more. That's the way to do it."

"I hope it don't rain before," Jody said.

"Why not? Don't want to get throwed in the mud?"

That was partly it, and also he was afraid that in the flurry of bucking Gabilan might slip and fall on him and break his leg or his hip. He had seen that happen to men before, had seen how they writhed on the ground like squashed bugs, and he was afraid of it.

He practiced on the sawhorse how he would hold the reins in his left hand and a hat in his right hand. If he kept his hands thus busy, he couldn't grab the horn if he felt himself going off. He didn't like to think of what would happen if he did grab the horn. Perhaps his father and Billy Buck would never speak to him again, they would be so ashamed. The news would get about and his mother would be ashamed too. And in the school yard—it was too awful to contemplate.

He began putting his weight in a stirrup when Gabilan was saddled, but he didn't throw his leg over the pony's back. That was forbidden until Thanksgiving.

518

Every afternoon he put the red saddle on the pony and cinched it tight. The pony was learning already to fill his stomach out unnaturally large while the cinching was going on, and then to let it down when the straps were fixed. Sometimes Jody led him up to the brush line and let him drink from the round green tub, and sometimes he led him up through the stubble-field to the hilltop from which it was possible to see the white town of Salinas and the geometric fields of the great valley, and the oak trees clipped by the sheep. Now and then they broke through the brush and came to little cleared circles so hedged in that the world was gone and only the sky and the circle of brush were left from the old life. Gabilan liked these trips and showed it by keeping his head very high and by quivering his nostrils with interest. When the two came back from an expedition they smelled of the sweet sage they had forced through.

Time dragged on toward Thanksgiving, but winter came fast. The clouds swept down and hung all day over the land and brushed the hilltops, and the winds blew shrilly at night. All day the dry oak leaves drifted down from the trees until they covered the ground, and yet the trees were unchanged.

Jody had wished it might not rain before Thanksgiving, but it did. The brown earth turned dark and the trees glistened. The cut ends of the stubble turned black with mildew; the haystacks grayed from exposure to the damp, and on the roofs the moss, which had been all summer as gray as lizards, turned a brilliant yellow-green. During the week of rain, Jody kept the pony in the box stall out of the dampness, except for a little time after school when he took him out for exercise and to drink at the water-trough in the upper corral. Not once did Gabilan get wet.

The wet weather continued until little new grass appeared. Jody walked to school dressed in a slicker and short rubber boots. At length one morning the sun came out brightly. Jody, at his work in the box stall, said to Billy

Buck, "Maybe I'll leave Gabilan in the corral when I go to school today."

"Be good for him to be out in the sun," Billy assured him. "No animal likes to be cooped up too long. Your father and me are going back on the hill to clean the leaves out of the spring." Billy nodded and picked his teeth with one of his little straws.

"If the rain comes, though—" Jody suggested.

"Not likely to rain today. She's rained herself out." Billy pulled up his sleeves and snapped his arm bands. "If it comes on to rain—why a little rain don't hurt a horse."

"Well, if it does come on to rain, you put him in, will you, Billy? I'm scared he might get cold so I couldn't ride him when the time comes."

"Oh sure! I'll watch out for him if we get back in time. But it won't rain today."

And so Jody, when he went to school, left Gabilan standing out in the corral.

Billy Buck wasn't wrong about many things. He couldn't be. But he was wrong about the weather that day, for a little after noon the clouds pushed over the hills and began to pour down. Jody heard it start on the schoolhouse roof. He considered holding up one finger for permission to go to the outhouse and, once outside, running for home to put the pony in. Punishment would be prompt both at school and at home. He gave it up and took ease from Billy's assurance that rain couldn't hurt a horse. When school was finally out, he hurried home through the dark rain. The banks at the sides of the road spouted little jets of muddy water. The rain slanted and swirled under a cold and gusty wind. Jody dog-trotted home, slopping through the gravelly mud of the road.

From the top of the ridge he could see Gabilan standing miserably in the corral. The red coat was almost black, and streaked with water. He stood head down with his rump to the rain and wind. Jody arrived running and threw open the

520

barn door and led the wet pony in by his forelock. Then he found a gunny sack and rubbed the soaked hair and rubbed the legs and ankles. Gabilan stood patiently, but he trembled in gusts like the wind.

When he had dried the pony as well as he could, Jody went up to the house and brought hot water down to the barn and soaked the grain in it. Gabilan was not very hungry. He nibbled at the hot mash, but he was not very much interested in it, and he still shivered now and then. A little steam rose from his damp back.

It was almost dark when Billy Buck and Carl Tiflin came home. "When the rain started we put up at Ben Herche's place, and the rain never let up all afternoon," Carl Tiflin explained. Jody looked reproachfully at Billy Buck and Billy felt guilty.

"You said it wouldn't rain," Jody accused him.

Billy looked away. "It's hard to tell, this time of year," he said, but his excuse was lame. He had no right to be fallible, and he knew it.

"The pony got wet, got soaked through."

"Did you dry him off?"

"I rubbed him with a sack and I gave him hot grain."

Billy nodded in agreement.

"Do you think he'll take cold, Billy?"

"A little rain never hurt anything," Billy assured him.

Jody's father joined the conversation then and lectured the boy a little. "A horse," he said, "isn't any lap-dog kind of thing." Carl Tiflin hated weakness and sickness, and he held a violent contempt for helplessness.

Jody's mother put a platter of steaks on the table and boiled potatoes and boiled squash, which clouded the room with their steam. They sat down to eat, Carl Tiflin still grumbled about weakness put into animals and men by too much coddling.

Billy Buck felt bad about his mistake. "Did you blanket him?" he asked.

"No. I couldn't find any blanket. I laid some sacks over his back."

"We'll go down and cover him up after we eat, then." Billy felt better about it then. When Jody's father had gone in to the fire and his mother was washing dishes, Billy found and lighted a lantern. He and Jody walked through the mud to the barn. The barn was dark and warm and sweet. The horses still munched their evening hay. "You hold the lantern!" Billy ordered. And he felt the pony's legs and tested the heat of the flanks. He put his cheek against the pony's grey muzzle and then he rolled up the eyelids to look at the eyeballs and he lifted the lips to see the gums, and he put his fingers inside the ears. "He don't seem so chipper," Billy said. "I'll give him a rub-down."

Then Billy found a sack and rubbed the pony's legs violently and he rubbed the chest and the withers. Gabilan was strangely spiritless. He submitted patiently to the rubbing. At last Billy brought an old cotton comforter from the saddle-room, and threw it over the pony's back and tied it at neck and chest with string.

"Now he'll be all right in the morning," Billy said.

Jody's mother looked up when he got back to the house. "You're late up from bed," she said. She held his chin in her hard hand and brushed the tangled hair out of his eyes and she said, "Don't worry about the pony. He'll be all right. Billy's as good as any horse doctor in the country."

Jody hadn't known she could see his worry. He pulled gently away from her and knelt down in front of the fireplace until it burned his stomach. He scorched himself through and then went in to bed, but it was a hard thing to go to sleep. He awakened after what seemed a long time. The room was dark but there was a greyness in the window like that which precedes the dawn. He got up and found his overalls and searched for the legs, and then the clock in the other room struck two. He laid his clothes down and got back into bed. It was broad daylight when he awakened again. For the first time he had slept through the ringing of the triangle. He leaped up, flung on his clothes and went out of the door still buttoning his shirt. His mother looked after him for a moment and then went quietly back to her work. Her eyes were brooding and kind. Now and then her mouth smiled a little but without changing her eyes at all.

Jody ran on toward the barn. Halfway there he heard the sound he dreaded, the hollow rasping cough of a horse. He broke into a sprint then. In the barn he found Billy Buck with the pony. Billy was rubbing its legs with his strong thick hands. He looked up and smiled gaily. "He just took a little cold," Billy said. "We'll have him out of it in a couple of days."

Jody looked at the pony's face. The eyes were half closed and the lids thick and dry. In the eye corners a crust of hard mucus stuck. Gabilan's ears hung loosely sideways and his head was low. Jody put out his hand, but the pony did not move close to it. He coughed again and his whole body constricted with the effort. A little stream of thin fluid ran from his nostrils.

Jody looked back at Billy Buck. "He's awful sick, Billy."

"Just a little cold, like I said," Billy insisted. "You go get some breakfast and then go back to school. I'll take care of him."

"But you might have to do something else. You might leave him."

"No, I won't. I won't leave him at all. Tomorrow's Saturday. Then you can stay with him all day." Billy had failed again, and he felt badly about it. He had to cure the pony now.

Jody walked up to the house and took his place listlessly at the table. The eggs and bacon were cold and greasy, but he didn't notice it. He ate his usual amount. He didn't even ask to stay home from school. His mother pushed his hair back when she took his plate. "Billy'll take care of the pony," she assured him.

He moped through the whole day at school. He couldn't answer any questions nor read any words. He couldn't even tell anyone the pony was sick, for that might make him sicker. And when school was finally out he started home in dread. He walked slowly and let the other boys leave him. He wished he might continue walking and never arrive at the ranch.

Billy was in the barn, as he had promised, and the pony was worse. His eyes were almost closed now, and his breath whistled shrilly past an obstruction in his nose. A film covered that part of the eyes that was visible at all. It was doubtful whether the pony could see any more. Now and then he snorted, to clear his nose, and by the action seemed to plug it tighter. Jody looked dispiritedly at the pony's coat. The hair lay rough and unkempt and seemed to have lost all of its old luster. Billy stood quietly beside the stall. Jody hated to ask, but he had to know.

"Billy, is he—is he going to get well?"

Billy put his fingers between the bars under the pony's jaw and felt about. "Feel here," he said and he guided Jody's fingers to a large lump under the jaw. "When that gets bigger, I'll open it up and then he'll get better."

Jody looked quickly away, for he had heard about that lump. "What is the matter with him?"

Billy didn't want to answer, but he had to. He couldn't be wrong three times. "Strangles," he said shortly, "but don't you worry about that. I'll pull him out of it. I've seen them get well when they were worse than Gabilan is. I'm going to steam him now. You can help."

"Yes," Jody said miserably. He followed Billy into the grain room and watched him make the steaming bag ready. It was a long canvas nose bag with straps to go over a horse's ears. Billy filled it one-third full of bran and then he added a couple of handfuls of dried hops. On top of the dry substance he poured a little carbolic acid and a little turpentine. "I'll be mixing it all up while you run to the house for a kettle of boiling water," Billy said.

When Jody came back with the steaming kettle, Billy buckled the straps over Gabilan's head and fitted the bag tightly around his nose. Then through a little hole in the side of the bag he poured the boiling water on the mixture. The pony started away as a cloud of strong steam rose up, but then the soothing fumes crept through his nose and into his lungs, and the sharp steam began to clear out the nasal passages. He breathed loudly. His legs trembled in an ague, and his eyes closed against the biting cloud. Billy poured in more water and kept the steam rising for fifteen minutes. At last he set down the kettle and took the bag from Gabilan's nose. The pony looked better. He breathed freely, and his eyes were open wider than they had been.

"See how good it makes him feel," Billy said. "Now we'll wrap him up in the blanket again. Maybe he'll be nearly well by morning."

"I'll stay with him tonight," Jody suggested.

"No. Don't you do it. I'll bring my blankets down here and put them in the hay. You can stay tomorrow and steam him if he needs it."

The evening was falling when they went to the house for their supper. Jody didn't even realize that some one else had fed the chickens and filled the wood-box. He walked up past the house to the dark brush line and took a drink of water from the tub. The spring water was so cold that it stung his mouth and drove a shiver through him. The sky above the hills was still light. He saw a hawk flying so high that it caught the sun on its breast and shone like a spark. Two blackbirds were driving him down the sky, glittering as they attacked their enemy. In the west, the clouds were moving in to rain again.

Jody's father didn't speak at all while the family ate supper, but after Billy Buck had taken his blankets and gone to sleep in the barn, Carl Tiflin built a high fire in the fireplace and told stories. He told about the wild man, who ran naked through the country and had a tail and ears like a horse, and he told about the rabbit-cats of Moro Cojo that hopped into the trees for birds. He revived the famous Maxwell brothers who found a vein of gold and hid the traces of it so carefully that they could never find it again.

Jody sat with his chin in his hands; his mouth worked nervously, and his father gradually became aware that he wasn't listening very carefully. "Isn't that funny?" he asked.

Jody laughed politely and said, "Yes, sir." His father was angry and hurt, then. He didn't tell any more stories. After a while, Jody took a lantern and went down to the barn. Billy Buck was asleep in the hay, and, except that his breath rasped a little in his lungs, the pony seemed to be much better. Jody stayed a little while, running his fingers over the rough red coat, and then he took up the lantern and went back to the house. When he was in bed, his mother came into the room.

"Have you enough covers on? It's getting winter."

"Yes, ma'am."

"Well, get some rest tonight." She hesitated to go out, stood uncertainly. "The pony will be all right," she said.

Jody was tired. He went to sleep quickly and didn't awaken until dawn. The triangle sounded, and Billy Buck came up from the barn before Jody could get out of the house.

"How is he?" Jody demanded.

Billy always wolfed his breakfast. "Pretty good. I'm going to open that lump this morning. Then he'll be better maybe."

After breakfast, Billy got out his best knife, one with a needle point. He whetted the shining blade a long time on a little carborundum stone. He tried the point and the blade

526

again and again on his calloused thumb-ball, and at last he tried it on his upper lip.

On the way to the barn, Jody noticed how the young grass was up and how the stubble was melting day by day into the new green crop of volunteer. It was a cold sunny morning.

As soon as he saw the pony, Jody knew he was worse. His eyes were closed and sealed shut with dried mucus. His head hung so low that his nose almost touched the straw of his bed. There was a little groan in each breath, a deep-seated, patient groan.

Billy lifted the weak head and made a quick slash with the knife. Jody saw the yellow pus run out. He held up the head while Billy swabbed out the wound with weak carbolic acid salve.

"Now he'll feel better," Billy assured him. "That yellow poison is what makes him sick."

Jody looked unbelieving at Billy Buck. "He's awful sick."

Billy thought a long time what to say. He nearly tossed off a careless assurance, but he saved himself in time. "Yes, he's pretty sick," he said at last. "I've seen worse ones get well. If he doesn't get pneumonia, we'll pull him through. You stay with him. If he gets worse, you can come and get me."

For a long time after Billy went away, Jody stood beside the pony, stroking him behind the ears. The pony didn't flip his head the way he had done when he was well. The groaning in his breathing was becoming more hollow.

Doubletree Mutt looked into the barn, his big tail waving provocatively, and Jody was so incensed at his health that he found a hard block clod on the floor and deliberately threw it. Doubletree Mutt went yelping away to nurse a bruised paw.

In the middle of the morning, Billy Buck came back and made another steam bag. Jody watched to see whether the pony improved this time as he had before. His breathing eased a little, but he did not raise his head.

The Saturday dragged on. Late in the afternoon Jody went to the house and brought his bedding down and made up a place to sleep in the hay. He didn't ask permission. He knew from the way his mother looked at him that she would let him do almost anything. That night he left a lantern burning on a wire over the box stall. Billy had told him to rub the pony's legs every little while.

At nine o'clock the wind sprang up and howled around the barn. And in spite of his worry, Jody grew sleepy. He got into his blankets and went to sleep, but the breathy groans of the pony sounded in his dreams. And in his sleep he heard a crashing noise which went on and on until it awakened him. The wind was rushing through the barn. He sprang up and looked down the lane of stalls. The barn door had blown open, and the pony was gone.

He caught the lantern and ran outside into the gale, and he saw Gabilan weakly shambling away into the darkness, head down, legs working slowly and mechanically. When Jody ran up and caught him by the forelock, he allowed himself to be led back and put into his stall. His groans were louder, and a fierce whistling came from his nose. Jody didn't sleep any more then. The hissing of the pony's breath grew louder and sharper.

He was glad when Billy Buck came in at dawn. Billy looked for a time at the pony as though he had never seen him before. He felt the ears and flanks. "Jody," he said, "I've got to do something you won't want to see. You run up to the house for a while."

Jody grabbed him fiercely by the forearm. "You're not going to shoot him?"

Billy patted his hand. "No. I'm going to open a little hole in his windpipe so he can breathe. His nose is filled up. When he gets well, we'll put a little brass button in the hole for him to breathe through."

528

Jody couldn't have gone away if he had wanted to. It was awful to see the red hide cut, but infinitely more terrible to know it was being cut and not to see it. "I'll stay right here," he said bitterly. "You sure you got to?"

"Yes. I'm sure. If you stay, you can hold his head. If it doesn't make you sick, that is."

The fine knife came out again and was whetted again just as carefully as it had been for the first time. Jody held the pony's head up and the throat taut, while Billy felt up and down for the right place. Jody sobbed once as the bright knife point disappeared into the throat. The pony plunged weakly away and then stood still, trembling violently. The blood ran thickly out and up the knife and across Billy's hand and into his shirtsleeve. The sure square hand sawed out a round hole in the flesh, and the breath came bursting out of the hole, throwing a fine spray of blood. With the rush of oxygen, the pony took a sudden strength. He lashed out with his hind feet and tried to rear, but Jody held his head down while Billy mopped the new wound with carbolic salve. It was a good job. The blood stopped flowing and the air puffed out the hole and sucked it in regularly with a little bubbling noise.

The rain brought in by the night wind began to fall on the barn roof. Then the triangle rang for breakfast. "You go up and eat while I wait," Billy said. "We've got to keep this hole from plugging up."

Jody walked slowly out of the barn. He was too dispirited to tell Billy how the barn door had blown open and let the pony out. He emerged into the wet grey morning and sloshed up to the house, taking a perverse pleasure in splashing through all the puddles. His mother fed him and put dry clothes on. She didn't question him. She seemed to know he couldn't answer questions. But when he was ready to go back to the barn she brought him a pan of steaming meal. "Give him this," she said.

But Jody did not take the pan. He said, "He won't eat

anything," and ran out of the house. At the barn, Billy showed him how to fix a ball of cotton on a stick, with which to swab out the breathing hole when it became clogged with mucus.

Jody's father walked into the barn and stood with them in front of the stall. At length he turned to the boy. "Hadn't you better come with me? I'm going to drive over the hill." Jody shook his head. "You better come on, out of this," the father insisted.

Billy turned on him angrily. "Let him alone. It's his pony, isn't it?"

Carl Tiflin walked away without saying another word. His feelings were badly hurt.

All morning Jody kept the wound open and the air passing in and out freely. At noon the pony lay wearily down on his side and stretched his nose out.

Billy came back. "If you're going to stay with him tonight, you better take a little nap," he said. Jody went absently out of the barn. The sky had cleared to a hard thin blue. Everywhere the birds were busy with worms that had come to the damp surface of the ground.

Jody walked to the brush line and sat on the edge of the mossy tub. He looked down at the house and at the old bunkhouse and at the dark cypress tree. The place was familiar, but curiously changed. It wasn't itself any more, but a frame for things that were happening. A cold wind blew out of the east now, signifying that the rain was over for a little while. At his feet Jody could see the little arms of new weeds spreading out over the ground. In the mud about the spring were thousands of quail tracks.

Doubletree Mutt came sideways and embarrassed up through the vegetable patch, and Jody, remembering how he had thrown the clod, put his arm about the dog's neck and kissed him on his wide black nose. Doubletree Mutt sat still, as though he knew some solemn thing was happening. His big tail slapped the ground gravely. Jody pulled a

530

swollen tick out of Mutt's neck and popped it dead between his thumb-nails. It was a nasty thing. He washed his hands in the cold spring water.

Except for the steady swish of the wind, the farm was very quiet. Jody knew his mother wouldn't mind if he didn't go in to eat his lunch. After a little while he went slowly back to the barn. Mutt crept into his own little house and whined softly to himself for a long time.

Billy Buck stood up from the box and surrendered the cotton swab. The pony still lay on his side and the wound in his throat bellowsed in and out. When Jody saw how dry and dead the hair looked, he knew at last that there was no hope for the pony. He had seen the dead hair before on dogs and on cows, and it was a sure sign. He sat heavily on the box and let down the barrier of the box stall. For a long time he kept his eyes on the moving wound, and at last he dozed, and the afternoon passed quickly. Just before dark his mother brought a deep dish of stew and left it for him and went away. Jody ate a little of it, and, when it was dark, he set the lantern on the floor by the pony's head so he could watch the wound and keep it open. And he dozed again until the night chill awakened him. The wind was blowing fiercely, bringing the north cold with it. Jody brought a blanket from his bed in the hay and wrapped himself in it. Gabilan's breathing was quiet at last; the hole in his throat moved gently. The owls flew through the hayloft, shrieking and looking for mice. Jody put his hands down on his head and slept. In his sleep he was aware that the wind had increased. He heard it slamming about the barn.

It was daylight when he awakened. The barn door had swung open. The pony was gone. He sprang up and ran out into the morning light.

The pony's tracks were plain enough, dragging through the frostlike dew on the young grass, tired tracks with little lines between them where the hoofs had dragged. They

531

headed for the brush line halfway up the ridge. Jody broke into a run and followed them. The sun shone on the sharp white quartz that stuck through the ground here and there. As he followed the plain trail, a shadow fell across in front of him. He looked up and saw a high circle of black buzzards, and the slowly revolving circle dropped lower and lower. The solemn birds soon disappeared over the ridge. Jody ran faster then, forced on by panic and rage. The trail entered the brush at last and followed a winding route among the tall sage bushes.

At the top of the ridge Jody was winded. He paused, puffing noisily. The blood pounded in his ears. Then he saw what he was looking for. Below, in one of the little clearings in the brush, lay the red pony. In the distance, Jody could see the legs moving slowly and convulsively. And in a circle around him stood the buzzards, waiting for the moment of death they knew so well.

Jody leaned forward and plunged down the hill. The wet ground muffled his steps and the brush hid him. When he arrived, it was all over. The first buzzard sat on the pony's head and its beak had just risen dripping with dark eye fluid. Jody plunged into the circle like a cat. The black brotherhood arose in a cloud, but the big one on the pony's head was too late. As it hopped along to take off, Jody caught its wing tip and pulled it down. It was nearly as big as he was. The free wing crashed into his face with the force of a club, but he hung on. The claws fastened on his leg and the wing elbows battered his head on either side. Jody groped blindly with his free hand. His fingers found the neck of the struggling bird. The red eyes looked into his face, calm and fearless and fierce; the naked head turned from side to side. Then the beak opened and vomited a stream of putrefied fluid. Jody brought up his knee and fell on the great bird. He held the neck to the ground with one hand while his other found a piece of sharp white quartz. The first blow broke the beak sideways and black blood spurted from the twisted,

532

leathery mouth corners. He struck again but missed. The red fearless eyes still looked at him, impersonal and unafraid and detached. He struck again and again, until the buzzard lay dead, until its head was a red pulp. He was still beating the dead bird when Billy Buck pulled him off and held him tightly to calm his shaking.

Carl Tiflin wiped the blood from the boy's face with a red bandana. Jody was limp and quiet now. His father moved the buzzard with his toe. "Jody," he explained, "the buzzard didn't kill the pony. Don't you know that?"

"I know it," Jody said wearily.

It was Billy Buck who was angry. He had lifted Jody in his arms, and had turned to carry him home. But he turned back on Carl Tiflin. "Course he knows it," Billy said furiously, "Jesus Christ! man, can't you see how he'd feel about it?"

BIOGRAPHICAL NOTES

Léonie Adams. Born in Brooklyn, New York, November 9, 1899. Educated at Barnard College, where she wrote her first poetry. Guggenheim Fellow, 1928-1930. Author of two distinguished volumes of poetry: *Those Not Elect* and *High Falcon.*

Conrad Aiken. Born in Savannah, Georgia, in 1889. Educated at Harvard University. One of the most versatile and prolific writers of his time. Author of many books, including *Priapus and the Pool*, 1925; *The Blue Voyage* (novel), 1929; *John Deth and other Poems*, 1930; *Time in the Rock*, 1936. Awarded the Pulitzer Prize for Poetry in 1929.

Sherwood Anderson. Born in Camden, Ohio, September 13, 1876. Had little formal education. Sold papers, mowed lawns, worked as a stable-boy on race-courses and later became an advertising copy-writer. His first novel, *Windy McPherson's Son*, was published in 1916. *Winesburg, Ohio*, 1919, made him famous. He is also the author of: *Poor White*, 1920; *Many Marriages*, 1923; *Dark Laughter*, 1925 and a volume of short stories, which are impressions from American life, *The Triumph of the Egg*, 1921. He died March 8, 1941.

Stephen Vincent Benét. Born July 22, 1898, in Bethlehem, Pennsylvania. Attended Summerville Academy and was graduated from Yale in 1919. Author of: *The Ballad of William Sycamore*, 1923; the long poem, *John Brown's Body*, 1929, and four novels, including *The Beginning of Wisdom*, 1921, and *Spanish Bayonet*, 1926. The short story, "The Devil and Daniel Webster," has been made into an opera which had its world premiere in New York on May 19, 1939.

534

John Peale Bishop. Born in Charles Town, West Virginia, in 1891. Attended Mercersburg Academy and graduated from Princeton in 1917. After the World War he became managing editor of Vanity Fair. In 1922 he and his wife went abroad and settled in an old country house on the outskirts of Paris. Among their friends in the expatriate group were Ernest Hemingway, Scott Fitzgerald and Archibald MacLeish. Since returning to this country Bishop has made his home on Cape Cod. Author of: *Many Thousands Gone* (stories), 1932; *Now With His Son* (poems), 1932; *Act of Darkness* (novel), 1935; *Minute Particulars* (poems), 1936; *Selected Poems,* 1941.

R. P. Blackmur. Born in Springfield, Massachusetts, in 1904. One of the most scrupulous critics in America. One of the Editors of the Hound and Horn; has contributed essays and verse to critical journals. Author of two books of criticism, *The Double Agent,* 1934; and *The Expense of Greatness,* 1940; and two books of poetry, *From Jordan's Delight,* 1937, and *The Second World,* 1942. He is now teaching at Princeton University.

Louise Bogan. Born at Livermore Falls, Maine, August 11, 1897. Educated privately and at the Girls' Latin School in Boston. One of the editors of The Measure, a poetry journal of the twenties. Author of four volumes of poetry: *Body of This Death, Dark Summer, The Sleeping Fury,* and *Poems and New Poems.* Miss Bogan has contributed many essays and reviews to periodicals, and is at present poetry reviewer for The New Yorker.

Kay Boyle. Born in St. Paul, Minnesota, February 19, 1903. Attended the Shipley school and studied the violin at the Cincinnati Conservatory of Music. Her short story "The White Horses of Vienna" was awarded first prize in the O. Henry Memorial Award of 1935. She is the author of several novels: *Plagued by the Nightingale,* 1931; *Year Before Last,* 1932; *Gentlemen, I Address You Privately,* 1938, and several volumes of short stories: *Wedding Day,* 1930; *The First Lover,* 1933, and *The White Horses of Vienna,* 1936.

Van Wyck Brooks. Born in Plainfield, New Jersey, February 16, 1886. Educated in local schools and took his degree from Harvard in 1907. An editor of the Century Magazine, the

Seven Arts Magazine and the Freeman. His critical works have from the first received popular acclaim. He has been honored by the Dial Award, 1923, the Pulitzer Prize, 1936, and the Second Gold Medal of the Limited Editions Club in the same year. Author of: *Wine of the Puritans*, 1908; *The Flowering of New England*, 1936; *The Ordeal of Mark Twain*, 1920; *America's Coming of Age*, 1915; *The Pilgrimage of Henry James*, 1925; and the *Life of Emerson*, 1932.

Erskine Caldwell. Born at White Oak, Georgia, December 17, 1902. Educated at the University of Virginia and the University of Pennsylvania. Worked as stage-hand, cotton picker, professional football player, lecturer, screen writer 1933-34. Author of numerous books, the most famous being *Tobacco Road* (1932), the stage version of which had a record run on Broadway. Other books: *American Earth*, 1931; *God's Little Acre*, 1933; *Trouble in July*, 1940; *Jackpot*, 1940; *Say! Is This the U. S. A.?*, 1941.

Willa Cather. Born in Winchester, Virginia, December 7, 1876, and reared in the Middle West, which is the *milieu* of most of her novels. Miss Cather is generally conceded to be the dean of American women novelists. Her best-known works are *My Antonia*, 1918; *One of Ours*, 1922; *My Mortal Enemy*, 1926; *Death Comes for the Archbishop*, 1927; *Shadows on the Rock*, 1931; and *Sapphira and the Slave Girl*, 1940. Miss Cather was awarded the Pulitzer Prize in 1922.

Hart Crane. Born in Garretsville, Ohio, July 21, 1899. When the poet was a small boy he was taken to Cleveland to live where he attended public school. He wrote poetry from the age of thirteen, and at fifteen published a poem in *Bruno's Bohemian*. He had little formal education. Mrs. William Vaughan Moody became interested in his talent and encouraged him to become a writer. In 1916 he went to New York to write and prepare for college, and met members of the Imagist group. In 1917 one of his poems appeared in the Little Review and he gave up plans for going to college and took a job in Brentano's Book Store. His early poems appeared in The Dial, Poetry, Pagany and other literary magazines. In 1925, on money furnished by Otto Kahn, the banker-philanthropist, he began work on his long poem, *The Bridge*, which was published in 1929. In 1931 he received a Guggenheim Fellowship and went to Mexico, announcing his intention of writing a long poem on the Spanish Conquest. The following spring, disturbed by fears that his powers were failing, he committed suicide by jumping from the steamer on which he had taken passage for New York. Author of: *White Buildings*, with a foreword by Allen Tate, 1926; *The Bridge*, 1930; *The Collected Poems of Hart Crane*, with an introduction by Waldo Frank, 1933.

Edward Estlin Cummings. Born October 14, 1894 in Cambridge, Massachusetts, the son of a clergyman. He was educated at Harvard and during the World War served in an American ambulance corps and later because of a military censor's mistake was thrown into the detention camp described in *The Enormous Room*, his best known prose work. He is the author of several volumes of poems: *Tulips and Chimneys*, 1923, *Is 5*, 1926; *No Thanks*, 1935, and *Collected Poems*, 1938.

John Dos Passos. Born in Chicago, January 14, 1896. Attended the Choate school and was graduated from Harvard in 1912, *cum laude*. His first novel, *Three Soldiers*, 1921, a novel of war experience, aroused heated argument. His reputation came in 1925 with *Manhattan Transfer*, which uses the fictional device which Dos Passos has called "the Camera Eye" to record impressions of American life. Author of: *The 42nd Parallel*, 1930; *The Big Money*, 1937; *The Adventures of a Young Man*, 1939.

T. S. Eliot. Born in St. Louis, Missouri, September 26, 1888. Educated at Harvard, the Sorbonne, and Merton College, Oxford. *Prufrock and Other Poems*, 1917, and *The Sacred Wood* (essays), 1920, began an influence on Anglo-American letters which has been greater than that of any other writer in this period. Eliot edited The Criterion from 1923 to 1939; this journal set the standards for most literary journals of the time. The appearance of *The Waste Land* in 1922 brought in a new era in modern poetry in English. Other works: *Collected Essays*, 1932; *Collected Poems*, 1936; *Murder in the Cathedral* (drama), 1935; *The Family Reunion*, 1939.

William Faulkner. Born in Mississippi. Educated at the University of Mississippi. His first novels had little popularity until *Sanctuary*, a horror tale, written as a money-maker and later re-written, was published in 1931. Faulkner combines Flaubertian discipline with Southern eloquence and is one of the most powerful and original writers in America. Author of: *Sartoris*, 1929; *The Sound and The Fury*, 1929; *As I Lay Dying*, 1930; *Light in August*, 1932; *Pylon*, 1935; *Absalom! Absalom!*, 1936; *The Wild Palms*, 1939; *Go Down Moses*, 1942. The selection in this book is from a volume of short stories, *These Thirteen*, 1931.

Robert Frost. Born in San Francisco in 1875 of New England extraction. Attended Dartmouth and Harvard, but found the regular discipline irksome and left without a degree. *A Boy's Will* and *North of Boston* were published in England where he went in 1912, feeling that poetry was better received there than in the United States. The First World War brought him, now famous, home to New England. In 1916, he was made professor of English at Amherst and occupied that chair until 1938. Author of: *West-Running Brook*, 1929; *Selected Poems*, 1923; *Collected Poems*, 1930; *The Augustan Books of Poetry*, 1932; *A Further Range*, 1936; *Selected Poems*, with introductory essays by W. H. Auden, C. Day Lewis, Paul Engle and Edwin Muir, 1936.

Caroline Gordon. Born in Kentucky, October 6, 1895. Educated at private schools in the south. Graduated from Bethany College, West Virginia. Author of: *Penhally*, 1931; *Aleck Maury*, 1934; *None Shall Look Back*, 1937; *The Garden of Adonis*, 1937; *Green Centuries*, 1941.

Julien Green. Born in Paris, France, September 6, 1900, of American parents. All his books were written in French, although Green remains an American citizen. Educated in France and at the University of Virginia. Author of ten books, mostly novels, including *Mont-Cinère*, 1925; *Leviathan*, 1925; *Le Voyageur sur La Terre*, 1930; *Minuit*, 1936; *Then Shall the Dust Return*, 1941. He has been in America since the fall of France.

Ernest Hemingway. Born at Oak Park, Illinois, July 21, 1898. Educated in public schools of Illinois. Volunteer with Italian forces and later Hearst newspaper correspondent during the World War. Author of: *In Our Time*, 1925; *The Sun Also Rises*, 1926; *A Farewell to Arms*, 1929; *To Have and to Have*

Not, 1937; *The Fifth Column and the First Forty-nine*, 1938; and *For Whom the Bell Tolls*, 1940.

Ring Lardner. Born March 6, 1885, in Niles, Michigan. Educated in public schools and the Armour Institute of Technology. He began writing his "You Know Me, Al" sketches when he was conducting a sports column on the Chicago Daily Tribune. The story in this anthology is from the collection of short stories: *The Round Up*, 1938. Author of other collections of stories and two novels: *You Know Me, Al, A Busher's Letters*, 1916; and *The Big Town, How I and the Mrs. Go to New York to See Life and Get Katie a Husband*, 1921.

Andrew Lytle. Born in 1903 in Murfreesboro, Tennessee. Attended Sewanee Military Academy and was graduated from Vanderbilt University in 1925. Author of: *Bedford Forrest and His Critter Company*, 1931; *The Long Night*, 1936; *At the Moon's Inn*, 1941.

Archibald MacLeish. Born May 7, 1892, in Glencoe, Illinois. Attended the Hotchkiss School and was graduated from Yale in 1915. The same year he entered the Harvard Law School and after graduation practised law for three years in Boston. In 1923 he gave up the law to devote himself to writing. Poetry awarded him the John Reed Memorial Prize in 1929, and in 1933 his long poem, *Conquistador*, received the Pulitzer Prize. MacLeish was passionately concerned in the Loyalist Cause in Spain and his poem, *Speech to the Scholars*, read before the Columbia chapter of Phi Beta Kappa, in 1937, called upon the scholars and poets to fight Fascism. With Ernest Hemingway, Joris Ivens and Lillian Hellman he collaborated on the story of the film, *The Spanish Earth*, written to give an account of the Spanish revolution sympathetic to the Loyalists. In 1939 he received an honorary degree from Harvard and was made Librarian of Congress. Author of: *The Pot of Earth*, 1925; *Streets in the Moon*, 1926; *The Hamlet of A. MacLeish*, 1928; *Frescoes for Mr. Rockefeller's City*, 1933; *Public Speech, Poems*, 1936, and *Land of the Free*, 1938; *The Fall of The City*, 1937; *The Irresponsibles*, 1940; and *The American Cause*, 1941.

Edna St. Vincent Millay. This most famous of living American women poets was born on February 22, 1892, in Rockland,

Maine. She was educated at Vassar College where she wrote "Renascence," the first poem with which she attracted attention. Besides several poetic dramas she has published about a dozen volumes of poetry, of which *Second April* (1921) and *Fatal Interview* (1931), a long sonnet sequence, are probably the most distinguished.

Marianne Moore. Born in St. Louis, Missouri, November 15, 1887. Attended the Metzger Institute and took the bachelor's degree at Bryn Mawr in 1909. Her first verse appeared in The Egoist, an English periodical. The publication of her first volume of verse was arranged without the author's knowledge by some friends. In 1924 she received the Dial Award for distinguished service to American Letters and in 1925 she became acting editor of The Dial and remained with the magazine until it ceased publication in 1929. Author of: *Poems*, 1921 (arranged by H. D. and Mr. and Mrs. Robert McAlmon); *Observations*, 1924; *Selected Poems*, with an introduction by T. S. Eliot, 1935; *The Pangolin and Other Verse*, 1936.

Katherine Anne Porter. Born at Indian Creek, Texas, May 15, 1894. Educated in a convent. Author of: *Flowering Judas*, 930; *Hacienda*, 1934; *Noon Wine*, 1937; *Pale Horse, Pale Rider*, 1939.

Phelps Putnam. Born in Boston, Massachusetts, July 9, 1894. Attended Phillips Exeter Academy and Yale, from which he was graduated in 1916. Putnam, one of the most original of American poets, writes little but enjoys a high reputation among his fellow craftsmen. A series of the poems in *The Five Seasons* celebrates the wanderings of his mythological American hero, Bill. Arthur of: *Trinc*, 1927; *The Five Seasons*, 1931.

John Crowe Ransom. Born in Pulaski, Tennessee, April 30, 1888. Graduated in 1909 from Vanderbilt and in 1913 took the bachelor's degree at Christ College, Oxford. A founder and editor of the Fugitive and a leader of the Southern Agrarian group. Author of: *Poems about God*, 1919; *Chills and Fever*, 1924; *Grace After Meat*, 1924; *Two Gentlemen in Bonds*, 1927; *God Without Thunder*, 1930; *The World's Body*, 1938; *The New Criticism*, 1941.

Edwin Arlington Robinson. This fine American poet was born at Head Tide, Maine, December 22, 1869, and died in New

York, April 6, 1935. After twenty years of obscurity he published, in 1916, *The Man Against the Sky*, and began to receive the recognition which was his due. He wrote many long narrative poems, some of them on Arthurian subjects, but he was primarily a great writer of dramatic lyrics. His *Collected Poems*, first published in 1921 and enlarged in 1929, is probably the most solid achievement in poetry by an American.

Carl Sandburg. Born at Galesburg, Illinois, January 6, 1878. He first attracted attention with a group of poems in Poetry: A Magazine of Verse, in 1914; and since that time he has gradually become the leading Middle Western poet. Author of many volumes of verse, including *Chicago Poems, Cornhuskers, Smoke and Steel, Slabs of the Sunburnt West, Good Morning, America*, and *The People, Yes*, his most recent volume. His monumental prose work, *Abraham Lincoln: The Prairie Years* and *Abraham Lincoln: The War Years*, is the most substantial testimony of our time to the greatness of Lincoln the man.

William Saroyan. Born in Fresno, California, August 31, 1908, the son of an educated Armenian immigrant. Attended public schools until he was fifteen and read widely in public libraries. He became famous with the publication of the short story, "The Daring Young Man on the Flying Trapeze," in 1934. Saroyan, one of the most prolific of writers, never revises a story, preferring to "throw it in the closet and write another if it isn't right." Author of: *Inhale and Exhale*, 1936; *Three Times Three*, 1936; *Love, Here Is My Hat*, 1938; and several plays: *My Heart's in the Highlands*, 1939; *The Beautiful People*, 1930; and *The Time of Your Life*, 1940.

Delmore Schwartz. Born in Brooklyn, December 8, 1913. He was educated at the University of Wisconsin, and at New York University, where he received his degree. He later did graduate work at Harvard, and received a Guggenheim Fellowship in 1940. His published works are: *In Dreams Begin Responsibilities*, 1938; a translation of Rimbaud, *A Season in Hell*, 1939; and a verse-play, *Shenandoah*, 1941. He is now an instructor in English at Harvard.

Karl Shapiro. Born in Baltimore in 1913. He went to public schools in Norfolk, Virginia, Chicago and Baltimore. In 1932 he entered the University of Virginia, but left shortly. The next five years were devoted to reading and writing. In 1935 his *Poems* was privately printed. After three years at Johns Hopkins, he went to the library school of the Enoch Pratt Library in Baltimore, where he was working when he was drafted into the army in March, 1941. A number of his poems have appeared in Poetry and The Partisan Review, and some of his work was published in the volume *Five Young American Poets*, 1941.

John Steinbeck. Born February 27, 1902, in Salinas, California. Attended local schools and later Stanford University, leaving without a degree. Author of: *Tortilla Flat*, 1935; *In Dubious Battle*, 1936; *Of Mice and Men*, 1937; *The Grapes of Wrath*, 1939; *The Moon Is Down*, 1942.

Wallace Stevens. Born in Reading, Pennsylvania in 1879. Educated at Harvard and entered the law. A vice-president of the Hartford Accident and Indemnity Company. His career has been marked by retirement and infrequent publication. Author of: *Harmonium*, 1923; *Ideas of Order*, 1935; *Owl's Clover*, 1936; *The Man With the Blue Guitar and Other Poems*, 1937.

Allen Tate. Born in Winchester, Kentucky, November 19, 1899. Educated in public and private schools; graduated from Vanderbilt University in 1922. Member of the Southern literary group known as the "Fugitive-Agrarians." He has taught at University of North Carolina and Princeton University. Author of nine books, including *Selected Poems*, 1937; *Reactionary Essays*, 1936; *Reason in Madness* (essays), 1941; *The Fathers* (novel), 1938.

James Thurber. Born December 8, 1894, in Columbus, Ohio. Educated in Columbus and attended Ohio State University. His sketches and illustrations are familiar to readers of The New Yorker. Author of: *Is Sex Necessary or Why You Feel the Way You Do* (with E. B. White), 1929; *The Middle Aged Man on the Flying Trapeze*, 1935; and *Let Your Mind Alone*, 1937.

Mark Van Doren. Born in Hope, Illinois, June 13, 1894. Took his bachelor's and master's degrees from the University of Illinois and his doctor's degree from Columbia University where he has for some years been a member of the English faculty. He has also lectured at the New School for Social Research and from 1924 to 1928 was literary editor of The Nation. His *Collected Poems* won the Pulitzer Prize in 1939. His chief interest is in writing poetry, but he has written several volumes of literary criticism which include studies of Dryden and Shakespeare and has edited many volumes of Americana. Author of: *Spring Thunder and Other Poems*, 1924; *7 P. M. & Other Poems*, 1926; *Now The Sky*, 1928; *Jonathan Gentry*, 1931; *A Winter Diary*, 1935; *The Last Look and Other Poems*, 1939. He is also the author of two novels: *The Transients*, 1935 and *Windless Cabins*, 1940 and a novel in verse, *The Mayfield Deer*, 1941.

Robert Penn Warren. Born in Guthrie, Kentucky, in 1905. Educated at Vanderbilt University, University of California, Yale University, and New College, Oxford. Member of the Southern group of "Fugitive-Agrarians." Author of *John Brown: the Making of a Martyr*, 1930; *Thirty-Six Poems*, 1936; *Night Rider* (novel), 1939; *Eleven Poems on the Same Theme*, 1942. Joint editor of the Southern Review from 1935 to 1942, when the Review suspended. He is now teaching at the University of Minnesota.

Jerome Weidman. Born in New York on April 4, 1914. Educated at the College of the City of New York. Has worked in publishers' offices and contributed stories to magazines. Author of *I Can Get It for You Wholesale*, 1937; *What's In It For Me?*, 1938; *The Horse That Could Whistle "Dixie,"* 1939; *Letter of Credit*, 1940; *I'll Never Go There Any More*, 1941.

Eudora Welty. Born in Jackson, Mississippi. Attended schools in Mississippi, Wisconsin, and New York. Worked in newspaper offices and publicity departments. First story appeared in *Manuscript* in 1936. A collection of stories, *The Curtain Is Green*, appeared in 1941, with an introduction by Katherine Anne Porter.

Glenway Wescott. Born in Kewaskum, Wisconsin, April 11, 1901. Educated in public schools in West Bend and Waukesha, Wisconsin, and attended the University of Chicago. Author of: *The Apple of the Eye*, 1924; *The Grandmothers*, 1927; *Good-bye Wisconsin*, 1928; *The Pilgrim Hawk*, 1940.

William Carlos Williams. Born September 17, 1883, in Rutherford, New Jersey. Prepared at the Horace Mann school and
took his M. D. degree at the University of Pennsylvania in
1906. After several years of graduate study abroad he returned
to Rutherford where he has practised medicine ever since.
Williams made his appearance as an Imagist in 1914 with the
publication of some of his work in The Glebe. He is profoundly interested in the technical problems of modern verse
and feels that his art depends upon local and immediate tradition. Author of: *Poems,* 1909; *Collected Poems,* 1921-1931;
Adam & Eve & The City, 1936; *The Complete Collected
Poems of William Carlos Williams,* 1906-1938, 1938, and several novels: *A Voyage To Pagany,* 1928; *In The Money,*
1939; and a book of essays, *In the American Grain,* 1925.

Edmund Wilson. Born May 8, 1895, in Red Bank, New Jersey.
Prepared for college at the Hill School and was graduated
from Princeton in 1916. One of the best known and most
scholarly of American critics. Author of three volumes of
literary criticism: *Axel's Castle,* 1931; *The Triple Thinkers,*
1938; *The Wound and the Bow,* 1941; a volume of poems,
Poets, Farewell, 1929; a novel, *I Thought of Daisy,* 1929;
Travels in Two Democracies, 1936; and *To the Finland Station,* 1940, a history of the origin of Marxism.

Thomas Wolfe. Born in Asheville, North Carolina, October 3,
1900. Died September 15, 1938. Educated in public schools
and at University of North Carolina. Author of: *Look Homeward, Angel,* 1929; *From Death Till Morning,* 1935; *Of Time
and the River,* 1935, *The Web and the Rock,* 1939, *You Can't
Go Home Again,* 1940; and *The Hills Beyond,* 1941.

Stark Young. Born in 1881 at Como, Mississippi. Educated at the
State University and at Columbia University. Playwright and
theatrical critic as well as author of: *Heaven Trees,* 1926;
The Torches Flare, 1928; *River House,* 1929, and *So Red the
Rose,* 1934; and *Glamour,* essays on the art of the theatre,
1925, *The Flower in Drama,* a book of papers on the theatre,
1923, and a volume of short stories, *The Street of the Islands,*
1935.

Date Due